Framework SCIENCE 8

Paddy Gannon

OXFORD
UNIVERSITY PRESS

Great Clarendon Street, Oxford OX2 6DP

Oxford University Press is a department of the University of Oxford.
It furthers the University's objective of excellence in research, scholarship,
and education by publishing worldwide in

Oxford New York

Auckland Cape Town Dar es Salaam Hong Kong Karachi
Kuala Lumpur Madrid Melbourne Mexico City Nairobi
New Delhi Shanghai Taipei Toronto

With offices in

Argentina Austria Brazil Chile Czech Republic France Greece
Guatemala Hungary Italy Japan Poland Portugal Singapore
South Korea Switzerland Thailand Turkey Ukraine Vietnam

Oxford is a registered trade mark of Oxford University Press
in the UK and in certain other countries

First published 2003

British Library Cataloguing in Publication Data

Data available

ISBN-13: 978-0-19-914896-7

ISBN-10: 0199148961

10 9 8 7 6 5

Printed in Italy by Rotolito Lombarda.

Contents

8E Atoms and elements

8F Compounds and mixtures

8G Rocks and weathering

8H The rock cycle

8I Heating and cooling

8J Magnets and electromagnets

8K Light

8L Sound and hearing

Introduction

Every day you make hundreds of decisions:

- what to eat
- whether a car is going to stop in time when the crossing lights go red
- whether to mess about in PE or actually get some exercise instead
- whether organic foods really are better for you and the environment
- how to use electricity safely
- what shampoo to use
- whether to read any more of this...

The reason why everyone in school does science is because it can help you to make better decisions about your life. Sometimes on television or in magazines or newspapers you'll see something being presented as a scientific fact when it isn't necessarily true. People often want to do this to encourage us to think like they do, or to buy their products. Knowing some science, and also knowing how to find out more about a particular subject in science, can help us to spot when this is happening and to make up our own minds.

But there's an even better reason to study science – it's really good fun and you get to find out how things work. This book aims to help your learning in science, as part of a course including lots of practical work and activities too. We hope that you enjoy it.

How to use this book

If you want to find a particular bit of science use the Contents and Index. There's also a **Glossary** (page 149) which gives you the meanings of most of the science words you'll meet in your course.

The book is divided into 12 topics:

At the start of each topic you'll find an **opener page** reminding you of what you already know about a topic, and a summary of the key ideas to come in the unit.

Then there is a set of double-page spreads on various parts of the topic, with questions for you to try and a **Language bank** of important words. The spreads are labelled **A**, **M** or **S** next to the title. **A** spreads introduce the easier ideas, **M** spreads follow on from these, and **S** spreads include some things which may make you think a bit harder.

At the end of the topic there are **Checkpoints** with questions to test yourself with, so you can find out if there are any ideas you need another look at before moving on.

Food and digestion

Before starting this unit, you should already be familiar with these ideas from earlier work.

- You need to eat a good mixture in your diet – foods for activity, for growth and also fruits and vegetables. Why do you need fruits and vegetables in your diet?
- Food provides energy for your body. It allows all your cells to carry out the life processes. See if you can list these life processes.
- Food, like all other matter, is made up of particles. Some food molecules are very big indeed and others are much smaller.
- Like other multicellular organisms, we have specialised cells grouped into tissues and organs to carry out particular functions.

You will meet these key ideas as you work through this unit. Have a quick look now, and at the end of the unit read them through slowly.

- We need **nutrients** for growth, repair and movement.
- You should be able to name foods that contain each nutrient:
  - **protein** for growth and repair
  - **carbohydrates** for energy
  - **fats** to store energy
  - **vitamins** and **minerals** in small amounts for chemical reactions
  - **roughage** to keep things moving through the digestive system
  - **water** as the medium for all the reactions of life.
  - A **balanced diet** supplies the correct mix of all these nutrients.
- The **digestive system** is an organ system. It supplies the cells of the body with nutrients and other raw materials.
- The **blood** transports these nutrients to all the body cells. Some nutrients have molecules too big to pass through the walls of the digestive system into the blood. The digestive system breaks down these big molecules into smaller ones that can be **absorbed**.
- **Enzymes** break down large molecules during digestion. Different enzymes are produced in the mouth, stomach, pancreas and small intestine. Each one acts on a particular kind of nutrient.
- **Amylase** enzymes breaks down carbohydrates. **Protease** enzymes break down proteins. **Lipase** enzymes break down fats. Each enzyme needs different conditions, which are supplied in different parts of the digestive system.

Food, glorious food

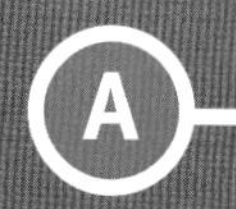

What's in food and why is it important?

How many different sorts of food can you think of? All the different foods you eat are a mixture of just seven food types or **nutrients**. Your body needs these nutrients as raw materials for:

- **growth** – you need nutrient molecules so your body can get bigger
- **repair** – to repair damaged tissues when you hurt yourself
- **movement** – food provides stored energy, which is released by every cell during respiration. This released energy allows the body to move.

> **Guess what?**
> *Some people suffer from **anaphylaxis**, which means that they are allergic to certain chemicals. Nuts can cause such a bad reaction in some people that their bodies go into shock and they need an injection to prevent death.*

We need food for the activities of everyday life, and for children's bodies to grow and develop properly. Unfortunately not everyone has enough food to keep them healthy.

The seven nutrients

- **Protein** is used for growth and to repair damaged tissue.
- **Carbohydrates** supply a ready source of energy for the body.
- **Fats** store energy in the body and are needed for cell membranes.
- **Roughage** or **fibre** keeps things moving in the digestive system.
- **Vitamins** are needed for chemical reactions in the body and for building other molecules. We only need to eat small amounts of them, but they are vital.
- **Minerals** are compounds that occur naturally in foods. They provide the elements we need in small amounts for chemical reactions in the body. (You can find out about elements and compounds in Unit 8E.)
- **Water** is essential for life as the chemical reactions of life take place in a watery solution. 75% of your body is water.

We need to eat all seven nutrients to stay healthy. Different foods contain different amounts of these nutrients.

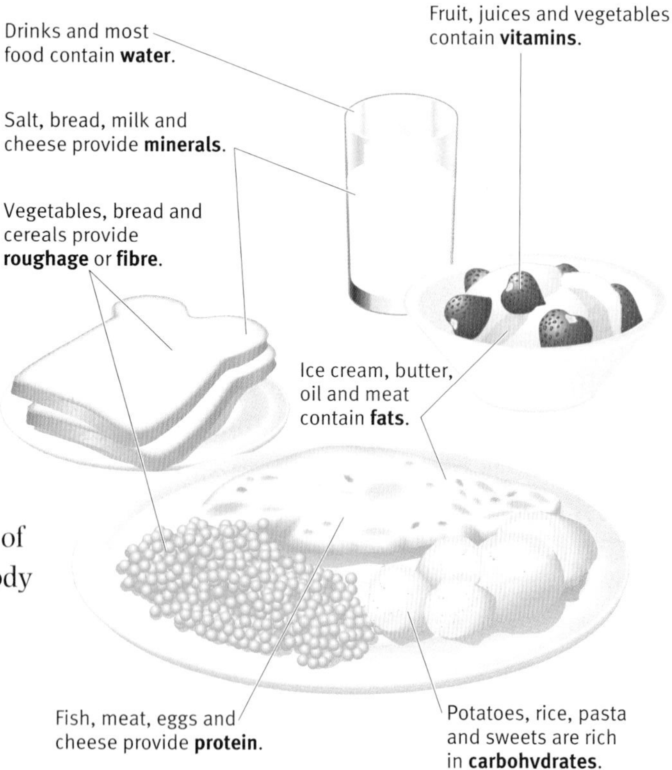

Does this meal supply all seven nutrients?

Vital vitamins and minerals

There are several vitamins and minerals, found in different foods. The table shows a few of them. You only need to eat a bit of each one, but if you don't, you are in trouble!

Vitamin	Found in	Used for
A	liver, butter, green vegetables	healthy eyes and skin – helps you see in the dark
B_2	cheese, milk, liver, eggs, green vegetables	healthy skin
C	citrus fruits, green vegetables, potatoes	healthy gums and skin – without it you get a disease called scurvy
D	fish liver oil, eggs, sunlight on the skin	healthy bones – without it you get rickets (soft bones)
Mineral containing	**Found in**	**Used for**
iron	liver, red meat, eggs	healthy blood – without it you are pale and weak (anaemia)
calcium	milk, cheese, fish	healthy bones and teeth

What's in my food?

Food labels show which nutrients are in the food. This helps you make sure you eat all the nutrients you need.

How do we know which nutrients are in a food? These tests can tell us.

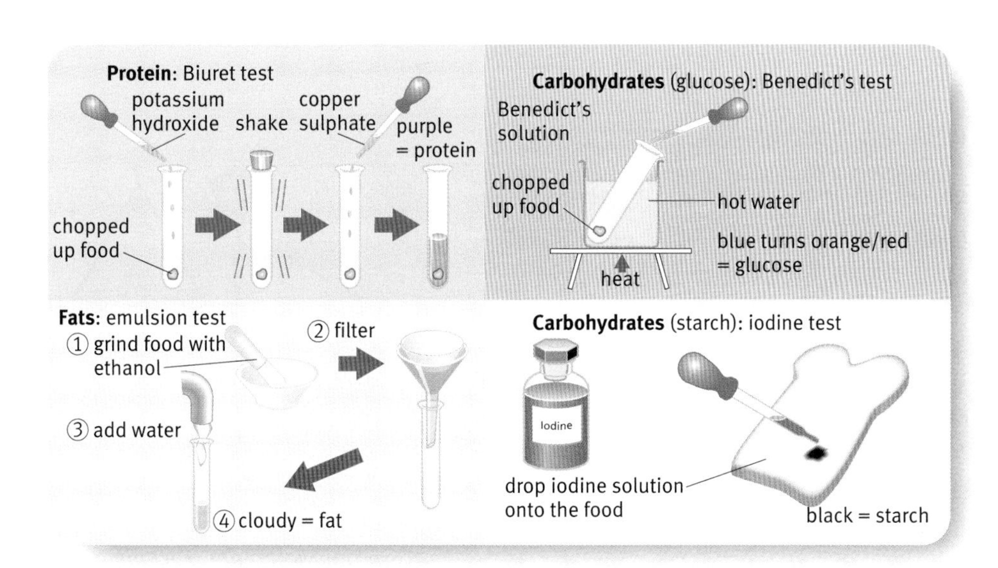

Nutrition Information

	Typical value per 100 g		30 g serving with 125 ml of semi-skimmed milk	
ENERGY	1650 kJ	390 kcal	750 kJ*	180 kcal
PROTEIN	6 g		6 g	
CARBOHYDRATES	83 g		31 g	
of which sugars	35 g		17 g	
starch	48 g		14 g	
FAT	3.5 g		3 g*	
of which saturates	0.7 g		1.5 g	
FIBRE	2.5 g		0.8 g	
SODIUM	0.65 g		0.25 g	
VITAMINS:		(% RDA)		(%RDA)
THIAMIN (B_1)	1.2 mg	(85)	0.4 mg	(30)
RIBOFLAVIN (B_2)	1.3 mg	(85)	0.6 mg	(40)
NIACIN	15 mg	(85)	4.6 mg	(25)
VITAMIN B_6	1.7 mg	(85)	0.6 mg	(30)
FOLIC ACID	333 μg	(165)	110 μg	(55)
VITAMIN B_{12}	0.85 μg	(85)	0.75 μg	(75)
IRON	7.9 mg	(55)	2.4 mg	(17)

Compare the amount of carbohydrate with the tiny amounts of vitamins and minerals in this breakfast cereal.

Language bank 

carbohydrates
energy
fats
fibre
growth
minerals
molecules
movement
protein
repair
roughage
vitamins
water

1 Copy and complete using words from the Language bank:

Food is a mixture of ______ which we need to stay healthy. There are ______ of these nutrients. Different foods contain different amounts of each one.

2 How would you show that a milkshake contains protein and fat?

3 Name two nutrients that you need for healthy bones.

4 Plan your meals for a day. Make sure you have all the nutrients you need. Explain why you included each food.

Balancing your diet

Which foods provide a balanced diet?

Your **diet** is all the food you eat. A **balanced diet** is a diet that contains all seven nutrients in the correct amounts. A balanced diet will provide your body with the right mixture of nutrients which you need to stay healthy.

The food guide pyramid

Different people need different amounts of each nutrient per day, depending on the person and what they do. But any diet that concentrates too much on just a few nutrient groups is not balanced. Imagine trying to live on just sweets and fizzy pop! The food guide pyramid tells you what proportions of each food group to eat.

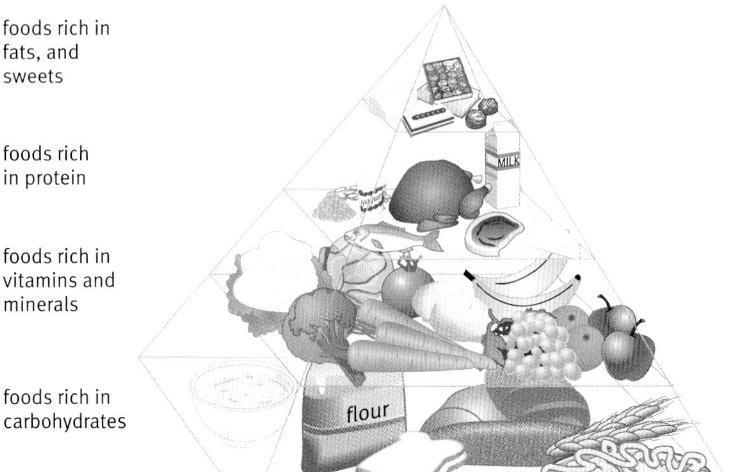

Don't eat too many fats and sweets at the top of the pyramid. The bread and cereals at the bottom should make the biggest part of your diet.

Healthy for who?

The diet people need to eat, particularly the amount of energy they need, depends on their lifestyle. For example, an accountant sitting at a desk all day might need only 10 500 kJ of energy per day, compared with18 900 kJ for a builder. Eating too much can cause weight gain if people are not very active.

It's not just energy needs that vary. Some people have particular nutrient needs, for example, a pregnant woman needs a diet with plenty of protein, vitamins and minerals.

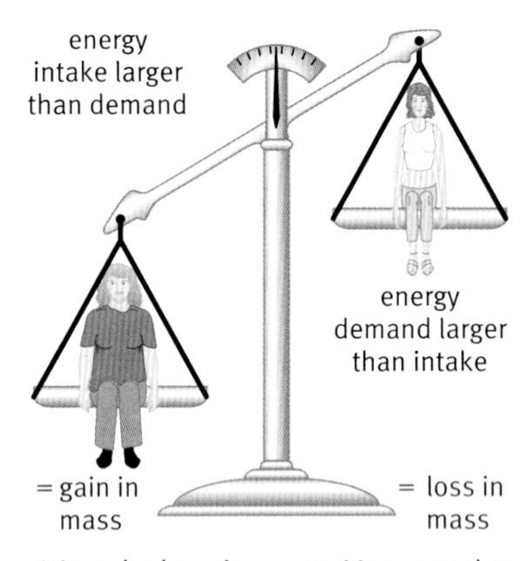

It's a balancing act. You need to take in enough energy in your diet to supply your energy needs, but no more. If your energy input is greater than your output you could gain weight (mass).

Guess what?

Fat stores a lot of energy. Carbohydrates supply us with 17 kJ per gram, but fat gives an amazing 38 kJ per gram. However, it is not healthy to rely just on fat in the diet to provide our energy.

There are lots of different balanced diets eaten by people around the world.

How our diet has changed with time

Average nine-year-old is getting taller

Early evening for the family in the 1950s.

IF CHILDREN ARE TALLER THAN THEY used to be, we must be eating a more healthy diet, mustn't we? Let's look at some facts about life in the 1950s and modern times.

So has our diet changed a lot since the 1950s? Look at the bar chart.

These days we eat more meat, fruit and vegetables than we did in the 1950s. Then starchy foods like bread and fatty meat like lamb were much more popular.

Some studies on the average height of children have suggested that diet might explain why we seem to be getting taller. Unfortunately we are also much less active than we used to be, which might explain why we have more overweight children than ever before.

1950	2003
Food was still rationed after the war – you could only buy a small amount of many foods.	7% of children are obese (seriously overweight).
Few families had TV or a car.	People are less active – only 15% of children walk to school.
No supermarkets or fast food restaurants.	Convenience foods are popular and less food is prepared in the home.
There were no freezers and fridges were not common. Food was kept in a big cupboard called a pantry.	Most homes have central heating, fridges and freezers.
Tea was the most popular drink.	Soft sugary drinks are the most popular.

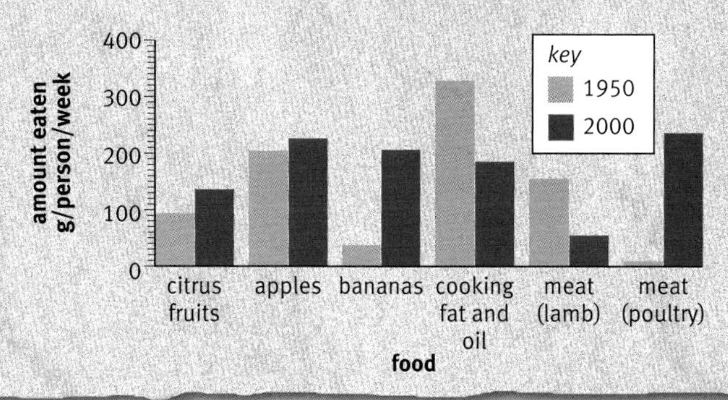

Some dietary differences between 1950 and 2000. We also drink two-thirds as much milk and eat half the amount of eggs and bread as in 1950.

- An average nine-year-old boy is now 24% fatter than in the 1970s.
- An average ten-year-old eats their own weight in chips every nine months.
- Thirty percent of all children are overweight.

1 Copy and complete using words from the Language bank:

A ______ diet provides a mix of all seven ______. It also needs to balance the input and output of ______. If we take in too much energy we may become ______.

2 List all the food you ate yesterday, and when you ate it. Do you think you had a balanced intake of food?

3 **a** Look at the article above. List three possible reasons from it why more children are obese today than in 1950.

b Suggest how central heating has changed the type of food we eat.

4 Give two examples of how the components of a balanced diet change depending on the person.

Language bank 

balanced diet
diet
energy
healthy
nutrients
obese

Digestion

What happens to food inside the digestive system?

Every one of the 100 million million or so cells in your body needs nutrients. Cells use nutrient molecules to stay alive and to perform the special tasks they do for the body. Food provides the nutrients that the cells need, but many molecules in food are too big to get into the tiny cells where they are used.

This is where **digestion** comes in. Digestion breaks food down into smaller molecules, so that they can get into the cells that use them. The result is that large insoluble molecules change into smaller soluble ones, which the body can **absorb** (take in).

Digestion is especially important for proteins, carbohydrates and fats, which have very big molecules. Most vitamins and minerals are already small enough to get into the cells. Digestion happens in a long tube passing through your body, called the **digestive system** or gut.

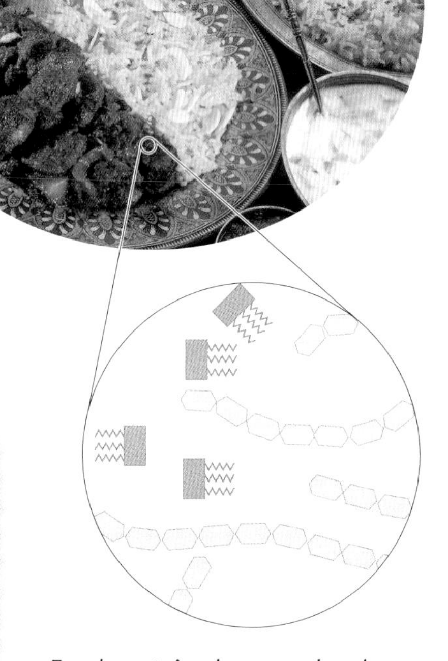

Food contains large molecules.

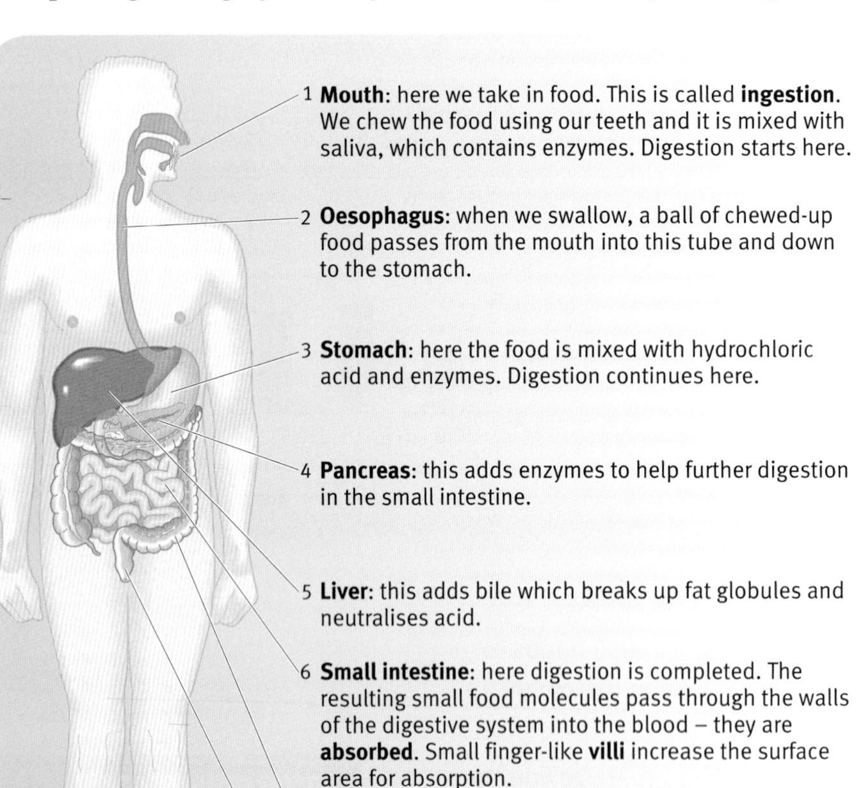

As food passes through the digestive system, substances called enzymes help with digestion.

Food in your stomach is still outside your body! It only gets into your cells after being absorbed into the blood.

Gruesome details about digestion

- An adult intestine is about 7 m long.
- Stomach acid in sick can corrode the metal of a car.
- Cows have more than one stomach which helps them digest cellulose material in plants.
- Hares eat their own faeces so they digest their food twice.
- Your faeces are brown because old red blood cells are added in the bile.
- Digestion can take up to 18 hours.

A model gut

Look at the diagram below. This tube is like your digestive system. The starch inside it can't get out because its molecules are too big. After digestion, the molecules are small enough to pass out of the tube into the surrounding water. This is like digested food molecules being absorbed into your blood in the small intestine.

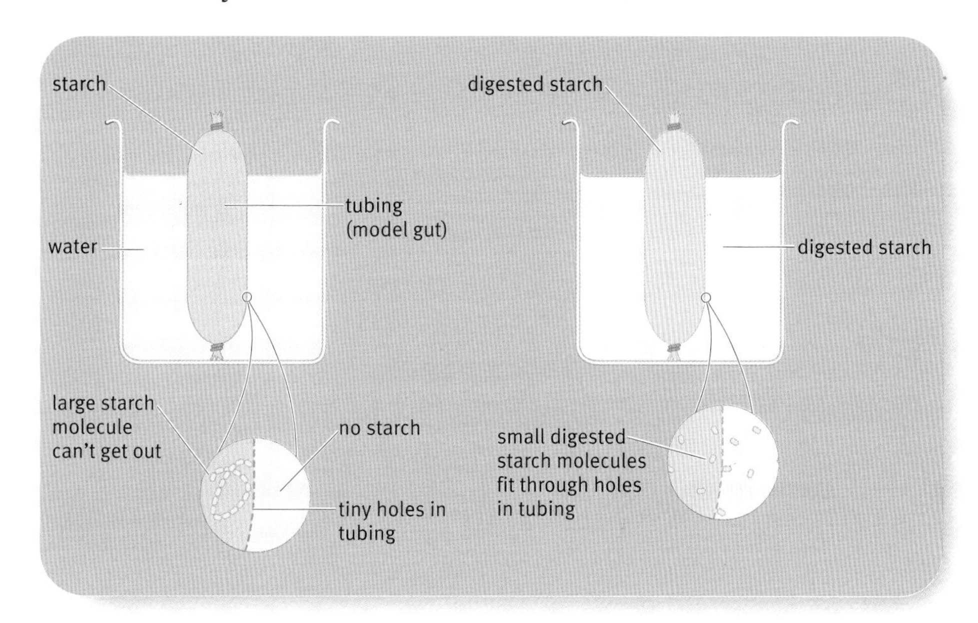

Digestion converts starch molecules into molecules that are small enough to pass through the tiny holes in the wall of the model gut.

1 Copy and complete using words from the Language bank:

Food contains ______ which the body needs. Digestion allows the nutrients to get into cells by breaking them down into smaller ______ using ______. They can then be ______ and used by cells.

2 List these processes in the order that they occur in the body: absorption, digestion, ingestion, egestion.

3 Match beginnings and endings to write two correct sentences.

Every cell needs nutrients ...	... because the molecules are too large.
The body cannot absorb undigested food ...	... for growth and repair and for energy.

4 If roughage is egested and not digested, why is it an important nutrient?

Language bank 

absorbed
anus
bile
cells
digestion
digestive system
egestion
enzymes
faeces
ingestion
large intestine
liver
molecules
mouth
nutrients
oesophagus
pancreas
rectum
small intestine
stomach

3A.4 Enzyme action

- What do digestive enzymes do?
- Where are the products of digestion used?

Digestive enzymes are special biological molecules made by the body. These enzymes break large nutrient molecules into manageable bits that the body can absorb and use.

As food passes through the digestive system, enzymes turn the insoluble lumps of food into smaller soluble molecules. These can cross the gut wall into the blood. Now they are really inside the body, and they are transported to all the body's cells, which can use the small food molecules.

This sieve is like the walls of the small intestine. The molecules of fats, carbohydrates and proteins are like stones caught in the sieve. They can't be absorbed because they are too big. Once the enzymes have finished with them, they are like the fine soil. They can pass through into the blood.

large insoluble molecules —**enzymes in water**→ **small soluble molecules**

Digestive enzymes speed up the digestion reactions. Each enzyme is **specific**, which means it will act only on certain types of foods. Different enzymes need different conditions – for example, some need acidic conditions, others need alkaline conditions. So different enzymes work in different regions of the gut where conditions are just right for them.

Some enzymes and what they do

Carbohydrates are broken down by amylase enzymes

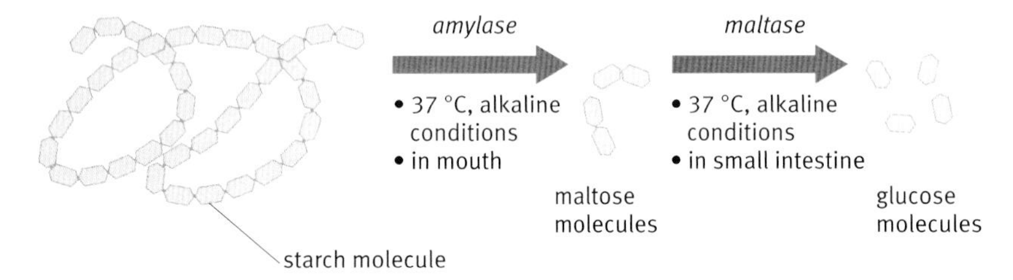

Starch is a carbohydrate with very large molecules. Enzymes break down starch into smaller maltose molecules, and eventually into glucose molecules which can be absorbed.

Proteins are broken down by protease enzymes

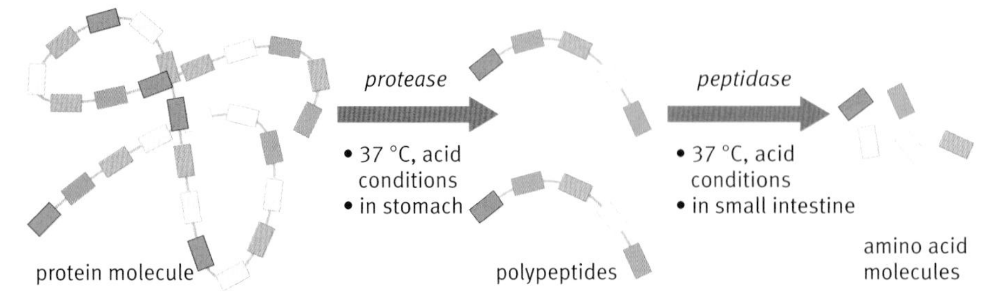

Proteins are large molecules which are folded or pleated. Enzymes break them down into smaller molecules called amino acids.

Guess what?

The stomach is made of protein. It is not digested by its own protein-digesting enzymes because it is lined with a layer of thick sticky stuff called mucus which protects it.

Fats are broken down by bile and lipase enzymes

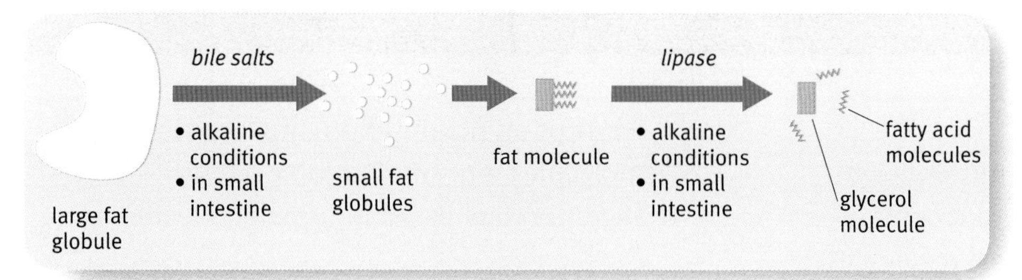

Fats have large ball-shaped molecules. Bile salts break them down into smaller fat droplets, and then enzymes digest them into smaller molecules called fatty acids and glycerol so that they can be absorbed.

Where are the products of digestion used?

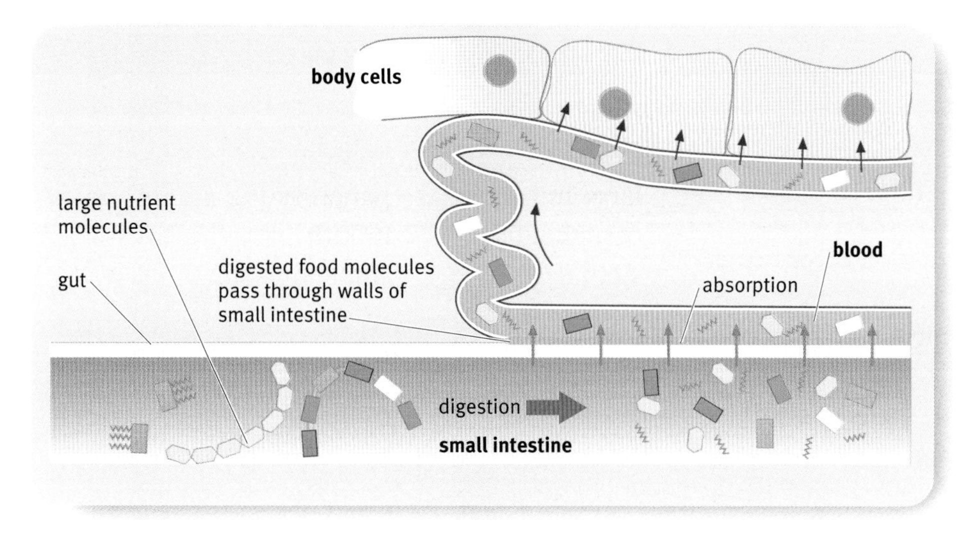

The diagram shows how digested food molecules get to the cells.

Up to six trillion reactions happen in every body cell every second. These reactions use digested food molecules.

The digested food molecules are absorbed through the gut wall and then pass into the blood. The blood transports them to the body's tissues, where they pass through the cell membranes and into the cells. Here they are used in the many reactions that go on in the cells, such as respiration or reactions which help growth and repair.

Guess what?

Biological washing powders contain enzymes. These enzymes can digest stains such as fat and protein at 'body' temperature, around 37 °C. This saves money because the washing water does not have to be very hot – boiling the clothes actually reduces the ability of these enzymes to wash. Great news, but some people are allergic to enzymes which give them a rash.

1 Copy and complete using words from the Language bank:

______ speed up the digestion of food in the body. They turn large ______ nutrient molecules of proteins, carbohydrates and fats into small ______ molecules so that the body can ______ them.

2 Name an enzyme that helps break down:

a carbohydrates **b** proteins **c** fats.

3 Imagine that you are a cheese sandwich (or any other food that you like containing carbohydrate, protein and fat). Draw a flow chart to show what happens as you travel from the mouth to the body cells.

Language bank 

absorb
amylase
carbohydrates
digestive enzymes
fats
insoluble
lipase
nutrient molecules
protease
proteins
soluble
specific

Checkpoint

1 Match the nutrients

Make a table to match up the nutrients with their functions and with foods that contain them. Add a sketch of a balanced meal, with labels showing why it is balanced.

Nutrients
fats
vitamins
proteins
minerals
water
carbohydrates
roughage

Functions
an energy store
for growth and repair
small amounts needed for chemical reactions in the body
compounds in foods that provide the elements we need for chemical reactions
for energy
to keep food moving through the gut
chemical reactions of life take place in this

Foods
potatoes, rice, pasta and sweets
fish, meat, eggs and cheese
salt, bread, milk and cheese
ice cream, butter, oil and meat
fruit, juices and vegetables
drinks and most food
vegetables, wholemeal bread and cereals

2 True or false?

Decide whether the following statements are true or false. Write down the true ones. Correct the false ones before you write them down.

a Ingestion means taking food in through the mouth.
b Only the largest nutrient molecules can pass through the walls of the small intestine into the blood.
c Absorption means changing large insoluble molecules into small soluble ones.
d Digestion means taking small molecules into the blood.
e Egestion means removing undigested food through the anus.

3 Missing labels

Look at the diagram of the digestive system at the top of the next column. Choose the correct label from the list below for each letter A–H.

Labels

liver	rectum
large intestine	pancreas
oesophagus	mouth
stomach	small intestine

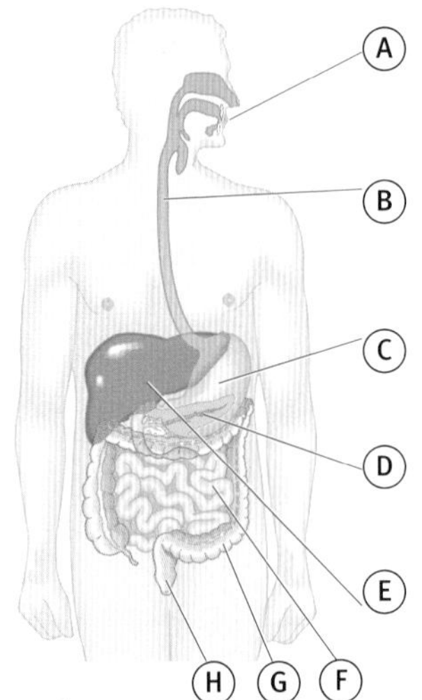

4 Fix the flow chart

This flow chart is mixed up. Redraw it so that it is correct.

mouth ⟶ small intestine ⟶ anus ⟶ stomach ⟶ large intestine ⟶ oesophagus

5 Enzyme action

Match up each enzyme with the reaction it speeds up.

Enzymes	Reactions
protease	**protein ⟶ amino acids**
amylase	**fat ⟶ fatty acids + glycerol**

Respiration

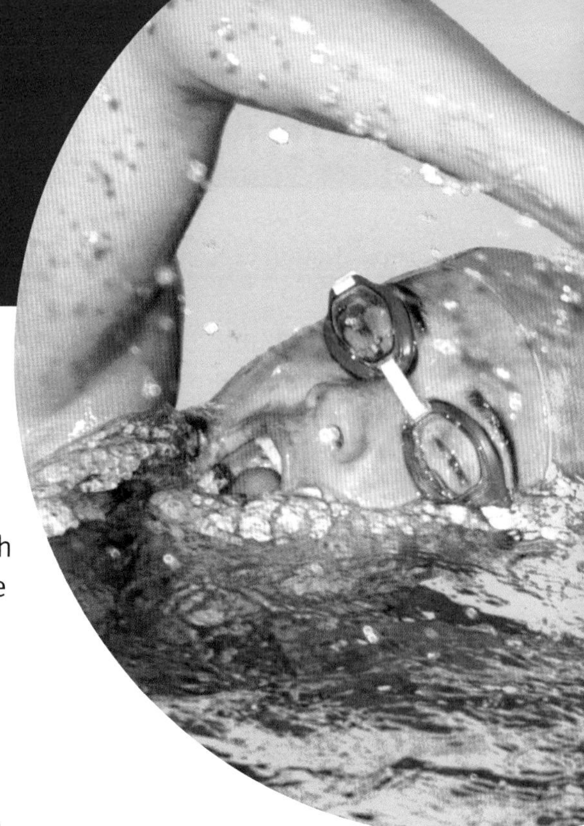

Before starting this unit, you should already be familiar with these ideas from earlier work.

- We are multicellular organisms with cells grouped into tissues, organs and organ systems to carry out particular functions. Which organ system supplies your body with molecules such as glucose to power the life processes in your cells?
- Your heart is an organ that pumps blood around the body. What happens to your heart and your breathing when you exercise?
- Food is like a fuel for the body. What do fuels store, and release when you burn them?
- Burning is a chemical reaction that uses oxygen from the air. Can you remember the name for a burning reaction?
- As well as oxygen, the air contains other gases including a small amount of carbon dioxide. Which gas is most plentiful in the air?

You will meet these key ideas as you work through this unit. Have a quick look now, and at the end of the unit read them through slowly.

- The **circulatory system** is an organ system that transports blood carrying oxygen, nutrient molecules such as glucose and other raw materials to the cells of the body. The blood also takes wastes away from the cells.
- The **breathing system** supplies oxygen for the body, and also removes carbon dioxide.
- In order to carry out all the life processes, cells need **energy**. This energy is provided by a process called **respiration**.
- Respiration uses up glucose and oxygen to release energy. It produces water and carbon dioxide. Respiration is like combustion, but is slower and more controlled.
- The air you breathe in is different from the air you breathe out. You remove oxygen from the air and add carbon dioxide and water to it. You also make the air a bit warmer.
- All cells and tissues need a good blood supply to provide glucose and oxygen for respiration, and to carry away carbon dioxide. If you exercise very hard your lungs and blood cannot keep up the supply and your muscle cells run short of oxygen.
- Respiration that uses oxygen is called **aerobic respiration**. Both animals and plants carry out aerobic respiration.

Respiration

O How do cells use the food molecules absorbed after digestion?

You know from Unit 8A that your body breaks down the food you eat into smaller molecules, so that it can get to all the cells in the body.

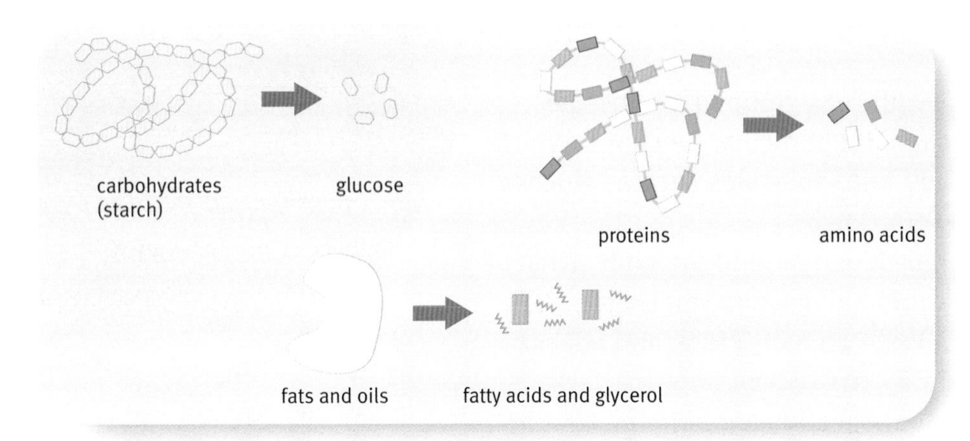

Your digestive system breaks down the large nutrient molecules in food into smaller units that the body can absorb.

These digested nutrients are absorbed in the small intestines into the **blood**. This is the body's **transport system**, and it carries the digested food molecules to every cell in the body. Here they are used for many things, including:

- growth
- to make new materials to repair your body if you hurt yourself
- for movement
- to produce heat to keep your body warm.

Athletes use 'high-energy drinks' to power up for a race or match...

What do cells use glucose for?

Your body needs a constant supply of energy for everything you do, from blinking to thinking to running and keeping warm. **Glucose** is an energy resource that the body's cells can use.

The cells use the glucose along with oxygen in a reaction called **respiration**. This reaction releases the store of chemical energy from the glucose. It happens in all the cells of the body, and the energy is used for lots of different things. For example, when an athlete runs, the muscle cells are respiring hard to provide enough energy for all that movement.

This word equation summarises respiration:

glucose + oxygen → carbon dioxide + water *This releases energy.*

MIXED BERRY FLAVOUR ISOTONIC DRINK WITH ADDED ENERGY - RELEASING B VITAMINS - with sugars and sweeteners.
INGREDIENTS: Water, Carbohydrate Blend (Glucose Syrup, Maltodextrin), Citric Acid, Acidity Regulator (Sodium Citrate), Preservatives (Potassium Sorbate, Sodium Benzoate), Flavouring, Antioxidant (Ascorbic Acid), Sweeteners (Aspartame, Acesulfame K), Stabiliser (Gum Acacia), Vitamins (Niacin, Pantothenic Acid, B6, B2, B12), Colour (Anthocyanins).
Contains a source of Phenylalanine.
NUTRITION INFORMATION (Typical Values per 100 ml): Energy 118 kJ (28 kcal), Protein - Trace, Carbohydrate 6.4 g, Fat - Nil, Riboflavin (Vit B2) - 0.05 mg (3.4% RDA), Niacin - 0.61 mg (3.4% RDA), Vit B6 - 0.07 mg (3.4% RDA), Vit B12 - 0.03 µg (3.4% RDA), Pantothenic Acid - 0.20 mg (3.4% RDA). **Each 500 ml bottle provides 17% RDA of the vitamins listed.** Typical Mineral Values per 100 ml: Sodium 50 mg, Potassium 8.6 mg, Calcium 2.0 mg, Magnesium 0.6 mg.
Refrigerate once opened and consume within 4 days.
Best Served Chilled.
LUCOZADE SPORT and the running man device are registered trademarks of the GlaxoSmithKline group of companies.
500 ml e

... because these drinks contain glucose in a form that does not need digesting, so the body can use it quickly.

Oxygen from the air is needed for this reaction, so it is called **aerobic respiration**. The oxygen enters the body in the lungs. Transporting the oxygen from the lungs to all the body cells is another job for the blood.

Respiration is the controlled release of energy from food. Because it happens in cells, it is sometimes called **cellular respiration**. Cells use the energy for various functions, from muscle cells contracting so we can move, to cells making enzymes so we can digest our food.

Guess what?

Just 100 g of glucose release 1555 kJ of energy. That's enough energy to boil over 4.5 litres of water.

Glucose burns like any other fuel, releasing energy. But glucose does not catch fire like this inside your cells. ***Do not attempt this yourself!***

The burning question: is combustion like respiration?

The photo shows powdered glucose being sprinkled into the flame of a camping stove. The glucose is burning like a fuel – it reacts with oxygen to produce carbon dioxide and water. Heat and light energy are released during the combustion reaction.

Burning is similar to respiration, but respiration is a much more controlled process – otherwise think what would happen to your cells!

Burning glucose must give out more energy than respiring glucose.

No, respiration just releases all the energy more slowly.

Energy demand

If someone is very active, their cells do lots of work so they need a good daily supply of energy. The graph shows the energy needed by various women aged 25.

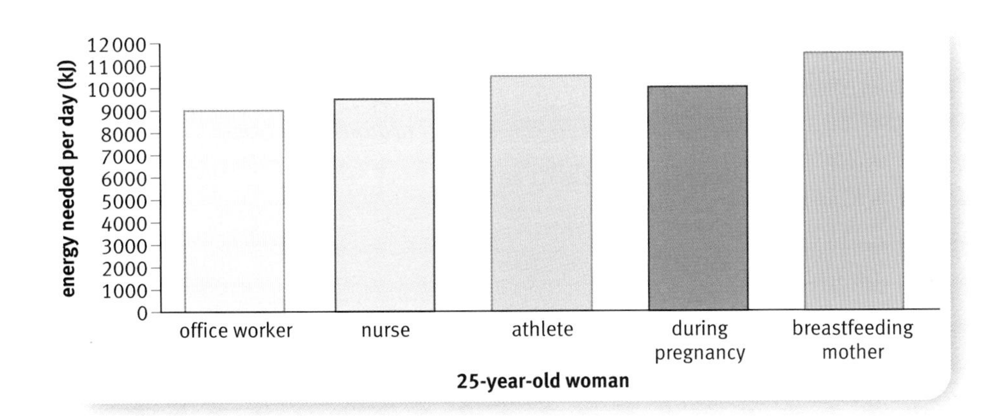

The more active you are, the more energy you need to take in each day in your food. Energy is also needed for a growing baby in pregnancy, and to make milk when breastfeeding.

1 Copy and complete using words from the Language bank:

Digested nutrients are absorbed into the ______ which transports them to all the ______. Here ______ reacts with oxygen in a controlled way to release ______ in a reaction called ______.

2 Briefly describe how oxygen in the air and glucose in a drink end up in an athlete's muscle cell to be used for respiration.

3 What is meant by these two terms for the release of energy from food?

a cellular respiration **b** aerobic respiration

4 Explain the difference in energy demand for an athlete and an office worker. Use these words: cells, respiration, energy release, glucose.

Language bank

absorb
aerobic respiration
blood
cells
cellular respiration
combustion
energy
glucose
nutrient molecules
oxygen
respiration
transport system

Transporting oxygen

- How does the oxygen needed for respiration reach the tissues of the body?
- What happens to the oxygen when it reaches the cells?

The **circulatory system** is the body's transport system. Oxygen and nutrients including glucose travel around the body in the blood.

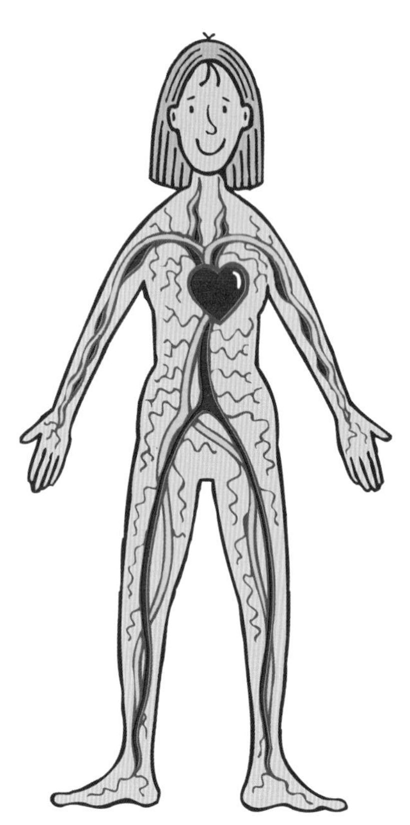

Blood vessels carry the blood all around your body.

What is in blood?

Blood is a mixture of different types of cells in a liquid.

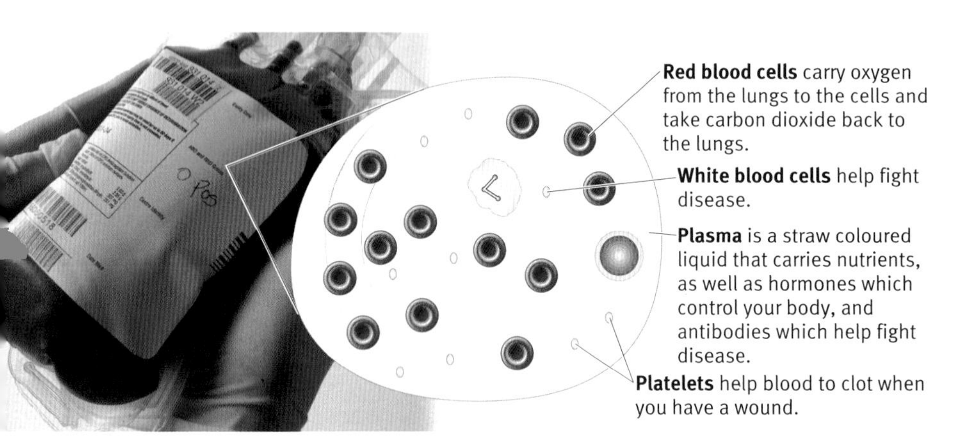

Circulation of blood

Blood **circulates** around the body, pumped by the heart. It travels in a network of tubes called **blood vessels**. There are three main types:

- arteries carry blood away from the heart
- veins carry blood back to the heart
- capillaries are tiny vessels that join arteries to veins.

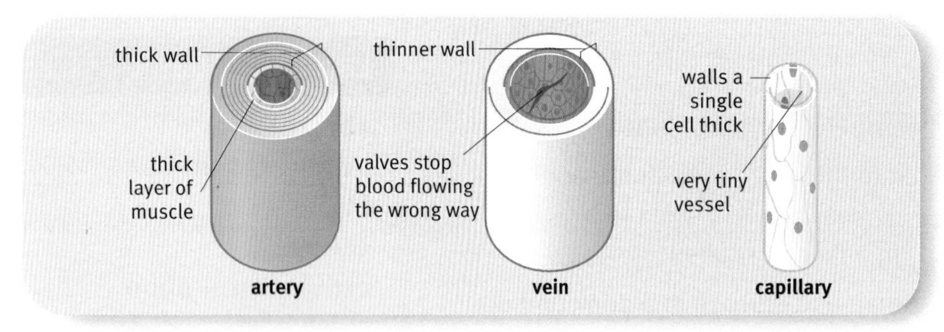

The three types of blood vessel.

The capillaries branch deep inside the body's tissues. Here substances such as oxygen, glucose and carbon dioxide can be **exchanged** between the blood and the cells. The following diagram shows this.

Guess what?

Blood makes up about 8% of our body mass.

Adults have about 5 litres of blood.

About 3 litres of the blood is plasma.

There are about 5 million red blood cells per cubic millimetre of blood.

1. The heart pumps blood to the lungs, Here it picks up oxygen, and carbon dioxide leaves it.
2. Oxygenated blood goes back to the heart.
3. The heart pumps oxygenated blood all around the body to organs such as the gut, the muscles and the brain.
4. Deep in the tissues oxygen, glucose and other nutrients pass from the blood to the cells for respiration. Waste material such as carbon dioxide passes from the cells to the blood to be carried away.
5. The deoxygenated blood travels back to the heart to be pumped back to the lungs again (go to 1).

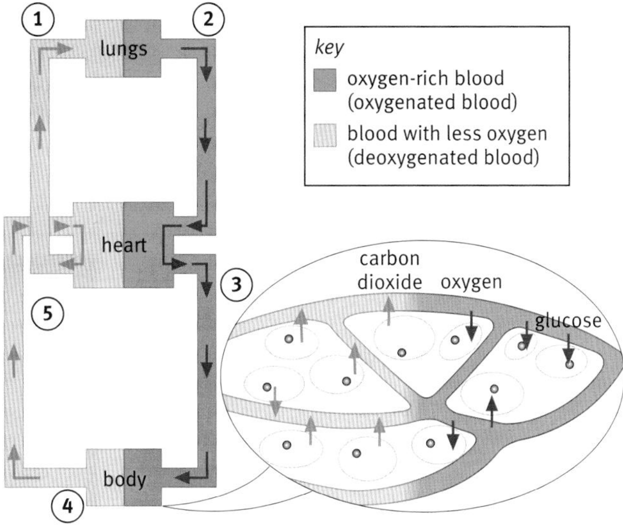

The human blood circulation. Can you spot the arteries and veins?

Pumping faster and harder

If you run a race, your muscle cells are respiring fast so they need lots of oxygen and glucose. They are producing more carbon dioxide and water, as well as releasing lots of energy to win the race.

To supply the cells, your heart pumps faster and harder, circulating the blood faster and you breathe faster too.

What if you tried to sprint hard for an hour? Your lungs would not be able to pick up enough oxygen, and your heart would not be able to circulate the blood fast enough. Your muscle cells would run short of oxygen. When this happens you get cramp and feel exhausted. You have to stop! But if you jog slowly, your body can supply enough oxygen and glucose for a long time.

1. Copy and complete using words from the Language bank:
   ______ is the body's transport system. It carries nutrients including ______ and oxygen around the body to the cells and tissues. Here they are used for ______ .
2. The chemical reaction respiration takes place in cells. Name the reactants and the products. What else is produced in the reaction?
3. List the parts of the blood. Underline the part that carries oxygen, and in another colour the part that carries glucose.
4. Find out more about cramp and what happens when your body can't supply enough oxygen. (Hint: try looking up 'lactic acid'.)
5. Do an internet or library search on how people first found out about the human blood circulation. Try entering these names: Galen, Vesalius, Harvey, Ibn-al-Nafis.

Guess what?

Our circulatory system is actually two systems joined up. One picks up oxygen and the other sends it around the body. The heart is therefore two pumps in one – a double pump.

There is so little oxygen at 10 000 m that this mountaineer breathes bottled oxygen to supply his tissues with enough oxygen to respire.

Language bank 

arteries
blood
capillaries
carbon dioxide
circulation
exchanged
glucose
oxygen
plasma
platelets
red blood cells
respiration
transport system
veins
white blood cells

The lungs

O What is the role of the lungs?

Every single cell of your body needs oxygen to respire and release energy from glucose.

glucose + oxygen → carbon dioxide + water *This releases energy.*

The human **breathing system** is where oxygen enters the blood, and also where the waste carbon dioxide leaves the body. The **lungs** are the major part of the breathing system. They are specialised organs designed to exchange gases:

- Oxygen passes from the air to the blood. It travels in the blood around the body to the cells, which use it for respiration.
- Carbon dioxide passes out from the blood into the air inside the lungs. It is then breathed out and leaves the body.

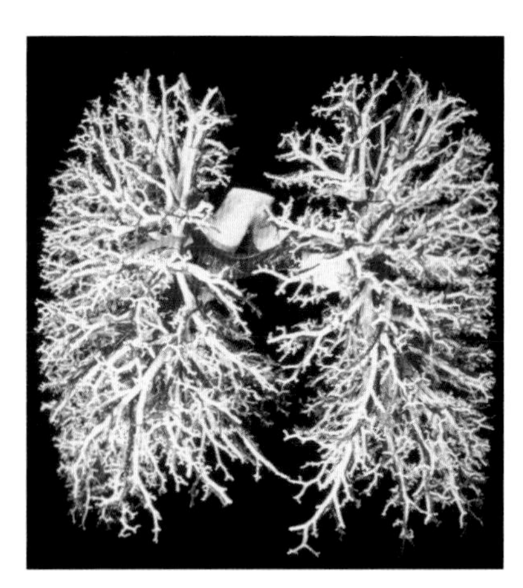

Tubes in the lungs divide again and again into smaller and smaller branches.

The structure of the lungs

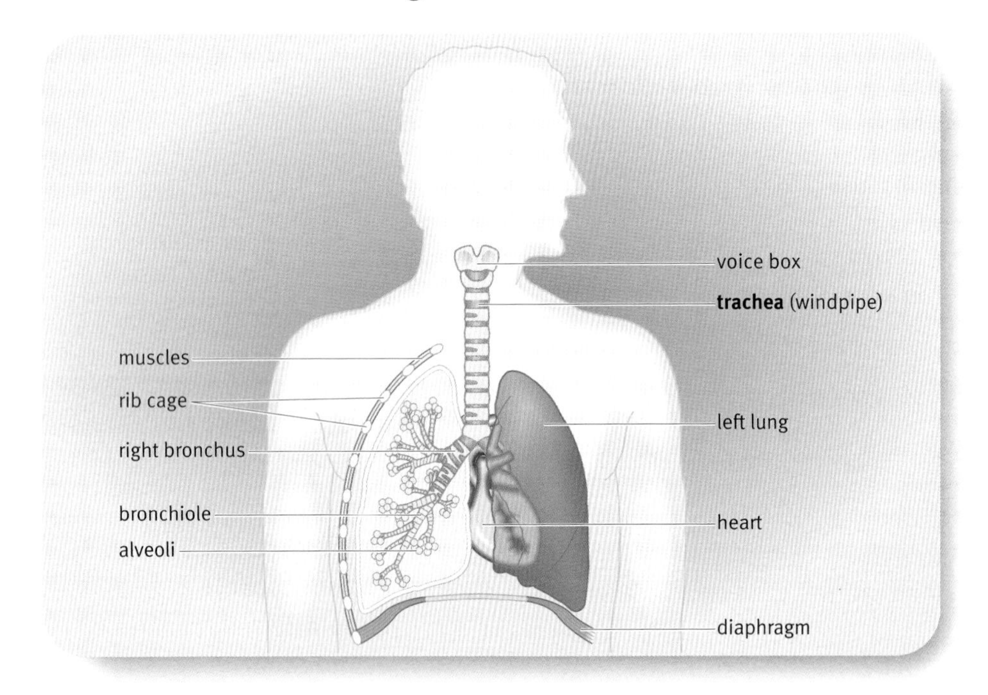

The **trachea** branches into two large tubes called **bronchi**, one going to each lung. These in turn divide again and again, finally ending in a chamber or air sac called an **alveolus** (plural alveoli).

The lungs are like large sponges. They are full of tiny alveoli. Air enters the body through the nose and mouth. It goes down the trachea to the bronchi. The bronchi divide again and again. Eventually they lead to the alveoli, and this is where **gas exchange** happens.

Exchanging gases

Oxygen and carbon dioxide gases are **exchanged** in the alveoli. The alveoli are well suited to this exchange of gases.

There are lots of alveoli providing a huge surface area for gas exchange. They have a rich network of blood capillaries around them. Gases are exchanged quickly through the thin walls of the capillary and alveolus.

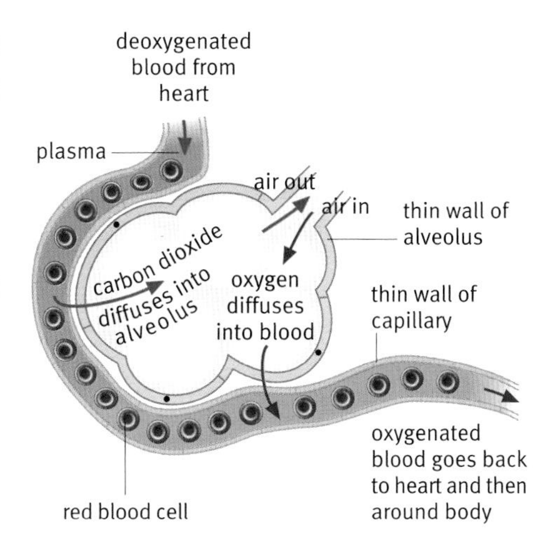

Guess what?

The surface area of both lungs is around 70 m^2 (about the size of a tennis court).

You breathe in and out about 15 times per minute.

You take in about half a litre of air in each breath.

The distance between the air inside an alveolus and the blood is 0.0015 mm.

Lungs and respiratory problems

The tissues of the lungs are very delicate. Any foreign material in the alveoli can damage them and make them less efficient at gas exchange. Then oxygen will not be taken in so quickly, and the body's cells could be starved of vital oxygen.

Healthy lungs (left) are normally bright pink. The black material on the lung on the right is tar from smoking. Smoke-damaged lungs are less efficient at gas exchange than healthy lungs.

People who smoke have a build-up of tar inside their lungs. The bronchioles are lined with tiny hairs which keep the airways clean. These hairs are damaged by smoking so the air coming in is not cleaned so well. Smokers have a greater chance of illnesses such as **bronchitis** (inflammation of the bronchi) or **emphysema** (a lung disease in which the alveoli begin to break down).

Language bank

- air sacs
- alveoli
- blood capillaries
- breathing system
- bronchioles
- bronchitis
- bronchus
- carbon dioxide
- emphysema
- gas exchange
- lungs
- oxygen
- smoking
- tar
- trachea

1 Copy and complete using words from the Language bank:
The lungs are the main part of the human ______ system. They are adapted for gas ______. The ______ is a tube bringing air from the nose and mouth to the lungs. It splits into two bronchi, which branch further, ending in the ______ which are tiny air ______.

2 How are the lungs well designed for gas exchange?

3 List the problems caused by smoking. Now list any benefits.

Investigating breathing

How are inhaled and exhaled air different?

As you breathe, you fill your lungs with air again and again. This is called **ventilation**. Air is **inhaled** (taken in) into the lungs. Some of the oxygen is removed and passes into the blood. Carbon dioxide, a poisonous waste gas produced in respiration, passes out of the blood and into the air in the lungs. This is **exhaled** (breathed out). The composition of gases in inhaled and exhaled air is therefore different.

The air we breathe out is warm and moist. On a cold day water, condenses and you can 'see your breath'.

The composition of air

	Percentage in inhaled air (air breathed in)	Percentage in exhaled air (air breathed out)
oxygen	21	17
nitrogen	78	78
carbon dioxide	0.04	4
other gases	0.96	0.96
water	variable	saturated

Exhaled air contains less oxygen and more carbon dioxide than inhaled air. Is that the only difference?

How do we know how much oxygen is in inhaled air?

Copper reacts with oxygen to make copper oxide. If you pass a known volume of air over heated copper in a tube, the volume of air falls.

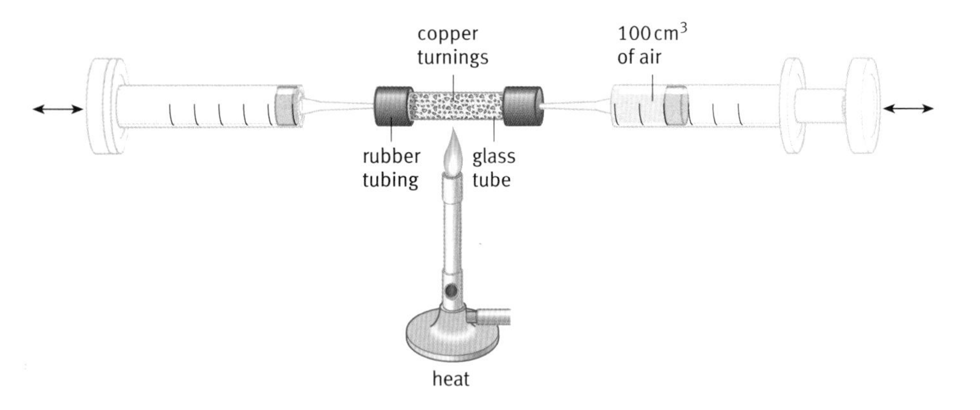

You start with 100 cm^3 of air. At the end there is less than 100 cm^3. The difference gives you the volume of oxygen used up.

Volume of air at the start (cm^3)	100
Volume of air after passing over heated copper (cm^3)	79
Difference (cm^3)	21

The table shows that 21 cm^3 out of 100 cm^3 of the air was oxygen, so 21% of the air was oxygen. If the experiment was done with exhaled air, the percentage of oxygen would be lower.

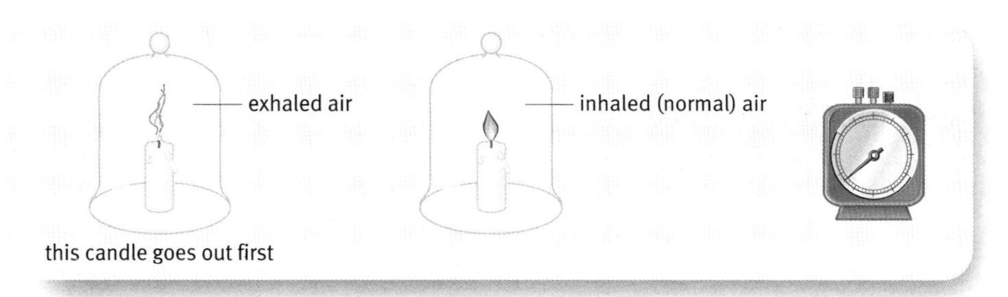

The candle burns for a shorter time in the exhaled air because there is less oxygen for it to use.

Finding what's in exhaled air

- Exhaled air contains less oxygen than inhaled air, as some of the oxygen is used by the cells in respiration.

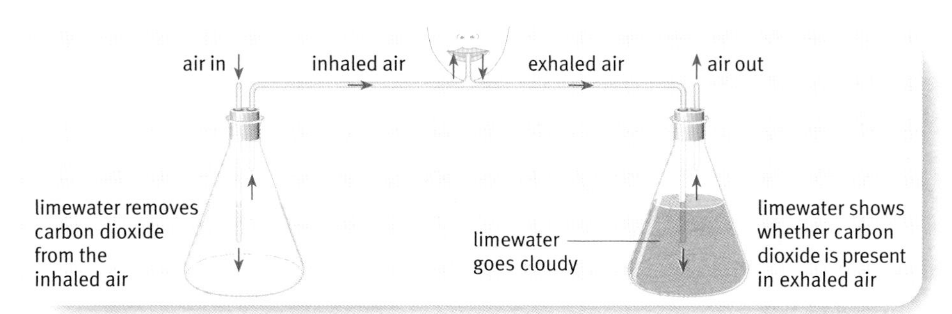

Inhaled air comes in through the left-hand flask and exhaled air goes out of the right-hand one. The right-hand flask goes cloudy much sooner than the left-hand one. This tells us that there is more carbon dioxide in exhaled air than in inhaled air.

- Exhaled air contains more carbon dioxide than inhaled air because carbon dioxide is produced in respiration.
- Exhaled air contains more water than inhaled air because water is produced in respiration.

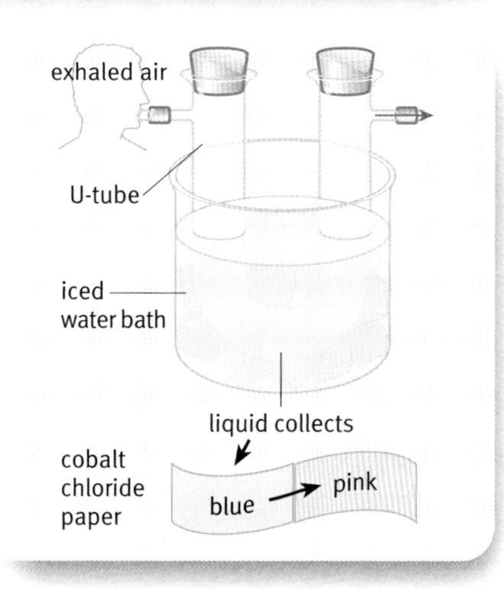

You could simply breathe out onto a cool mirror to see the water in your breath condense. In this apparatus the water vapour in your breath cools in the U-tube and condenses. Testing with blue cobalt chloride paper shows that the liquid in the tube is water. Drawing normal (inhaled) air through the U-tube would give less water collected in the tube.

1 Copy and complete using words from the Language bank:

Inhaled air contains 21% ______ and 0.04% ______, whereas exhaled air contains 17% ______ and 4% ______.

2 Why is the composition of the air you inhale different from that of the air you exhale?

3 Describe a positive test for:

a water

b carbon dioxide.

4 George put a locust in a beaker, covered it and counted the number of breaths per minute it took. What do you think would happen if he put the locust in a covered beaker full of exhaled air?

Language bank

breathing
carbon dioxide
cobalt chloride paper
composition
copper
exhaled air
inhaled air
limewater
oxygen
respiration

3B.5 Respiration in other organisms

M

- Do other organisms respire in a similar manner?

Plants use sunlight to make food by photosynthesis. This produces oxygen. However, plant cells need oxygen for respiration just like animal cells. Like animal cells they produce carbon dioxide and water. Looking at a simple experiment can show this.

Plants and respiration

The diagram shows an investigation to see whether plants make the same products of respiration as humans.

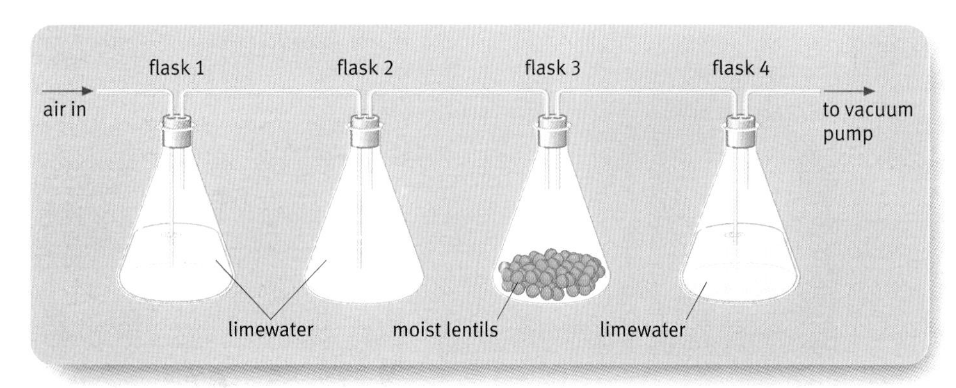

Animals respire, but not plants. Plants photosynthesise.

No, plants respire as well, just like animals.

Air is drawn into flask 1. The limewater removes carbon dioxide from this air. Flask 2 checks that this has happened. Any cloudiness in flask 4 will show carbon dioxide produced by respiration of the lentils.

Investigations of this type should have a **control**. This is part of the experiment that makes sure that the results are valid. A control for this experiment could be repeating it with the same apparatus, but without lentils in flask 3. If the limewater in flask 4 stays clear, this shows us that just passing air through the apparatus does not turn it cloudy. It was respiration of the lentils that caused the cloudy limewater in flask 4.

Plants respire, but they are less active than animals, so their respiration is much slower. They do not need lungs because they do not need to take in a lot of oxygen quickly. The lentils would have to respire for several hours to see a result.

Other animals and respiration

This diagram shows an investigation to see whether other animals make the same products of respiration as humans.

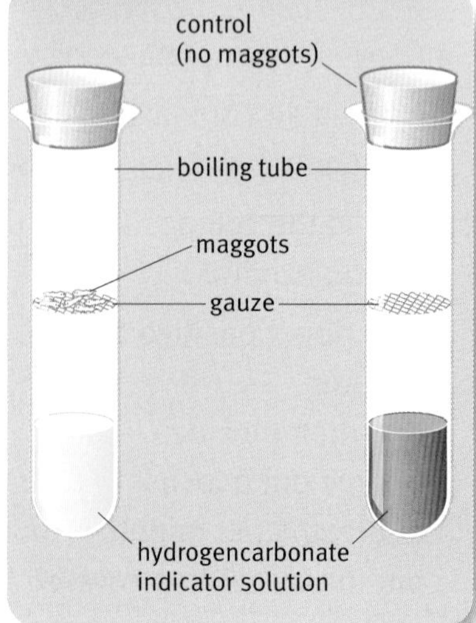

In the sealed boiling tube with maggots, the hydrogencarbonate indicator changes from red to yellow. This shows that carbon dioxide is present. The control has the indicator and the gauze, but no maggots. The indicator does not change colour in this tube, showing that it was the maggots that caused the change in the first tube.

The more active the maggots are, the faster they respire to give them more energy, and the quicker the indicator changes colour.

Dos and don'ts when using live animals in the lab

✔ Treat them with respect: imagine you are the animal and think how you would want to be treated.
✔ Return them to their original habitat if possible.
✔ Give them nutrients and water.
✔ Wash your hands and wipe the bench with disinfectant after handling living material.
✔ Use invertebrates in preference to vertebrates.

✘ Don't inflict pain.
✘ Don't kill the animals.
✘ Don't take more from the habitat than you will need for your investigation.

Do all animals have lungs like humans?

Different animals need different amounts of energy. This depends largely on how active they are. Animals are adapted to their environment, which includes being adapted to take in enough oxygen for their needs. Some need a quick and constant oxygen supply, whereas others can let oxygen enter their bodies slowly.

Organism	Gas exchange organ	Is air taken in and out? (ventilation)	Is blood used?
human	lung	yes	yes
earthworm	skin	no	yes
bee	tracheoles (a bit like bronchioles)	some	no
haddock	gills	yes	yes
dog	lungs	yes	yes

1 Copy and complete using words from the Language bank:
Plants and animals ______, taking in oxygen and producing carbon dioxide and water. Some ______ have specialised organs like the lungs, designed to absorb oxygen and give out carbon ______.

2 How could you show that a locust respires (gives out carbon dioxide)?

3 Why do different organisms exchange gases in different ways?

4 Lucy filled a vacuum flask with fresh peas and put a thermometer in it. Soon she could see that the temperature had risen. Explain why.

Guess what?

Insects could not exist if they were the size of humans, because they would not be able to take in enough oxygen. The respiratory system of many insects is very basic and relies on oxygen diffusing into open holes. This could not supply them with enough oxygen if they were huge.

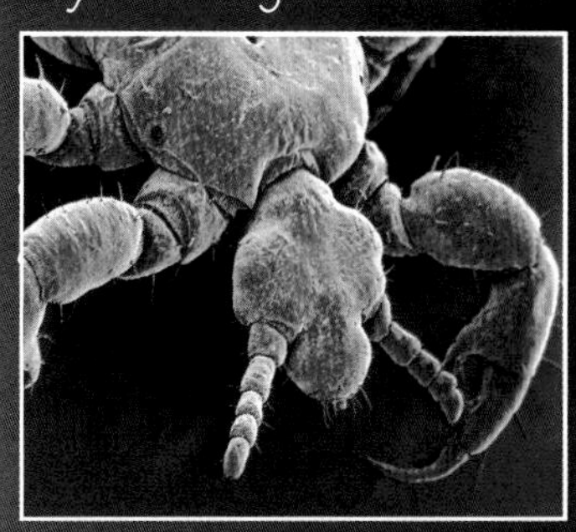

Like us, whales have lungs. Despite its huge size (lots of cells to supply), a whale can stay under water for 20 minutes before breathing air again. A human could develop brain damage due to oxygen starvation after just a few minutes.

Language bank

adapted
animals
carbon dioxide
control
energy
hydrogencarbonate
indicator
limewater
organism
oxygen
plants
respiration
respire

Checkpoint

1 Correcting mistakes

Read the following statements. Correct the bold words before you write the statements down.

a The **circle line** is an organ system that transports oxygen and glucose to the cells of the body.

b The breathing system is an **organisational system** that provides oxygen for the body, and removes carbon dioxide.

c Cells need **oestrogen** so that they can carry out the life processes.

d The energy resource for the body's cells is **glue**.

2 All true – glucose and fuels

Copy each statement below. Underline it in red if it is true for glucose. Underline it in blue if it is true for a fuel such as natural gas.

It stores chemical energy.
The energy is released in combustion.
The energy is released in respiration.
The energy is needed for heating and cooking.
The energy is needed for running and singing.
The energy is released quickly.
The energy is released slowly.

3 Aerobic respiration

Copy and complete the word equation for aerobic respiration using these words.

glucose, water, energy

________ + oxygen ⟶ carbon dioxide + ________

________ is given out.

4 Missing labels

Look at the diagram of the breathing system in the second column. Choose the correct label from the list above it for each letter A–G.

Labels

bronchiole	left lung
trachea (windpipe)	alveoli
heart	bronchus
rib cage	

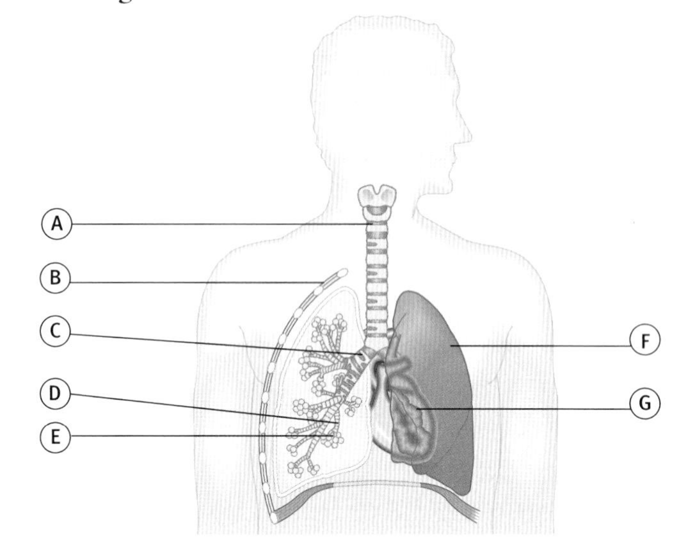

5 Higher and lower

Copy this table which compares gases in the air breathed in and the air breathed out. Write 'higher', 'lower' or 'the same' in each empty box.

Gas in air	Air breathed in	Air breathed out
oxygen		
carbon dioxide		
nitrogen		
water		

6 All mixed up

Copy and complete these sentences, unscrambling the words.

The **ticcularroy tyssem** is an organ system that transports materials around the body. It has three types of blood vessel: **risetare**, **vines** and **pillaricase**.
The capillaries are the smallest, and here glucose, oxygen and carbon dioxide are **dhagexcen** with the cells.

Microbes and disease

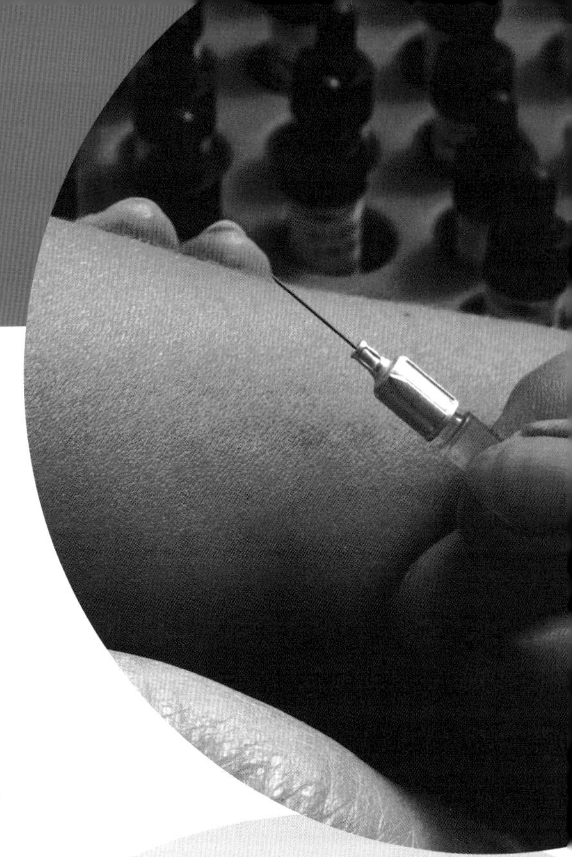

Before starting this unit, you should already be familiar with these ideas from earlier work

- Micro-organisms are living organisms that are too small for us to see them easily.
- Some microbes make us ill, some help things to decay and many are useful to us. Can you think of examples of these that you have learned about?
- Because they are living, micro-organisms feed, grow and reproduce. Like us they respire, using oxygen and food and producing carbon dioxide. What evidence have you seen that yeast produces carbon dioxide?

You will meet these key ideas as you work through this unit. Have a quick look now, and at the end of the unit read them through slowly.

- Micro-organisms are classified in three groups: **bacteria**, **fungi** and **viruses**. Bacteria and fungi have cells but viruses do not. Viruses can reproduce only when they are inside other living cells.
- Bacteria and fungi feed on all kinds of matter in the world, including you! Some microbes are useful, such as bacteria that feed on milk and turn it into yoghurt for us. Others cause disease and are harmful. These are called **pathogens**.
- You need to know some examples of diseases caused by bacteria, fungi and viruses, and how they are spread or **transmitted**.
- Multicellular organisms such as humans have ways of fighting off infections. Organs such as your skin, airways, eyes and stomach are adapted to prevent microbes invading your body. If any do get in, you have white blood cells to **engulf** them. You make **antibodies** to fight them, and if you cut yourself, your blood clots to seal off the wound.
- If you have antibodies to a particular microbe, you are **immune** to the disease. **Immunisation** helps prevent dangerous diseases spreading. It means injecting people so they have antibodies, making them immune to the disease without actually catching it.
- If you are ill with an infectious disease, the doctor may give you **antibiotics**. These are chemicals that work inside your body to kill microbes. Antibiotics do not work against viruses.

Micro-organisms

What are micro-organisms and how do we grow them?

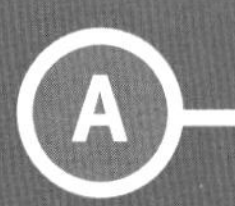

Micro-organisms are living things ('organisms') that are too small to see with the naked eye ('micro'). You need a microscope to see most of them. There are three classes of micro-organism.

- bacteria
- viruses
- fungi.

People use many other words to mean micro-organism. Some of them are shown on the word wall.

Bacteria

Size: About 1/1000 mm (about 100 times smaller than an animal cell).

Shape: Some are spherical, some are like little rods and others are shaped like a comma. Some are spiral and others have whip-like structures on them.

Structure: Bacteria are single-celled organisms. Some bacteria cause disease, but many do not and lots are useful to us.

Examples of bacteria: *Salmonella* (which causes food poisoning), *Streptococcus* (which can cause a sore throat), *Haemophilus influenzae* type B (which causes meningitis), and *Lactobacillus* (a useful bacterium used to make yoghurt).

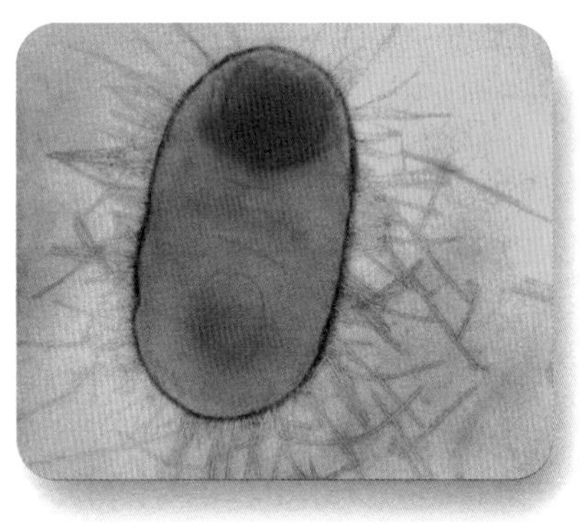

E. coli *bacterium.*

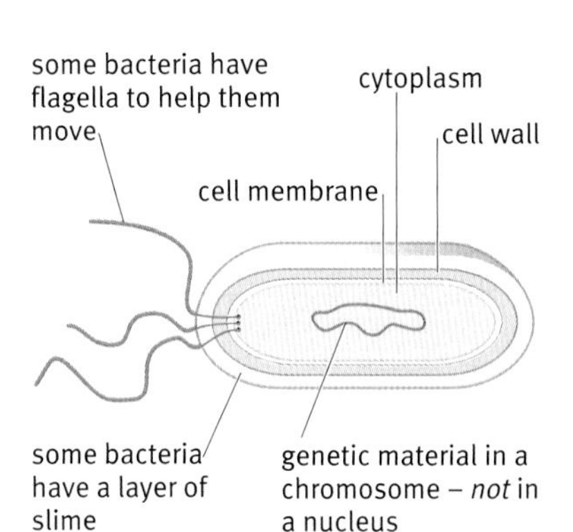

Bacterial cells are different from animal cells.

Viruses

Size: About 1/1000 000 mm, much smaller than bacteria.

Shape: Viruses usually have a regular geometric shape.

Structure: Viruses are not cells. They have a protein coat surrounding their genetic material. They cannot grow and reproduce on their own but have to invade other living things to do this. As far as we know, all viruses cause disease.

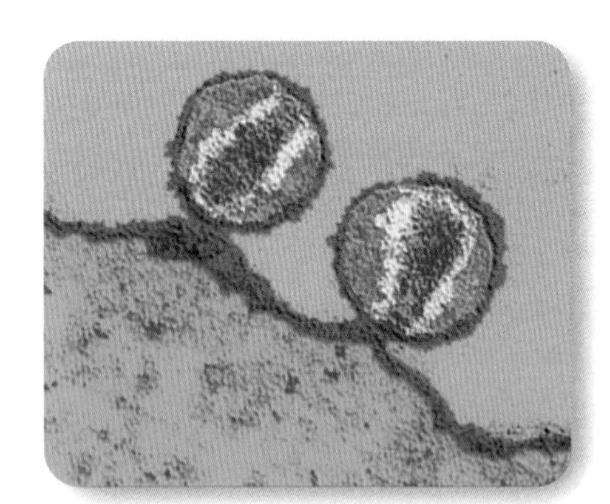

HIV viruses invading a cell.

Examples of viruses: Common cold virus, influenza (flu) virus, measles virus, chickenpox virus, HIV (the AIDS virus).

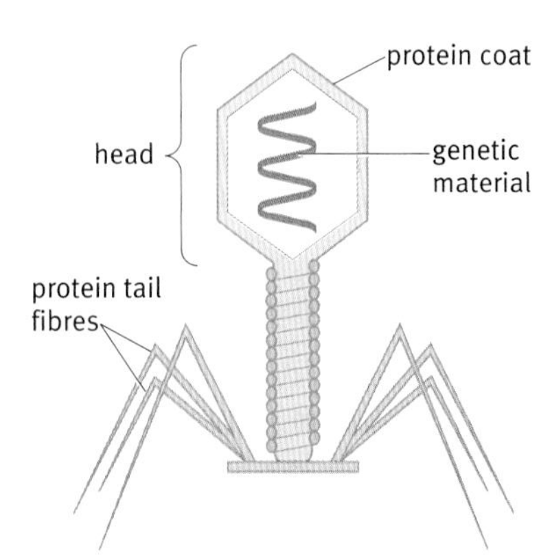

Viruses are not cells.

Fungi

Size: Some fungi can be seen with the naked eye, such as moulds. Others such as yeasts have single cells, but these are much bigger than bacterial cells.

Shape: Fungi have lots of different shapes.

Structure: Fungi are a bit like plants, but they have no chloroplasts so cannot make their own food by photosynthesis. They feed off other living things. Some fungi send out threads called **hyphae** which grow into the body of a dead organism. They digest and absorb the dead material to get the nutrients the fungus needs.

Examples of fungi: Athlete's foot fungus, yeast, *Penicillium* (a mould that makes an antibiotic called penicillin).

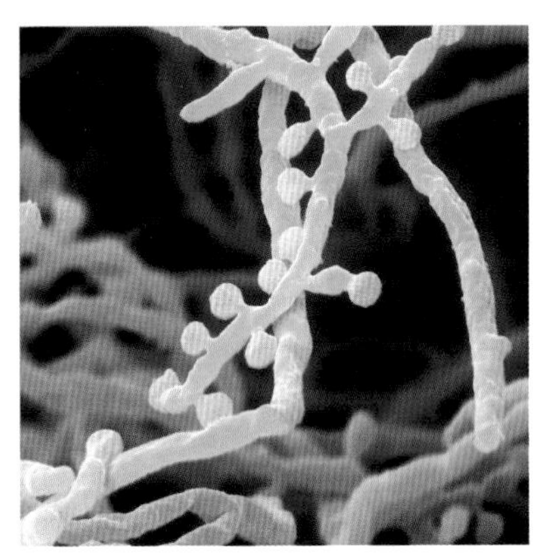

Athlete's foot fungus. The hyphae are shown in green, with orange spores.

How to grow micro-organisms

Micro-organisms are used in industry to make all sorts of products, including yoghurt, cheese, bread and Quorn (a protein-rich food). To make these things you need lots of micro-organisms. You provide them with warmth and a food supply so they can thrive and reproduce.

Agar jelly is often used to grow microbes. It provides nutrients for the micro-organisms.

Yeast respires the sugar solution and makes carbon dioxide bubbles. It also produces alcohol, turning the sugar solution into wine.

Making yoghurt

Yoghurt is made from milk. Two types of bacteria, *Lactobacillus* and *Streptococcus*, turn milk into yoghurt in a process called fermentation:

sugar in milk (lactose) —(fermentation at about 37 °C)→ **lactic acid**

The lactose turns into an acid, which curdles the milk and gives yoghurt its special taste. The acid also stops any harmful bacteria growing in the milk.

Guess what?

Making yoghurt is easy. Warm some UHT milk to about 40 °C and some live yoghurt containing the yoghurt-making bacteria. Put it in a vacuum flask for 4 hours. Cool it, add chopped fruit and bingo, you have fruit yoghurt.

1. Copy and complete using words from the Language bank:

   ______ are small living things which cannot be seen by the naked eye. ______, viruses and ______ are examples of these. Bacteria are tiny ______, smaller than animal ______. Viruses are not ______.
2. List the three types of micro-organism in order of size, smallest first.
3. Joe says that the definition of micro-organisms is 'tiny organisms that cause disease'. Is he right? Explain your answer.
4. Do you think viruses are living things? Explain your answer.

Language bank 

bacteria
cells
fungi
germs
microbes
micro-organisms
viruses

Harmful micro-organisms

Can micro-organisms be harmful?

There are lots of different diseases that cause problems with people's bodies. Some of them, such as cancer or a heart attack, are not passed on from one person to another. But other diseases are **infectious** – you can catch them from another person. Infectious diseases are caused by micro-organisms getting into the body and attacking it. These harmful microbes can be bacteria, viruses or fungi.

How infectious diseases are passed on

Organisms that cause disease are called **pathogens**. They can be passed or **transmitted** from one person to another in a number of ways.

Breathing in droplets

When you sneeze, thousands of tiny droplets of moisture fly out of your mouth and nose at about 100 miles per hour. If you have a cold these droplets contain cold viruses, which other people can breathe in. Not just colds but also flu, whooping cough and Legionnaire's disease are transmitted like this.

Eating or drinking

If you eat food or drink a drink that contains harmful micro-organisms, you can become ill. Salmonella food poisoning is spread this way. To prevent food poisoning, food should be cooked thoroughly and then wrapped and refrigerated if it is not going to be eaten straight away.

The faeces of a person who has an infectious disease contain many microbes. In times of flood or in overcrowded living conditions, infected faeces can get into food or water supplies and spread disease. Typhoid and cholera can spread very quickly if drinking water is contaminated with these bacteria. Diseases can also spread if people handle food without washing their hands after going to the toilet.

Dust is largely old skin, which microbes can use as food. They can float through the air on dust particles.

Microbes in faeces can spread disease both in this country and abroad. We can take care to wash our hands after using the toilet, but it's not so easy for everyone.

By touch

Some diseases are spread by touch – they are **contagious** diseases. The skin disease impetigo is an example. The bacteria that cause it can be spread by sharing hairbrushes, towels or pillowcases. Meningitis (an infection of the brain's lining) is spread by kissing and coughing. The fungus that causes athlete's foot is also spread by touch. It can grow on the floors of changing rooms and infect people changing there.

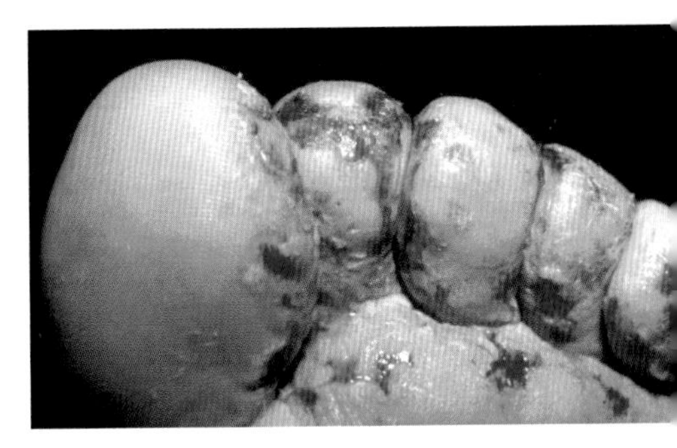

Athlete's foot is a contagious disease caused by a fungus.

By animals

Rats, mice, cockroaches and flies can all contaminate food with micro-organisms. One minute a fly could be munching on a cowpat, and the next it could land on your jam doughnut! Animals that spread diseases like this are called **vectors**. Mosquitoes are vectors that spread the diseases malaria and yellow fever. The mosquito sucks blood from an infected person and then passes on the infection to the next person it feeds on. Even dog faeces can spread a disease which blinds people, which is why dogs should not foul areas where children play.

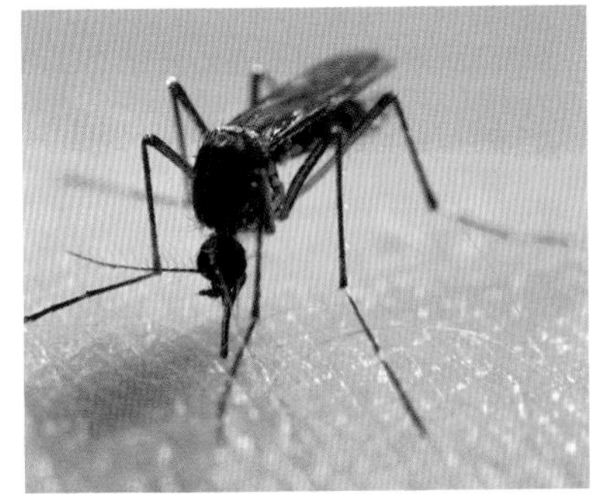

Mosquitoes cause an irritating bite, but they can also be vectors for more serious diseases.

By blood

Hepatitis and AIDS are serious diseases caused by viruses. These micro-organisms are spread in infected blood. Drug addicts who inject themselves with needles used by other people are at risk from these diseases. Doctors and nurses also need to take great care not to allow a patient's blood to enter their bodies through a scratch in the skin.

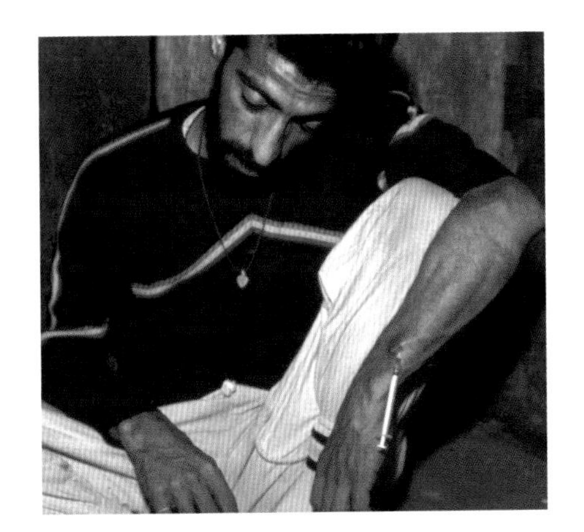

Injected drugs harm the body, but on top of this sharing needles can introduce a deadly disease.

Some diseases, such as rubella (German measles), can pass through the placenta from a pregnant woman to her growing fetus. A baby can also be infected with a disease through breast milk.

Guess what?

'Malaria' means 'bad air' as people originally thought the disease was transmitted by the air. Later it was discovered that mosquitoes were the vectors for malaria.

Language bank 

AIDS
bacteria
contagious diseases
contaminate
faeces
fungi
infectious diseases
micro-organisms
pathogens
transmitted
vectors
viruses

1 Copy and complete using words from the Language bank:

An ______ disease can be spread from one person to another. There are several different ways that diseases can be ______ from one person to another. Organisms that can infect you and cause diseases are called ______. Animals that can carry and transmit diseases are called ______.

2 Give three examples of a pathogen.

3 List six ways in which micro-organisms can spread between people.

4 How are infectious diseases different from heart disease?

Keeping microbes out

How can we protect ourselves against infectious diseases?

You have probably had illnesses caused by micro-organisms at one time or another. Your body has a few ways of defending itself against pathogenic microbes so that you stay healthy most of the time.

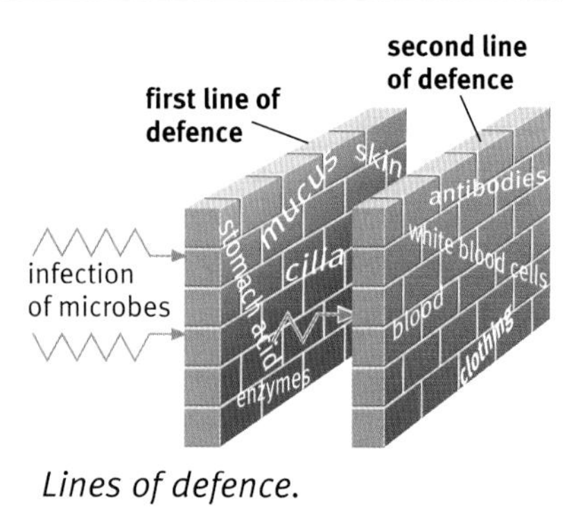

Lines of defence.

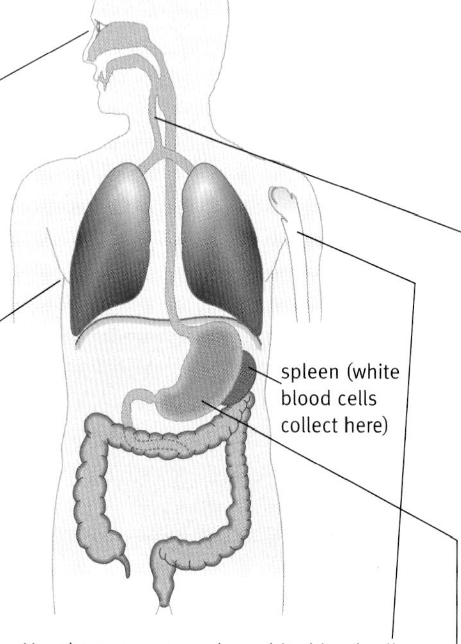

Your sweat and tears contain enzymes called lysozymes. These destroy any micro-organisms that get into your eyes or mouth or on your skin. The insides of your ears are protected by bacteria-destroying wax.

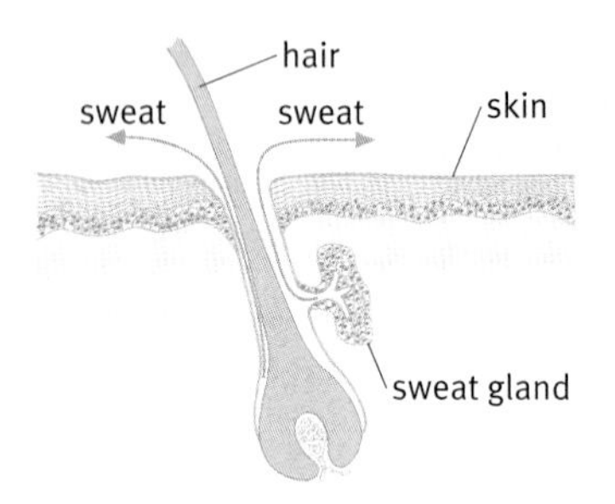

The skin is a barrier to microbes and stops them attacking the delicate tissue beneath. The skin is slightly acidic (pH 5.5) and this kills many micro-organisms. It is also dry, and microbes prefer damp conditions to reproduce.

Your bone marrow makes white blood cells. These are carried in the blood to areas where micro-organisms have invaded the body. They destroy the microbes, for example by engulfing (eating) them.

Air going into your lungs may contain pathogenic micro-organisms. The inside of your nose and your airways are lined with a sticky liquid called **mucus**. This traps the micro-organisms, and tiny hairs called **cilia** line the passages. These move the mucus up to be blown out of your nose or swallowed into your gut where stomach acid destroys them.

Micro-organisms in the body stimulate some white blood cells to make substances called **antibodies**. These help to destroy the micro-organisms.

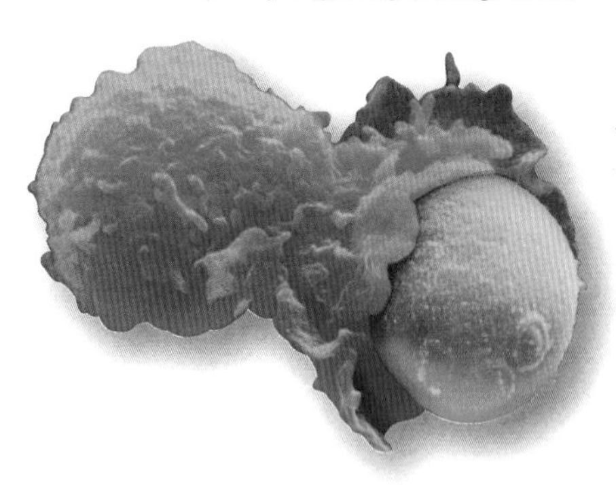

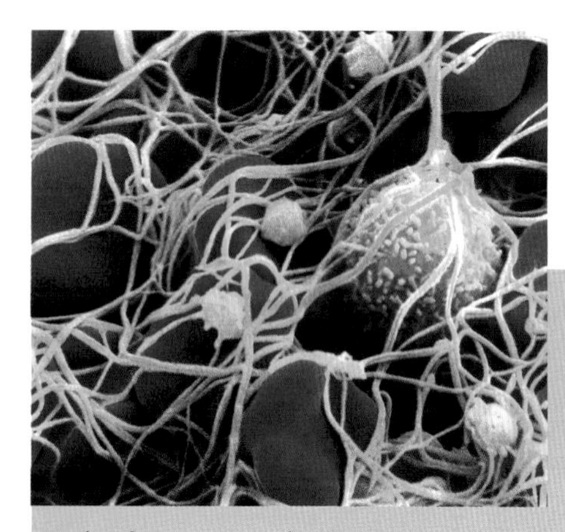

A clot forms to seal a wound.

If you cut yourself, blood washes out microbes from the cut. White blood cells fight any invading micro-organisms. Platelets in the blood stick together to form a **clot**, sealing the wound with a scab so microbes can't get in. Fluid from blood leaks into the surrounding tissue to fight microbes, causing swelling.

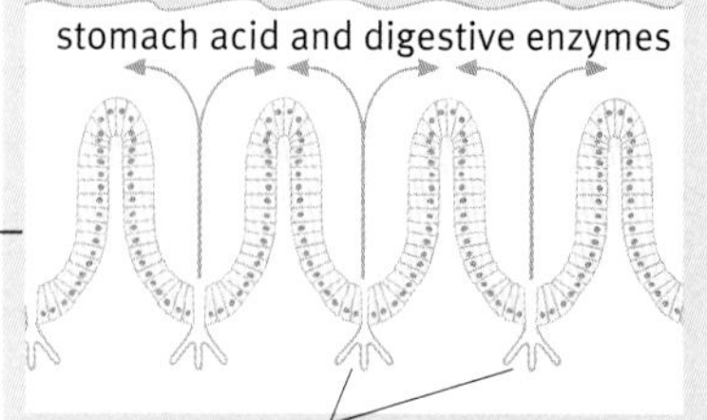

The acid in your stomach kills most of the bacteria in the food you eat.

More about antibodies

- Some antibodies stick to the surface of the micro-organisms, which makes them more likely to be engulfed by white blood cells.
- Some antibodies simply dissolve micro-organisms.
- Some antibodies make micro-organisms stick together in lumps so they cannot get inside body cells and reproduce.
- Some antibodies produce antitoxins, which disarm the poisonous toxins made by micro-organisms.

How to kill micro-organisms

There are things we can do to kill micro-organisms both inside and outside the body, and reduce the risk of infection.

- Micro-organisms thrive in warmth but are killed at high temperatures. Hospital equipment is **sterilised** in an autoclave, a kind of pressure cooker which heats things to around 120 °C.
- If you are ill with a bacterial disease, the doctor will prescribe **antibiotics**. These are drugs that kill bacteria in your body, or stop them growing. Antibiotics do not affect viruses, so they are not prescribed for colds or flu. Penicillin is one antibiotic. It is made by a fungus called *Penicillium*.
- **Disinfectants** are chemicals used to sterilise things outside the body, for example on kitchen surfaces. Some contain chlorine, a bleach which kills micro-organisms.

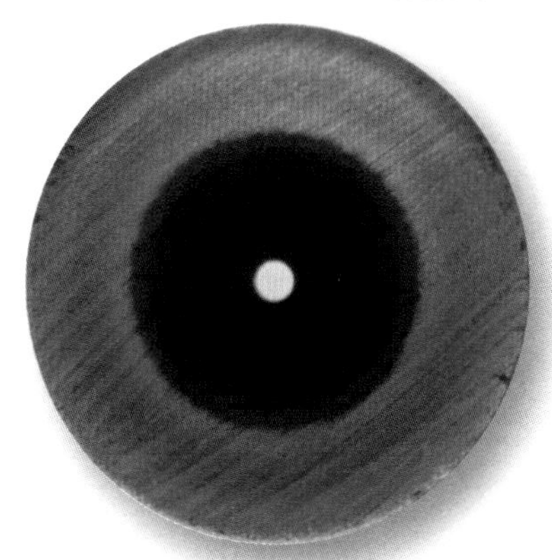

The disc contains penicillin. The clear area shows where it has killed the bacteria in the agar.

Language bank 

antibiotics
antibodies
antitoxins
clot
disinfectants
engulfing
lysozymes
micro-organisms
mucus
pathogens
platelets
skin
sterilised
swelling
toxins
white blood cells

1. Copy and complete using words from the Language bank:
   ______ are micro-organisms that cause disease if they enter the body. To prevent this, the ______ covers us and ______ in our airways traps microbes. If any microbes do enter the body, an army of white ______ cells fight infection.
2. Describe six ways the body has of trying to prevent pathogens entering the body and making us ill.
3. What is the difference between an antibiotic and a disinfectant?
4. The skin is sometimes described as an organ that is a waterproof, germ-proof, self-repairing barrier against germs and dirt. Explain why it is important that the skin behave in this way.
5. The blood is a tissue made up of several types of cell. Some white blood cells engulf microbes. Others make antibodies. Explain the function of antibodies.

3C.4 Immunity and immunisation

How can we protect ourselves against infectious diseases?

Innoculation, vaccination, immunisation...?

They all mean injecting a vaccine to make you immune to a disease.

If a micro-organism invades your body, your white blood cells make antibodies to fight it. Once your body has made these particular antibodies, it 'remembers' how to make them. If that micro-organism invades again, you are protected and don't get the disease. You are **immune** to that disease.

Active immunity

Active immunity happens when people make their own antibodies to a disease.

Natural: If you have been infected with a disease, your body made antibodies to it. Your body 'remembers' the disease, and is ready to make antibodies quickly if you are ever infected again.

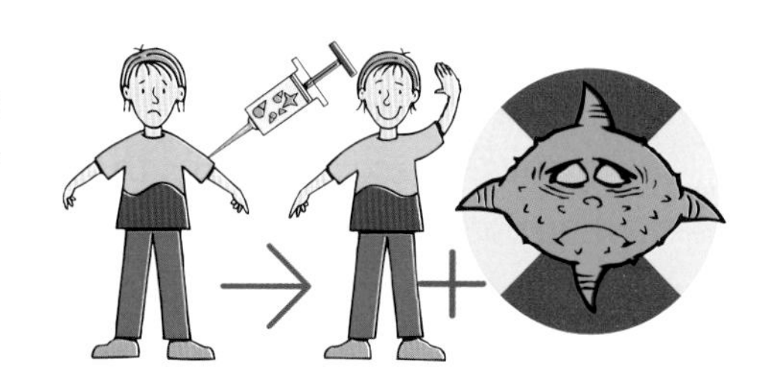

Artificial: You can be injected with a **vaccine** containing weakened or dead microbes, or some bits of microbes. The active live microbes are not present, so the vaccine does not make you ill. But your body reacts to the microbes and sets about making antibodies to fight them. It then 'remembers' how to make these antibodies, ready to react if you are ever infected with the disease.

Passive immunity

With passive immunity, people are given ready-made antibodies.

Natural: Pregnant women pass on their antibodies to their growing baby through the placenta. There are also antibodies in breast milk. This gives newborn babies some immunity from microbial infections.

Artificial: Antibodies are made outside the body, for example in laboratory-bred animals. These antibodies are injected into people and animals to give protection from fast-acting microbes. An example is the anti-tetanus vaccine. You may be injected with this if you have a deep or dirty wound where tetanus bacteria may grow. Your body may not make its own antibodies fast enough to fight them.

Pros and cons of immunisation

Immunisation is a very effective way of preventing an **epidemic**, when a disease spreads through the population.

Measles can be a deadly disease. A vaccine was introduced in the late 1960s, and this caused a dramatic reduction in the disease, as the graph on the next page shows.

Vaccines only work if lots of people are immunised. Because of this all children are immunised against the following diseases:

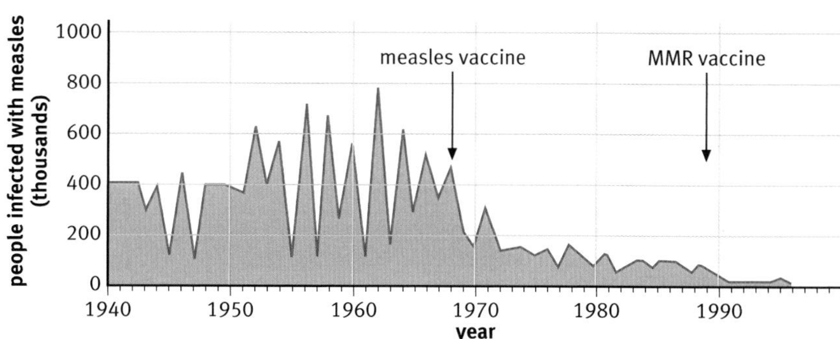

- The MMR vaccine immunises against measles, mumps and rubella.
- Tuberculosis (TB) is a serious bacterial disease which is difficult to cure with antibiotics. The BCG vaccination immunises people against TB.
- Polio is a disease caused by a virus, which can paralyse the muscles. The polio vaccine is very effective and doctors are hoping that polio will be eradicated (completely wiped out) by 2005.
- The DTP-Hib vaccine immunises against diphtheria (a contagious bacterial disease which used to kill many children), tetanus, pertussis (whooping cough) and also *Haemophilus influenzae* type B, a bacterium that causes meningitis.

Before the measles vaccine was introduced, an average of 250 000 people a year had the disease in England and Wales, and 85 children a year died of measles. In 1999, 2438 cases of measles were recorded and only two people died.

But vaccines can have side-effects, and some may even cause symptoms of the disease they are vaccinating against. Recently people have been worried about the MMR vaccine. However, the diseases themselves are very serious and without immunisation we are all at risk.

Guess what?

Not all vaccinations give immunity for life. Tetanus (lockjaw) is a bacterial disease that causes muscle spasm. The tetanus bacterium can thrive in deep wounds that have been in contact with the soil. If people cut themselves when outside, they may need a tetanus 'booster' if they have not had one in the last five years.

The problem with flu

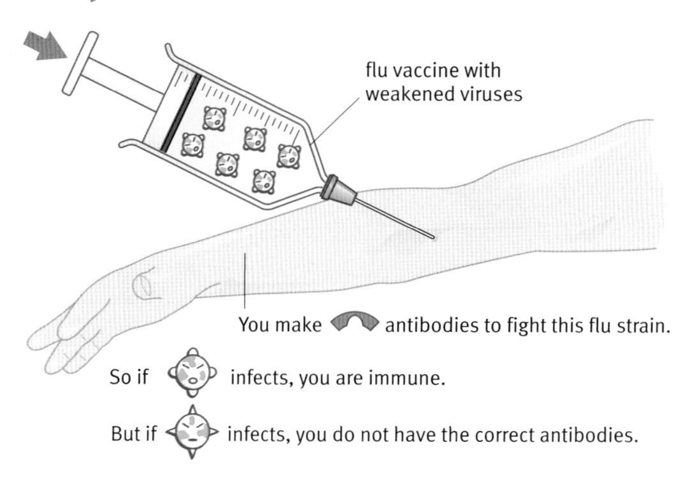

Flu is caused by a virus, so antibiotics do not work. People are vaccinated against one strain of the virus, but if a new virus emerges they can still catch that one. A new way forward maybe an antiviral drug that treats some types of influenza virus.

Language bank 

active immunity
antibodies
artificial immunity
immune
immunisation
immunity
inoculation
natural immunity
passive immunity
vaccination
vaccine

1. Copy and complete using words from the Language bank:

   The body is ______ if it is resistant to infection by a particular micro-organism. In ______ immunity, you make your own antibodies. In ______ immunity, you are given ready-made antibodies.

2. Give three names for injecting someone with a vaccine to make them immune to a disease.

3. Explain why the number of cases of measles fell sharply in the late 1960s. Use the words 'vaccine' and 'antibody' in your answer.

Checkpoint

1 Choose an answer

Copy and complete this sentence, choosing the correct ending from the list below.

There are three groups of micro-organism. They are:

fungi, decomposers and pathogens.
bacteria, fungi and viruses.
bacteria, germs and viruses.
rubella, bacteria and fungi.

2 Match the microbe

The diagrams show two kinds of micro-organism. Make a sketch of each and copy the notes below under the correct diagram. Name each one with the type of micro-organism.

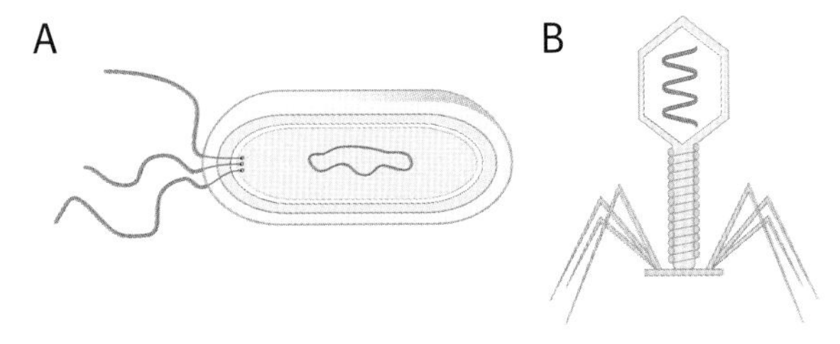

Notes

small cell, $\frac{1}{100}$ the size of an animal cell
have a cell wall, cell membrane, cytoplasm and genetic material
some cause disease, some are useful
examples include *Salmonella* and *Lactobacillus*

not a cell, much smaller than the smallest cell
have a protein coat with genetic material inside
can only reproduce inside living organisms
examples include the common cold and HIV

3 Dodging diseases

Make a table with three columns: 'Diseases', 'Transmitted by' and 'How to avoid catching the disease'. Match up the following diseases with how they are transmitted and write them in your table. Then suggest how you might avoid catching each disease.

Diseases	Transmitted by
impetigo	eating infected food
common cold	touch
typhoid	mosquito vector
salmonella	breathing in droplets
malaria	drinking infected water

4 Lines of defence

Make a large copy of the diagram below. Add these labels on the correct walls.

Labels

white blood cells
antibodies
mucus and cilia in airways
enzymes in tears and sweat
skin
stomach acid
clotting

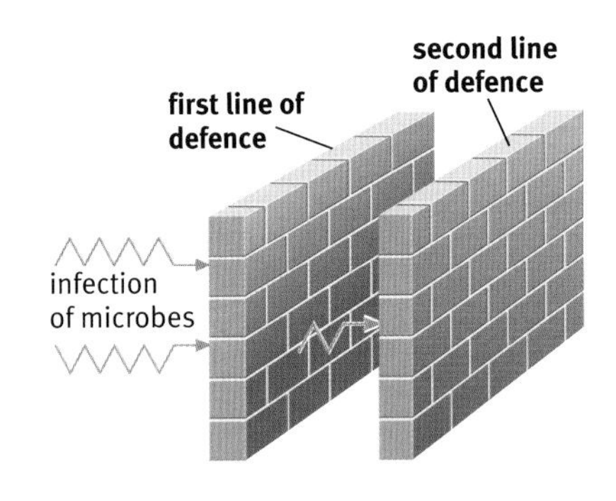

5 All mixed up

Match each word with its correct meaning.

Words

immunisation
passive immunity
active immunity
vaccine

Meanings

having antibodies that your body made for itself
a solution containing weakened or dead microbes
having antibodies that your body did not make for itself
injecting someone with a vaccine to make them immune

Ecological relationships

Before starting this unit, you should already be familiar with these ideas from earlier work.

- There are many different habitats on Earth. Can you think of four different environmental conditions you could measure?
- Living things are adapted to their environment. They carry out their life processes in a way that suits their surroundings.
- Organisms of the same species have many characteristics in common. Do you know what species you belong to?
- All the different species are put in groups, such as animal or plant. If it's an animal, it might be a vertebrate or an invertebrate. Can you remember the five groups of vertebrates?
- We show the energy flow in a community using food chains and food webs. What's at the start of every food chain?

You will meet these key ideas as you work through this unit. Have a quick look now, and at the end of the unit read them through slowly.

- Plants are classified into several taxonomic groups. **Flowering plants** and **conifers** make seeds for reproduction. **Mosses, liverworts** and **ferns** make spores. Each group has different features which adapt it to different habitats.
- Communities of organisms live together and develop. The numbers of some species change at different times – in summer when it is drier there will be fewer moss plants in a woodland.
- **Predators** affect the numbers of **prey** animals. Eagles eat grouse, so if there are no eagles, the number of grouse will rise.
- Energy is transferred between organisms in food webs. Producers (plants) store energy by making their own food and consumers (animals) take in energy in their food.
- Animals use some of this energy for the life processes, and lose some as heat. So there is less to pass on to the next animal – energy is lost at each stage of the food chain.
- A **pyramid of numbers** compares the numbers of organisms at each level in a food chain. It shows that there is less energy at the top.
- As one animal eats another, materials pass from one organism to the next. When the organisms die, they decay and the materials are returned to the environment ready to build new organisms.

Classifying organisms

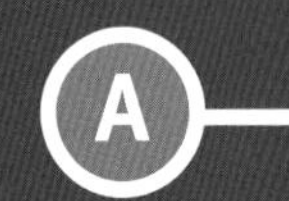

- How can animals be classified?
- How can green plants be classified?

Remember
To be alive, every living thing must carry out the seven life processes.

Which organisms might live an ocean habitat? You could probably suggest many different ones. A **habitat** is a place where an organism lives, and it provides the organism with the essentials of life so that it can carry out the seven life processes. A habitat provides ...

animals with:
- food
- shelter
- water.

plants with:
- light
- water
- a place to grow.

The resources in a habitat affect which organisms can live there. For example, a green plant could not live in a dark cave, as it would not be able to make food by photosynthesis. A bat could sleep in a dark cave but might need to leave it to search for food.

Classifying animals

We could classify organisms by where they live; for example, a camel is a desert animal. But as you know from Unit 7D, animals are divided up into vertebrates (with a backbone) and invertebrates (without a backbone).

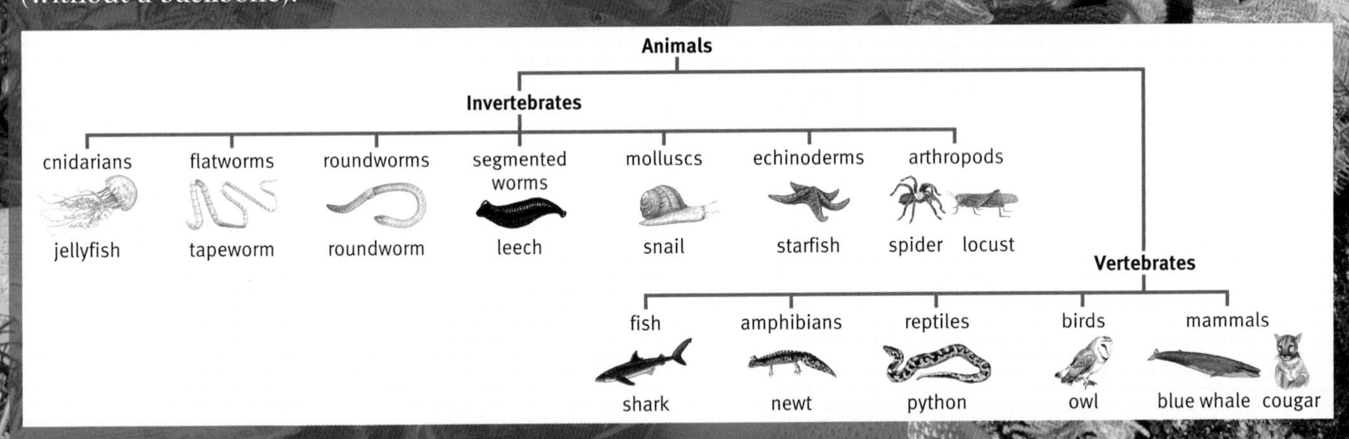

Classifying plants

There are more than 300 000 plant species, with many different features. All these plants can be classified depending on:
- whether they reproduce using seeds or spores
- what sort of veins (vascular tissue) they have in their leaves.

Using seeds

The **flowering plants** have male and female organs, which make **seeds** for reproduction. Flowering plants are well adapted to almost every sort of habitat.

- **Monocotyledons** are flowering plants with narrow leaves that have parallel veins.

Palms, grasses and cereals such as wheat are monocotyledons.

- **Dicotyledons** have broad leaves with a central midrib and branched veins. Flowers may have colourful petals.

Geraniums are dicotyledons.

Conifers can live in very dry places and can survive in many different habitats.

Conifers also make seeds, but inside cones rather than flowers.

Using spores

There are several groups of plants that reproduce using **spores**.

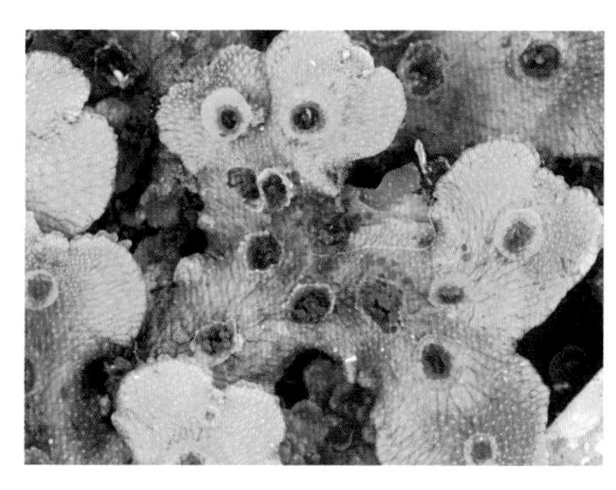

Mosses *(left) and* ***liverworts*** *(right) are small plants with tiny roots. They live only in damp areas as they have no waxy surface on their leaves to hold in water.*

Ferns *such as this male fern can live in drier conditions than mosses, but they need moisture to make their spores.*

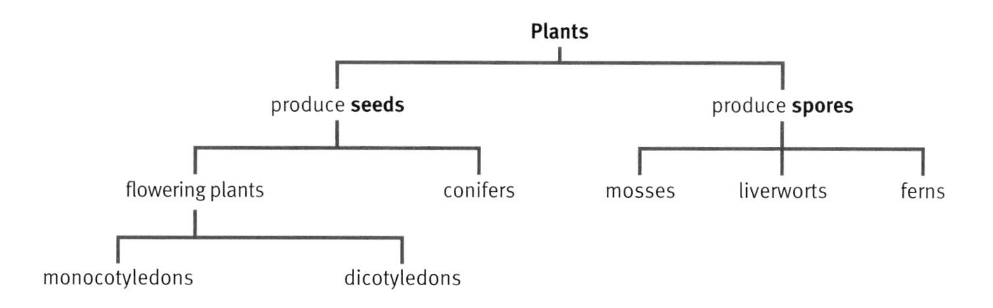

1 Copy and complete using words from the Language bank:

Animals are classified as ______ or ______. Plants are classified depending on whether they produce seeds or ______. The ______ plants produce seeds and are grouped into ______ and dicotyledons.

2 Which groups of plants are adapted to live in many different habitats?

3 Explain why mosses and liverworts need a moist habitat.

Language bank

adapted
animals
classify
conifers
dicotyledons
ferns
flowering plants
habitat
invertebrates
life processes
liverworts
monocotyledons
mosses
plants
seeds
spores
vertebrates

Finding out where things live

- How do plants, animals and environmental conditions interact in a habitat?

Remember

A **population** is a group of a particular species in a habitat.

A **community** is all the populations of different species in the habitat.

The **distribution** of an organism is simply where we find that plant or animal.

Damp or dry, hot or cold, sunny or shady – the conditions in an environment determine which organisms live in the habitats there. The different populations of plants and animals interact with the environment and also with each other. There are many factors that affect the numbers and distribution of populations in the community.

Counting plants

How does the distribution of plants depend on an environmental factor such as temperature, sunlight or the amount of dissolved oxygen? To find out we use **fieldwork**. This often means going out and counting the number of individuals of a species in a location. But how do we count individuals?

Sampling using a quadrat

For example, to find out the number of daisies on your school field and see if there are more there than in the field next door, you could count all the daisies in each field and compare the results. This would take a long time and might bore even the keenest ecologist! So we count just some of them – we take a **sample** to represent the whole field. We use a **quadrat** to take our sample.

A quadrat is a 1 m square made from wood or metal. We throw this in different positions randomly around the field and count the number of daisies in each square. If we do this say, ten times, we can work out the average number of daisies per square metre. If we know the total area of the field we can estimate the total number of daisies.

Why throw it randomly?

Otherwise you might choose all the areas with more daisies, or all the areas without daisies. Throwing randomly is fairer.

Quadrat	Number of daisies
1	1
2	3
3	2
4	4
5	3
6	1
7	3
8	2
9	4
10	1
total	24
average density of daisies per square metre	$\frac{24}{10} = 2.4$
number in a field 600 m × 800 m (= area 480 000 m^2)	$2.4 \times 480\,000 = 1\,152\,000$

Add up the daisies in each quadrat.

Divide by 10 to find the average per quadrat.

If one square metre has 2.4 daisies the whole field will have 1 152 000 daisies. Imagine counting all those!

Sampling using a line transect

Instead of counting the daisies, you might want to look at how the distribution of plant life changes as you move across the field. A **line transect** can help you investigate this.

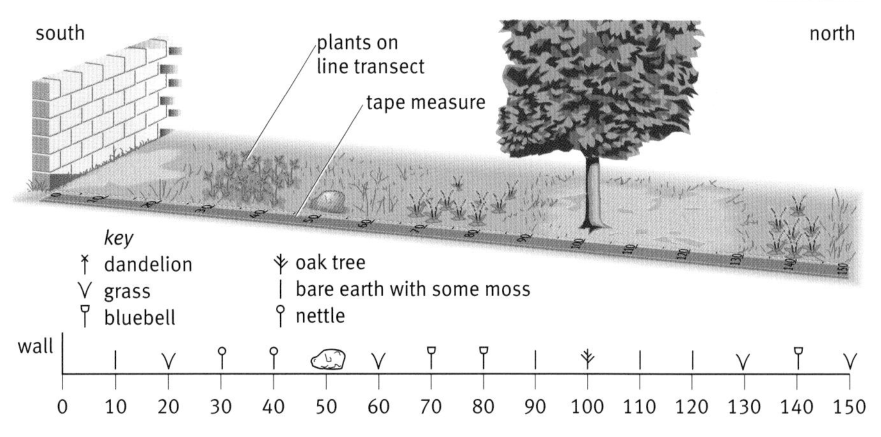

Place a tape measure on the ground. Record the position of all the plants it touches. You could take a light meter reading at each point to see if there is a relationship between the light level and the plants that grow there.

Sampling using a belt transect

A **belt transect** is two parallel line transects. These could be about one metre apart, with a quadrat placed between to record the plants present.

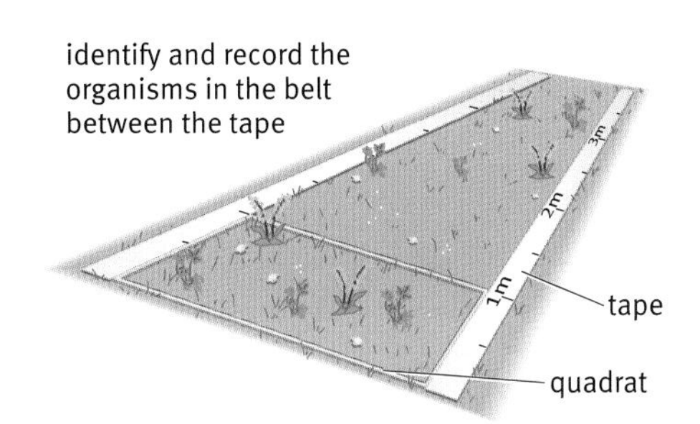

A grid between the two lines allows you to map the distribution of plants in the belt transect.

Counting animals

Counting plants and stationary seashore animals like limpets and mussels is relatively easy. However, most animals move around so are not so easy to count.

We catch small animals in a trap to count them and get an idea of the distribution of different species in a habitat. The traps must be designed not to harm the animals, and they should always be returned to their natural environment afterwards. We observe larger animals over a long period of time from a distance.

You can use a ***pooter*** *to collect small animals when investigating a habitat.*

1 Copy and complete using words from the Language bank:

A ______ is the number of one particular species in a habitat. A ______ is all the different populations in a habitat. We can use fieldwork to study the ______ of plants and animals in a habitat.

2 What is sampling and why is it particularly useful in fieldwork?

3 Explain why taking just one sample might give misleading results in a large field.

4 If you were looking at a pond habitat, find out how you might collect organisms to investigate their distribution in the pond.

Language bank 

belt transect
community
distribution
environment
fieldwork
habitat
line transect
pooter
population
quadrat
sampling

Difficult relationships

How do living things in a community depend on each other?

You have used **food chains** to show what the organisms of a particular habitat eat. A food chain starts with a **producer** (a green plant), and continues with a **consumer** (usually an animal). The first consumer is a **herbivore** (plant-eater). Higher consumers may be **omnivores** (plant- and meat-eaters) or **carnivores** (meat-eaters).

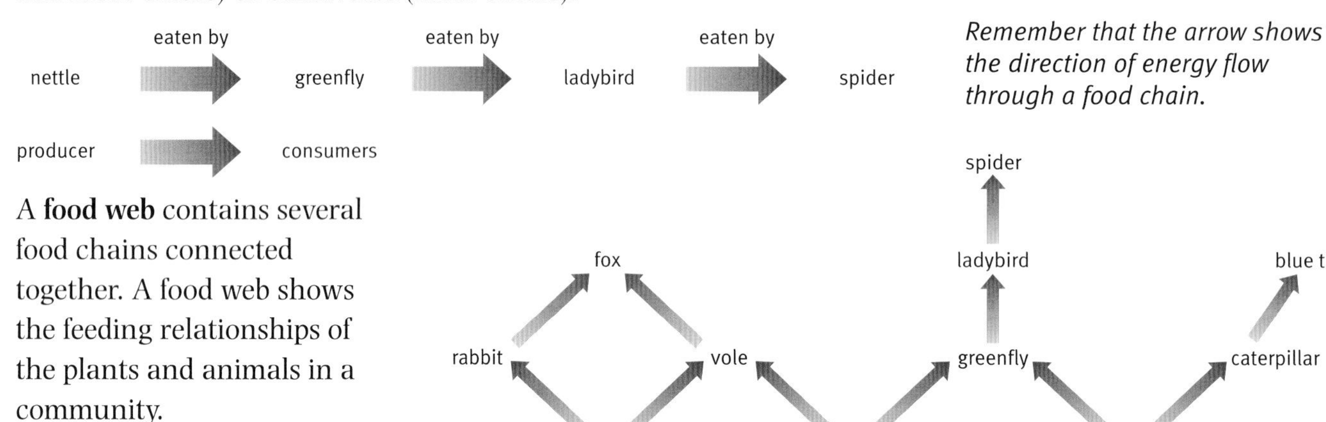

Remember that the arrow shows the direction of energy flow through a food chain.

A **food web** contains several food chains connected together. A food web shows the feeding relationships of the plants and animals in a community.

Predators and prey

Predators are organisms high up the food chain. They are good hunters, well adapted to finding, catching and killing their **prey**.

Prey animals are well adapted for detecting and avoiding predators.

The poison dart frog (left) has a brightly coloured toxic skin which puts off predators. The leaf frog (right) is camouflaged to blend into the background.

The ups and downs of the predator–prey relationship

In any environment the relative numbers of predator and prey are constantly changing, depending on environmental factors such as the availability of green plants (producers).

Grouse are birds that live in a moorland environment such as in Scotland. Grouse eat mainly heather, and are prey for eagles:

heather → grouse → eagle

The golden eagle is well adapted as a predator.

If there is lots of heather and therefore plenty of grouse, the eagle population will thrive. More eagle predators will catch lots of grouse so after a while the grouse population will fall. Then there are fewer grouse for the eagles to eat, so after a while the number of eagles falls too. This allows the number of grouse to increase again, and so the cycle continues. The graph shows how this relationship might cause a cyclic rise and fall in the populations of both animals.

1 number of grouse rising with plenty of heather to eat
3 fewer grouse now as the eagles eat more of them
key
grouse
eagles
population
2 number of eagles rises too as there are plenty of grouse to eat
4 with less grouse around, eagle population falls too
time

The populations of predators and prey are closely linked.

A further look at food webs

Every food web contains many interconnecting food chains. If the population of one organism changes, many others are affected, not just those they eat or that eat them.

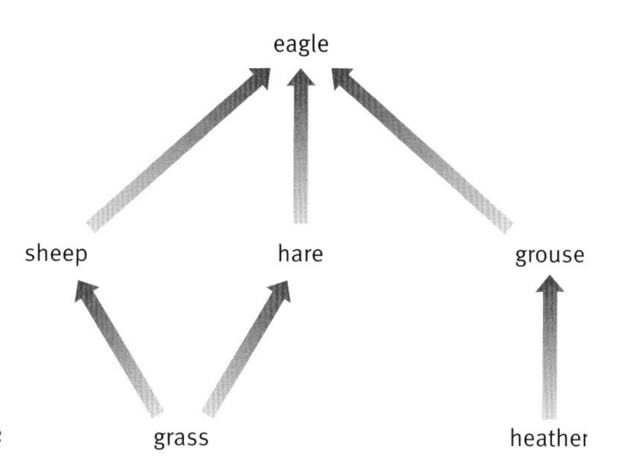

Eagles in Scotland do not just eat grouse; they feed off hares and dead sheep as well. So if the populations of hares, grouse and sheep are high, then eagles will be plentiful.

Hares eat grass and are prey for eagles.

What might happen if the number of hares suddenly falls, perhaps because of a disease?

- There is more grass for sheep to eat (as fewer hares are eating it).
- Eagles have fewer hares to eat, so they eat more grouse.
- The number of grouse therefore falls.
- Fewer grouse eat less heather, so the heather grows and spreads.
- Farmers might find that hungry eagles are targeting their sheep.

So a decrease in the population of just one species can have a huge effect on the populations of many organisms in a community.

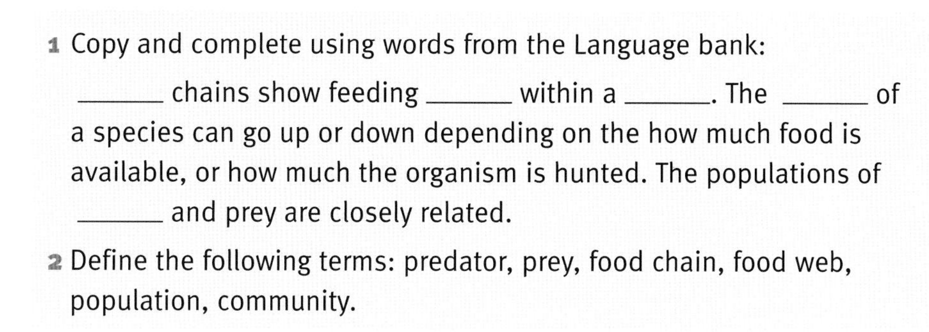
1 Copy and complete using words from the Language bank:

______ chains show feeding ______ within a ______. The ______ of a species can go up or down depending on the how much food is available, or how much the organism is hunted. The populations of ______ and prey are closely related.

2 Define the following terms: predator, prey, food chain, food web, population, community.

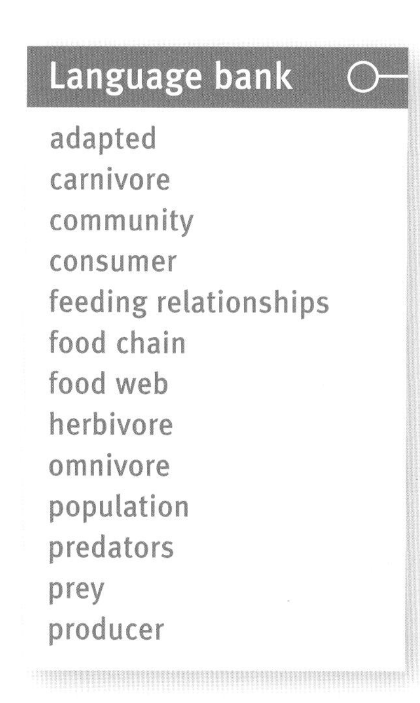
Language bank

adapted
carnivore
community
consumer
feeding relationships
food chain
food web
herbivore
omnivore
population
predators
prey
producer

Pyramids of numbers and biomass

○ How do living things in a community depend on each other?

Drawing pyramids

To see the relationship between two variables in an experiment, you draw a graph. In the same way, to study the relationship between populations in a food chain, we count the organisms and draw a diagram called a **pyramid of numbers**.

The first pyramid opposite shows a typical pyramid shape, with lots of producers and just a few carnivores (eagles) at the top. The second pyramid is different because there is only one oak tree with many caterpillars living off it. The oak tree is one organism, but it is very large. To give a more realistic idea of the feeding relationship we use another pyramid called a **pyramid of biomass**.

Ecologists draw a pyramid of biomass by weighing all the organisms at each stage of the food chain. The mass of producers is larger than the mass of consumers, and the oak tree food chain now shows a typical pyramid shape.

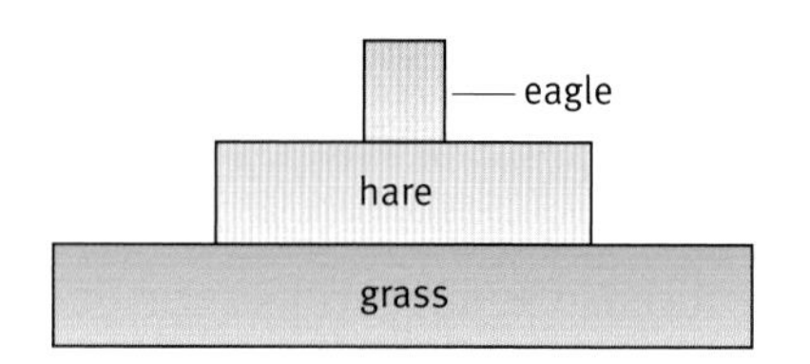

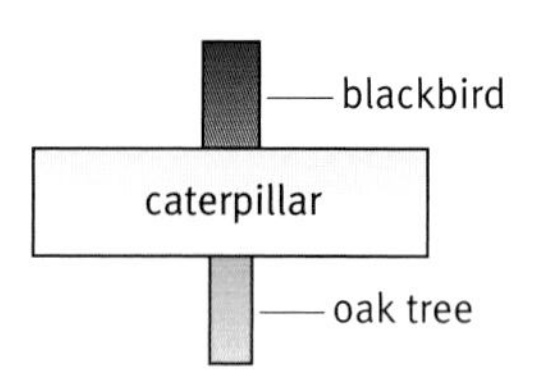

The width of each bar shows the number of organisms. The pyramid of numbers can look strange in some food chains.

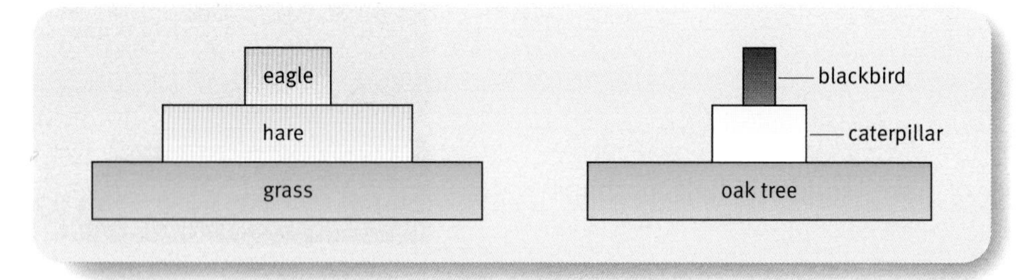

In a pyramid of biomass, the width of each bar shows the mass of the organisms.

Energy flow through food chains

The mass of each organism gives an idea of how much energy is available in it. The pyramid of biomass shows how energy flows through the food chain. There is less energy at the top of the pyramid.

This is because energy is lost at each link in the food chain. For example, grass makes food by photosynthesis, converting sunlight energy to stored chemical energy in the grass. A hare eats the grass to provide itself with energy.

The hare uses the energy from the grass to stay alive and carry out the life processes. It only stores a small amount of that energy in its body. This means that less energy is available for the eagle to build up its body mass. Because of this, the total mass always decreases as you go up the food chain:

- The mass of hares is smaller than the mass of grass.
- The mass of eagles is smaller than the mass of hares.

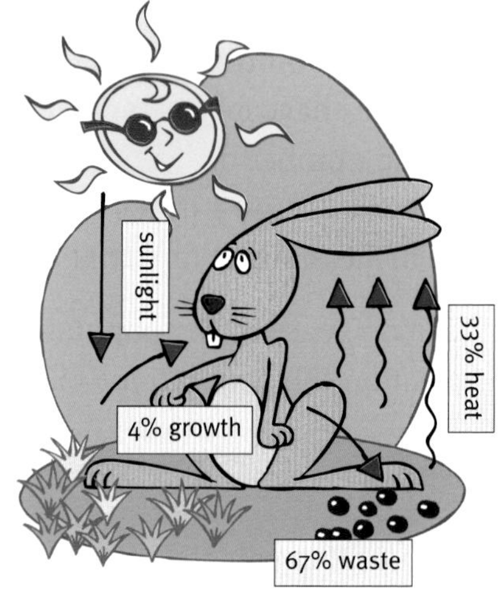

Of all the stored chemical energy the hare eats, 63% of it leaves the hare in droppings, 33% keeps it warm and just 4% increases its body mass. That 4% is the only energy available to the eagle that eats the hare.

Meat or veg?

A one-hectare field could produce about 5 tonnes of wheat to make 2 tonnes of bread for us to eat.

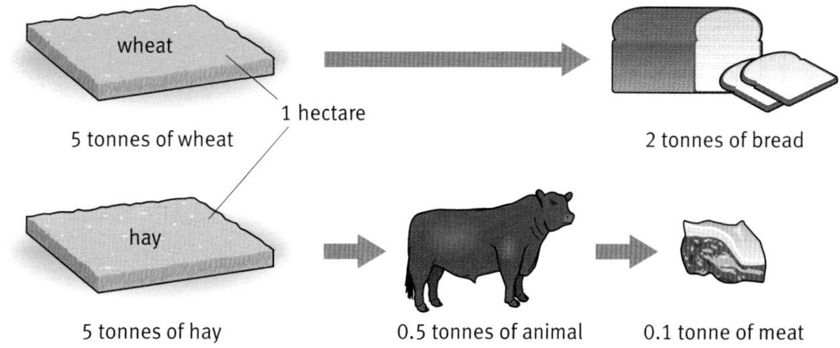

The lower we are in the food chain, the less energy is wasted.

The same field could instead produce 5 tonnes of hay. An animal could eat this to increase its body mass to 0.5 tonnes. This animal could then make 0.1 tonne of meat for us to eat.

Using the field to produce wheat, people are lower in the food chain and so less energy is lost. Using the field to feed animals, less meat can be made from the field because the animals waste energy simply by living.

Guess what?

Intensive farming methods try to minimise the energy wasted by animals. For example, small pens or cages restrict their movement. Free range or organic methods are less energy effective but have obvious advantages for the welfare of the animals..

Plants benefit from the death of others

Dead plants and animals are broken down by micro-organisms. They eventually find their way back into the soil. This supplies minerals for new plants to grow.

Decay returns minerals to the soil.

The organic material that makes up living material is **biodegradable** – it will rot away. Composting waste plant matter makes it decay more quickly, providing gardeners with compost to fertilise the soil and help next year's plants grow well. Nitrogen and other elements are cycled through the environment in this way.

Small pens stop the pigs wasting energy by moving around.

1. Copy and complete using words from the Language bank:
   A pyramid of ______ shows the number of each organism in a food chain. A pyramid of ______ tells us the mass of each organism in a food chain. This gives some idea of the amount of energy at each stage of the ______ .
2. Sketch a pyramid of biomass for one food chain in this food web.

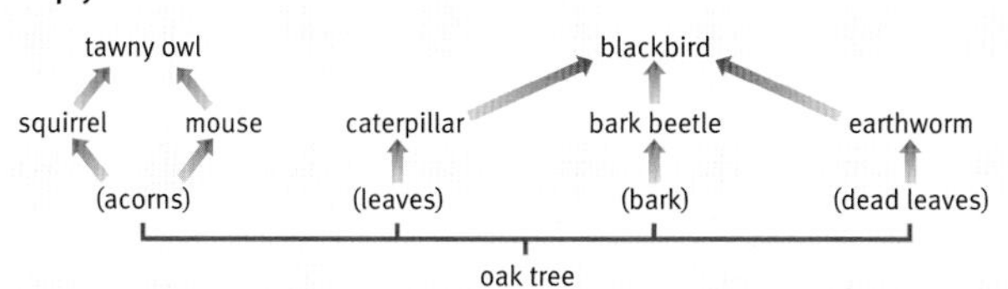

3. Explain why vegetables are usually cheaper per kilogram than meat.
4. Make a poster explaining why people should compost their vegetable waste rather than putting it in the dustbin.

Language bank 

- biodegradable
- composting
- consumers
- energy
- food chain
- organic
- producers
- pyramid of biomass
- pyramid of numbers

Checkpoint

1 Grouping plants

Copy the diagram opposite showing the main taxonomic groups of plants. Complete it using the words below.

mosses, seeds, conifers, ferns, dicotyledons

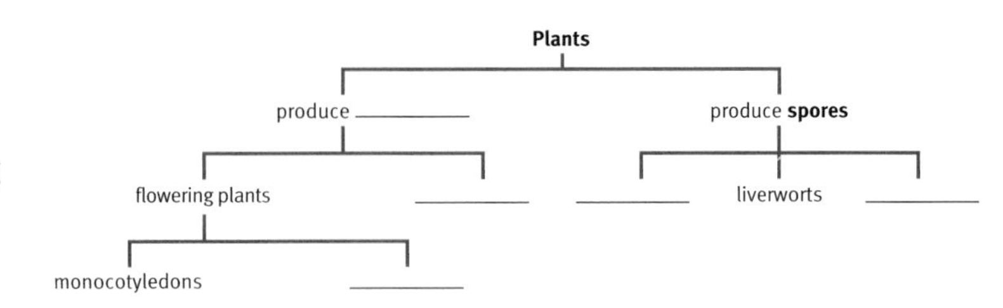

2 True or false?

Decide whether the following statements are true or false. Write down the true ones. Correct the false ones before you write them down.

- **a** Conifers reproduce using seeds. The seeds are made in flowers.
- **b** Flowering plants reproduce using seeds. The seeds are made in flowers.
- **c** Mosses have tiny roots. They live in dry places because they have no waxy surface on their leaves.
- **d** Ferns reproduce using seeds. They need moist conditions for this.

3 Depending on each other

Look at this food web. Suggest all the things that might happen if

- **a** the eagles all die
- **b** all the heather is dug up and sold
- **c** a new predator is released that is adapted to eating hares
- **d** a shooting party kills lots of grouse

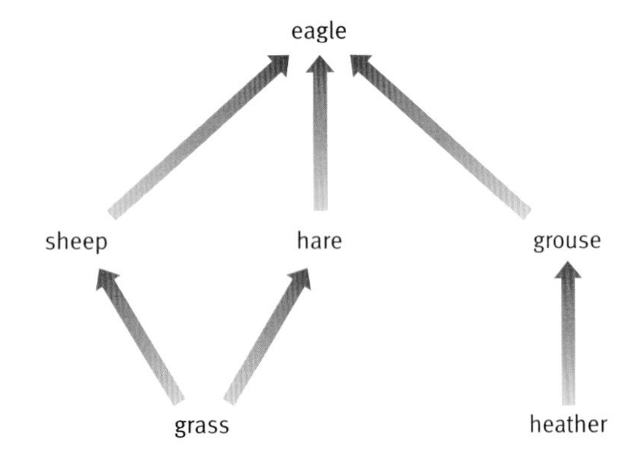

4 Energy flow

Match up the beginnings and endings to write four sentences.

Beginnings

Green plants are producers which store energy by
Consumers eat plants or animals to
Animals use energy for the life processes and
Food chains cannot be very long because

Endings

store some energy in their bodies.
making their own food.
energy is lost at each stage.
supply their energy.

5 Pyramids

Copy and complete these sentences, unscrambling the bold words.

A **marydip** of **brumsen** is a diagram that shows the numbers of organisms at each stage in a food chain.
A pyramid of numbers starting with an oak tree is not a typical **dimypar** shape.
You can overcome this problem using a **ripydma fo sibosma** which shows the **sasm** of organisms at each stage.

Atoms and elements

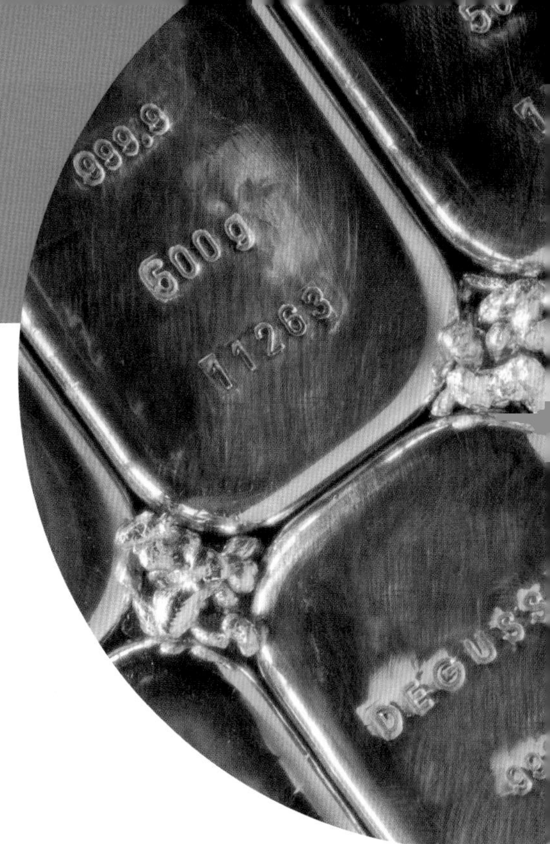

Before starting this unit, you should already be familiar with these ideas from earlier work.

- If we cannot see and touch something in science, we can use a model to help show us how it works. What model have you used to represent electrical circuits?
- The particle model suggests that all matter is made up of particles. How are the particles arranged in solids, liquids and gases?
- Matter sometimes changes state from solid to liquid or liquid to gas and back again. Boiling is one change of state. List some others.

You will meet these key ideas as you work through this unit. Have a quick look now, and at the end of the unit read them through slowly.

- All matter is built from particles called **atoms**.
- Some materials are **elements**. All their atoms are the same type.
- Elements have their own special properties. For example, copper is an orange-brown **metal**. It looks shiny if polished. In contrast sulphur is a yellow crumbly solid which is not shiny – sulphur is a **non-metal**.
- We use **symbols** to write atoms and elements for short. These symbols have one or two letters: C stands for carbon and He for helium.
- We group all the elements in the **periodic table**.
- The millions of materials in the world are made from just a small number of different elements combined in various ways.
- Elements combine to form **compounds**. A compound is a material made up of more than one element. The different atoms are joined firmly in a compound.
- Atoms can join up to make particles called **molecules**. Some elements have molecules. For example, an oxygen molecule has two oxygen atoms chemically joined.
- The molecules of compounds contain different atoms. A carbon monoxide molecule has a carbon atom and an oxygen atom.

3E.1 The material world

How many different materials are there?

Everything around us, and everything we use, is a **material**. Think of all the different substances that exist in the world, from air to sand to jelly to steel. There are millions of different materials. We classify all these materials into groups to help us make sense of them all. The word wall shows some groups of materials.

Materials are made of elements

There are millions of materials, but they are all made up of just 100 or so elements. An **element** is a substance that cannot be split into anything simpler. For example, carbon is an element. If you kept cutting some carbon into smaller pieces, you would still have carbon.

The combination of elements in a material makes it what it is. The elements determine the **properties** of the material, such as its colour, whether it is hard or soft, and what sort of job it is useful for. The fantastic variety of materials that exists are all made from quite a small number of elements. The picture shows some materials and the elements in them.

Guess what?

When scientists make or discover a new material, they register it so that other scientists know about it. About 5000 or so brand new materials are recorded every day.

All these materials are made up of elements. *Some elements are metals, and some are not. Some elements are solids, some are gases and a few are liquids.*

Combining elements

Think of elements as letters in words. There are about 750 000 words in the English language. They are all made up from just 26 letters of the alphabet. We combine letters in different ways to make slightly different words:

TOP STOP TOPS

Which letters we choose, and the order we put them in, determine what the word means. In a similar way, when elements join up to make other materials, the order and number of the elements determine the material's properties.

Carbon dioxide gas is made up of the elements carbon and oxygen. Add some hydrogen, sulphur, nitrogen and a few others, and you have all the elements needed to make a human being.

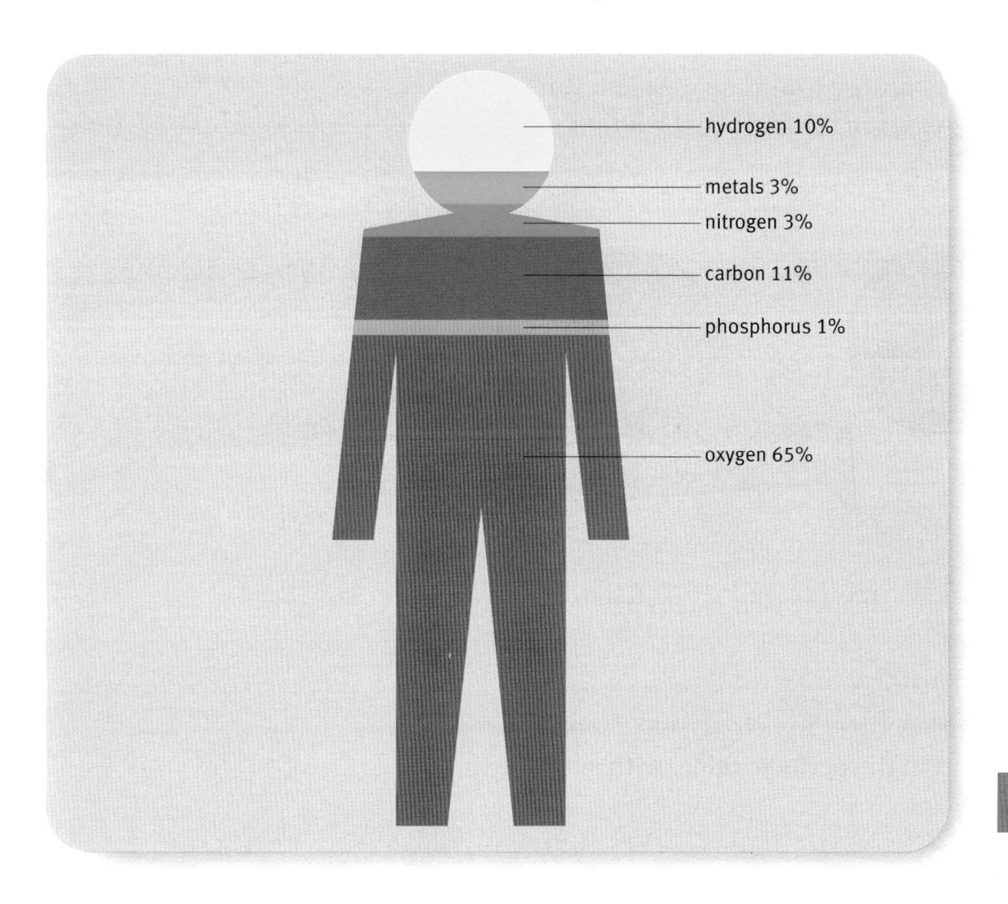

1 Copy and complete using words from the Language bank:

All materials are made from about ______ elements. The number and type of elements present determine the ______ of the material.

2 **a** List four groups of materials.
b Why do we classify materials into groups?

3 What is an element?

4 Explain why it is possible to have so many different materials from a limited number of elements.

Language bank 

100
ceramic
element
glass
material
metal
non-metal
organic
polymer
properties
substance

3E.2 Elements

What are elements made from?

You know that everything is made up of particles. An element is a substance that contains only one kind of particle. The tiny particles that make up an element are called **atoms**. Each element has its own kind of atom, and the atoms in different elements are different.

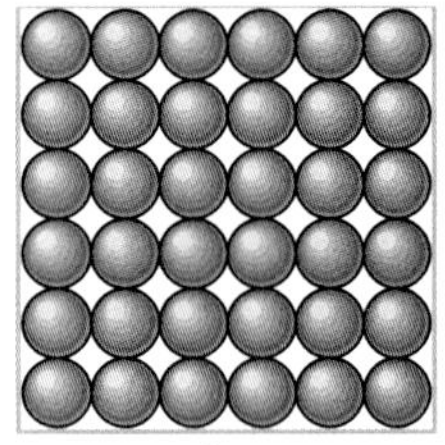
magnesium atoms

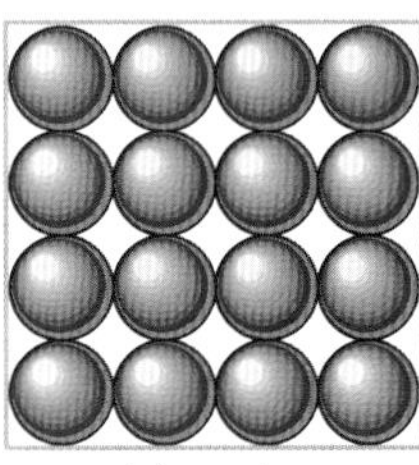
calcium atoms

Each element has its own type of atom.

Atoms are building blocks

Atoms are the building blocks of all materials. We can use a **model** to help us think about this. Just as bricks make up a house, so atoms make a material. For example, iron atoms make up the element iron.

In iron, all the atoms are the same, because iron is an element. But marble is a material that is not an element. In marble, the atoms are not all the same.

A house is made up of bricks.

An iron nail is made up of iron atoms.

So a nail is an element.

No, a nail is an object made of iron. Iron is an element.

The periodic table and symbols

Different elements have different properties. To help us make sense of the different elements, we list them in the **periodic table**, with similar elements grouped together.

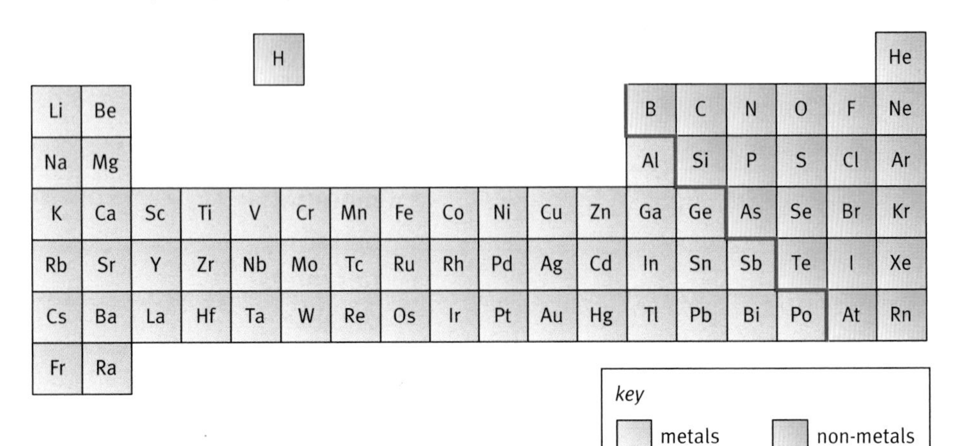

				H													He
Li	Be											B	C	N	O	F	Ne
Na	Mg											Al	Si	P	S	Cl	Ar
K	Ca	Sc	Ti	V	Cr	Mn	Fe	Co	Ni	Cu	Zn	Ga	Ge	As	Se	Br	Kr
Rb	Sr	Y	Zr	Nb	Mo	Tc	Ru	Rh	Pd	Ag	Cd	In	Sn	Sb	Te	I	Xe
Cs	Ba	La	Hf	Ta	W	Re	Os	Ir	Pt	Au	Hg	Tl	Pb	Bi	Po	At	Rn
Fr	Ra																

*Some elements are **metals** – they are shiny and cold to the touch. **Non-metals** are not. Metals are on the left of the red line and non-metals are on the right.*

Each element has a **symbol**, of one or two letters. This is a quick way of showing one atom of the element, or just the element's name. The same symbols are used all over the world. The table shows some examples.

Can you find these three elements in the periodic table? ...

Element	Symbol	Picture of atoms
aluminium (a metal that is a solid)	Al	
mercury (a metal that is a liquid)	Hg	
helium (a non-metal that is a gas)	He	

Molecules

In some elements, such as oxygen, the atoms pair up. A particle made up of more than one atom like this is called a **molecule**. We can show a molecule by combining the symbols for its atoms. We use a small number to show how many atoms there are. So for oxygen, we would write O_2. We call this a **formula**.

... What about these three?

Element	Formula	Picture of molecules
oxygen (a non-metal that is a gas)	O_2	
nitrogen (a non-metal that is a gas)	N_2	
bromine (a non-metal that is a liquid)	Br_2	

1 Copy and complete using words from the Language bank:

Elements are made up from small particles known as ______. We write a ______ to represent an element. All the elements are listed in the ______ table.

2 Explain each of the following terms:

a particle **b** atom **c** element **d** non-metal **e** molecule.

3 Which of the following are metals and which are non-metals?

a hydrogen (H) **b** iron (Fe) **c** oxygen (O) **d** mercury (Hg)

4 Look at the tables above. Draw diagrams showing the particles in:

a a solid metal element with single atoms for particles

b a liquid element with particles made from pairs of atoms

c a gas with single atoms for particles.

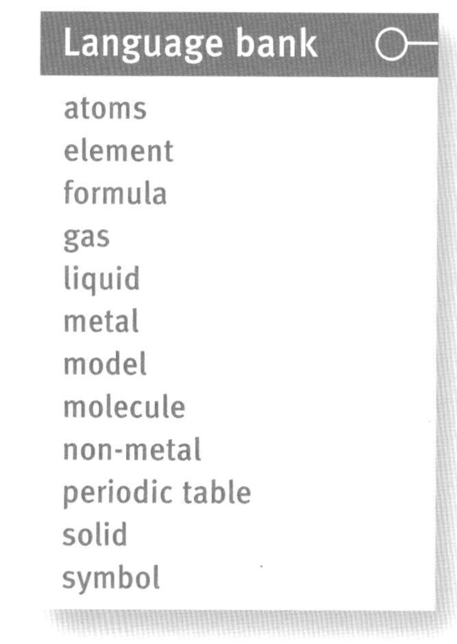

The periodic table

M

What are elements like?

The periodic table contains about 100 or so elements, but only 90 of them are found naturally on the Earth. The rest are made by scientists in the laboratory.

In the periodic table, similar elements are grouped together in vertical columns. For example, lithium, sodium and potassium are in one group on the left-hand side of the table. Fluorine, chlorine and bromine are in another group towards the right.

The cards show how we use some of the elements.

Aluminium is used for drinks cans and overhead power cables.

Silicon is a semiconductor, used to make 'chips' in computers.

Phosphorus is used to make matches, fertilisers, insecticides and pesticides.

Sulphur is used to make sulphuric acid, and also mixed with rubber to make it last longer.

Chlorine is a bleach used to treat water for drinking and in swimming pools.

Argon fills electric light bulbs.

Bromine is used in fuel additives, photography and disinfectants.

Mercury is used in tilt switches. It is also used in some thermometers, but it is poisonous. It is dangerous if the thermometer breaks.

Guess what?

Many element symbols have two letters, not just one. For example, Cl is the symbol for chlorine and Na is the symbol for sodium. C is the symbol for carbon, an element discovered many years before chlorine, so chlorine cannot be C.

1 Copy and complete using words from the Language bank:

The ______ table lists the elements in order, with similar elements in ______. The metals are on the left-hand side and the ______ are on the right. All the ______ are solids at room temperature, apart from mercury which is a liquid.

2 **a** Where are the elements that are gases found in the periodic table?
b List three gaseous elements along with a use for each.

3 Name a non-metal element that is liquid.

4 Metals are good conductors of electricity, and non-metals are generally not.
a Look at the information about silicon. What do you think the word 'semiconductor' means?
b Find out another element that is a semiconductor.
c Silicon lies near the line that separates metals from non-metals. Where is your semiconductor element on the periodic table?

Language bank

100
element
gas
groups
liquid
metals
non-metals
periodic table
solid

Sodium vapour fills street lights and makes an orange glow.

Hydrogen was used in airships to transport people, but is explosive and dangerous so not used for this any more.

Helium makes party balloons float.

Fluorine is used to etch glass, and it is also added to toothpaste.

Neon fills the tubular lights used for advertising.

Oxygen helps ill people breathe in hospitals.

Potassium is used to make 'salt' for people on low-salt diets.

Nitrogen fills crisp packets and keeps the crisps fresh.

H
hydrogen

H – symbol; hydrogen – name

Carbon as charcoal is used to purify water.

Magnesium is used in fireworks and to make aircraft bodies.

Zinc is part of brass, an alloy (metal mixture).

																	He helium
Li lithium	Be beryllium											B boron	C carbon	N nitrogen	O oxygen	F fluorine	Ne neon
Na sodium	Mg magnesium											Al aluminium	Si silicon	P phosphorus	S sulphur	Cl chlorine	Ar argon
K potassium	Ca calcium	Sc scandium	Ti titanium	V vanadium	Cr chromium	Mn manganese	Fe iron	Co cobalt	Ni nickel	Cu copper	Zn zinc	Ga gallium	Ge germanium	As arsenic	Se selenium	Br bromine	Kr krypton
Rb rubidium	Sr strontium	Y yttrium	Zr zirconium	Nb niobium	Mo molybdenum	Tc technetium	Ru ruthenium	Rh rhodium	Pd palladium	Ag silver	Cd cadmium	In indium	Sn tin	Sb antimony	Te tellurium	I iodine	Xe xenon
Cs caesium	Ba barium	La lanthanum	Hf hafnium	Ta tantalum	W tungsten	Re rhenium	Os osmium	Ir iridium	Pt platinum	Au gold	Hg mercury	Tl thallium	Pb lead	Bi bismuth	Po polonium	At astatine	Rn radon
Fr francium	Ra radium																

metals | non-metals

Chlorine

Phosphorus

Iron is used to make steels for construction.

Nickel is mixed with copper to make coins.

Copper pipes carry water in our homes.

Bromine

Calcium is found in limestone and marble.

key

solids liquids gases

Some elements are solid, some liquid and some gas at room temperature. The metals are found on the left-hand side of the table and the non-metals are on the right. Their individual properties make them useful in many different ways.

Compounds

How do we get all the other materials?

To make all the 26 million or so different materials that exist, the 100 or so elements must join up in different ways. New materials form when the atoms of these elements join in different ways.

A material that is made of more than one element joined together is called a **compound**. For example, water is a compound made up of the elements hydrogen (symbol H) and oxygen (O). In a compound, the atoms are not just mixed, they are chemically joined up.

A compound such as water has particles called **molecules**. We can represent molecules by drawing coloured circles, to show the arrangement of the atoms. We can also represent a water molecule by writing a chemical formula: H_2O. This tells us that a molecule of water contains two atoms of hydrogen and one atom of oxygen. You can see this explained in more detail below.

Water

Water is made up of many identical water molecules. Water is a liquid, so the molecules are close together.

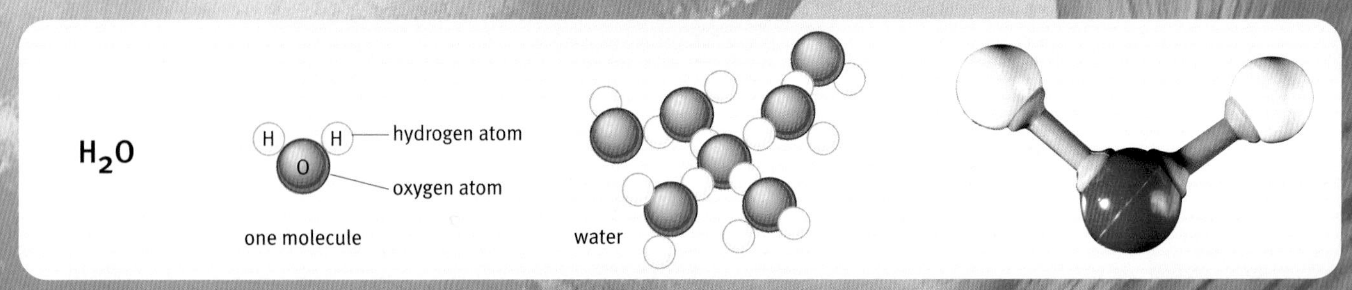

One oxygen atom is joined to two hydrogen atoms to make each water molecule.

Carbon dioxide

Carbon dioxide is a gas, so the molecules are further apart than in water.

Carbon dioxide, formula CO_2. One carbon atom is joined to two oxygen atoms to make each carbon dioxide molecule.

Sodium chloride

Sodium chloride (common salt) is a solid. The sodium and chlorine particles in it are close together with strong forces between them.

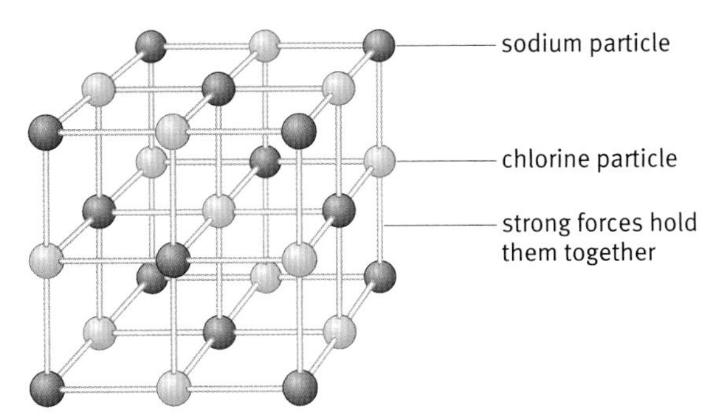

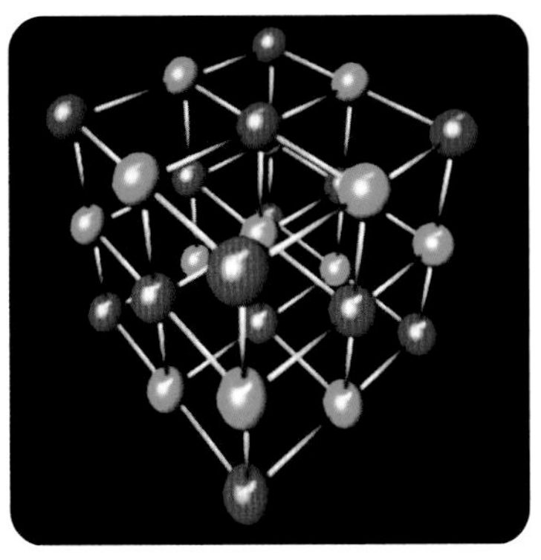

Sodium chloride, formula NaCl. There is one sodium particle for every chlorine particle.

Molecules in medicine

The different shapes of molecules have many and wide-ranging effects on our bodies. The photo shows a model of aspirin, a common painkiller. Ancient healers used willow bark to relieve pain. Today we know that of the many molecules in willow bark, it is aspirin that gives this relief to sufferers. Medical researchers test naturally occurring materials and also make thousands of new molecules each year, hoping to find one whose shape will fit into the chemistry of the body and have a healing effect.

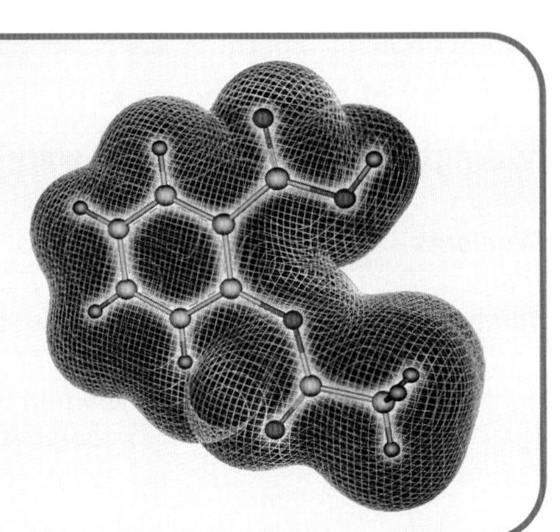

1 Copy and complete using words from the Language bank:

Elements are made of particles called ______. Compounds are made of more than one ______ chemically joined together. The particles in a compound such as carbon dioxide are called ______. We write a ______ to represent an atom, and a ______ to represent a compound.

2 Choose the correct ending below to complete each sentence.

a A water molecule is made from ...

b A carbon dioxide molecule is made from ...

Endings:

... one carbon atom and two oxygen atoms.

... one hydrogen atom and two oxygen atoms.

... two carbon atoms and one oxygen atom.

... two hydrogen atoms and one oxygen atom.

3 The formula for the compound ammonia is NH_3. Using different coloured circles to represent atoms of nitrogen and hydrogen, draw out what you think a molecule of ammonia might look like.

4 Using a computer with an internet connection, type 'new compounds' into a search engine and write a few lines about a new material you have researched.

Language bank 

atoms
chemically joined
compound
element
formula
material
model
molecules
symbol

Chemical reactions and equations

- How can we represent the changes when new materials are made?

Elements may join together to form compounds, and compounds can change into other compounds. Changes like these, which make new substances, are called **chemical changes** or **chemical reactions**. An example is hydrogen exploding. The hydrogen combines with oxygen from the air and a new substance, water, is formed. In a chemical reaction, the atoms recombine in different ways to form new substances.

We represent a chemical reaction using a **word equation**. This is a summary of what happens in the reaction.

hydrogen + oxygen ⟶ water

Reactants *– these are what combine together during the reaction.*

This means 'gives' or 'changes into'. The arrow tells you the direction of the reaction so you don't get the reactants and products mixed up.

Product *– this is what has been made in the reaction (there may be one product or more than one).*

Burning sulphur

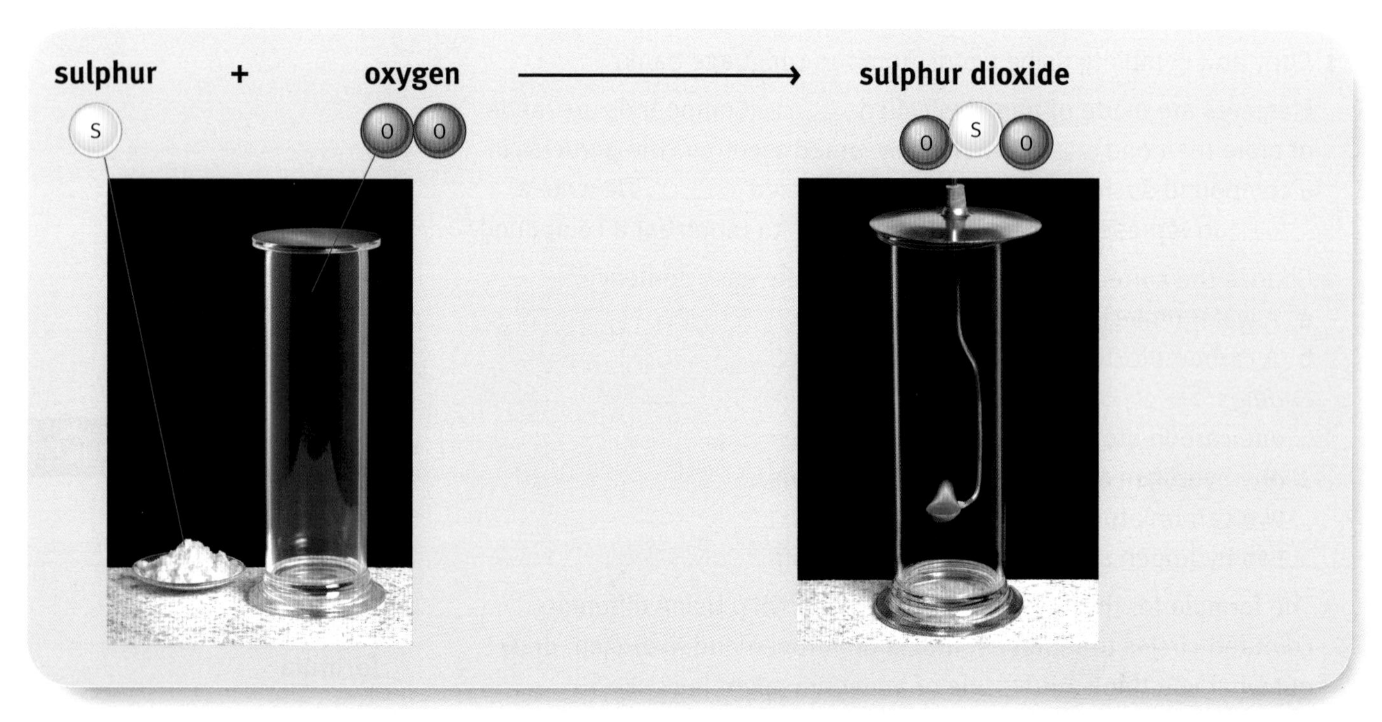

The reactants are the elements sulphur and oxygen. When you mix them, nothing happens until the sulphur is heated. Then the reaction starts, producing a blue flame in the gas jar. The product is the compound sulphur dioxide.

Why is it a chemical change? The answer is that a new substance is made – the reactants chemically change to form the product.

Substance	Properties (at room temperature)
sulphur	solid: a yellow powder
oxygen	a colourless gas which supports burning
sulphur dioxide	a choking acidic gas

Burning carbon

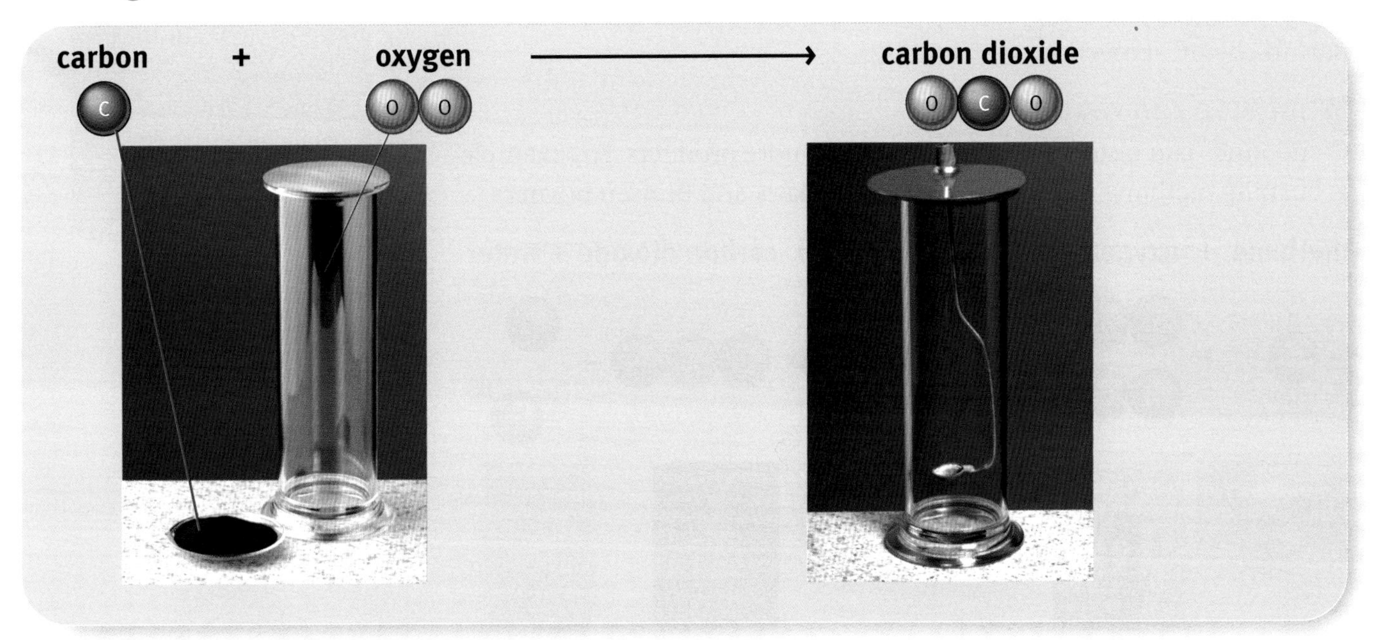

The reactants are the elements carbon and oxygen. When you mix them, nothing happens until the carbon is heated. It then reacts to form the product, the compound carbon dioxide.

Substance	Properties (at room temperature)
carbon	solid: a dark powder
oxygen	a colourless gas which supports burning
carbon dioxide	a colourless gas that is used in fire extinguishers

1 Copy and complete using words from the Language bank:

A ______ happens when a new substance is made. Elements may combine to form ______. The substances that react are called ______, and any new materials formed are called ______. We show these changes by writing a ______.

2 List the reactants and products for:

a hydrogen burning **b** sulphur burning.

3 Charcoal is carbon. Write a word equation for the reaction when charcoal burns.

Language bank

chemical change
chemical reaction
compounds
elements
products
reactants
word equation

3E.6 More reactions and equations

- How can we represent the changes when new materials are made?

You can tell compounds because they have molecules.

No, oxygen has molecules but it's an element. You can tell compounds because they contain more than one element.

You have seen how the elements sulphur and carbon react with the element oxygen when they burn. But it's not just elements that take part in chemical reactions.

What else can react?

Compounds can also react and form one or more products. An example is burning methane, the gas used in gas cookers and Bunsen burners.

methane + oxygen ⟶ carbon dioxide + water

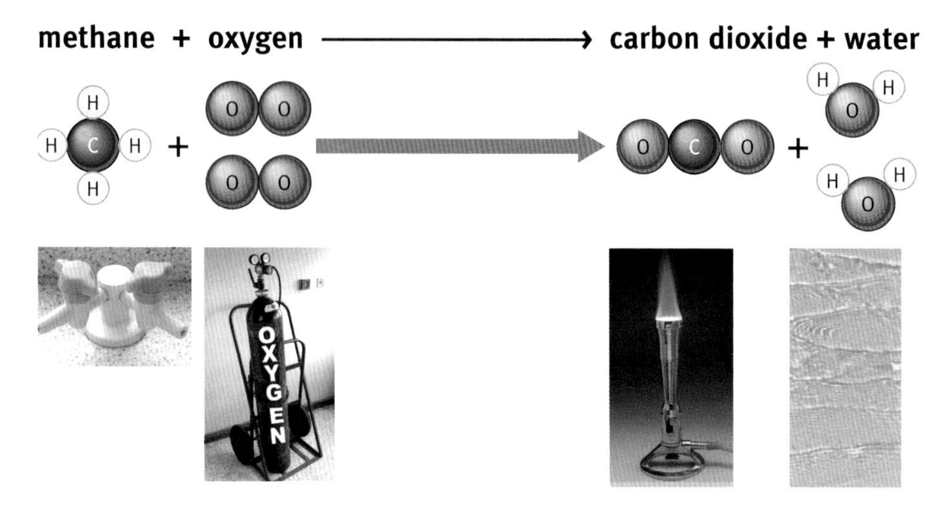

The reactants are the compound methane and the element oxygen. These react to form the compounds water and carbon dioxide, and release energy.

What's in a name?

When silvery coloured magnesium metal is heated in a Bunsen burner flame, it burns with a bright white flame as it reacts with oxygen from the air. The product is a white powdery substance, a compound called magnesium oxide.

The magnesium wasn't mixed with anything. How do you know it has reacted?

Because the mass has increased.

mass of magnesium before heating 2.4 g

mass of white solid after heating 4.0 g

The '-ide' ending in magnesium ox**ide** shows that the two elements have combined. An **oxide** is formed in an **oxidation** reaction, when something reacts with oxygen. In the same way, a **sulphide** is formed when something reacts with sulphur, and a **chloride** is formed when something reacts with chlorine.

Can we split compounds up?

Reactions don't always make compounds out of elements. Sometimes they work the other way round.

In this apparatus, electricity (electrical energy) is passed through water (containing a bit of acid to help the reaction). The water splits up to form its elements hydrogen and oxygen. This shows that water is made from hydrogen and oxygen.

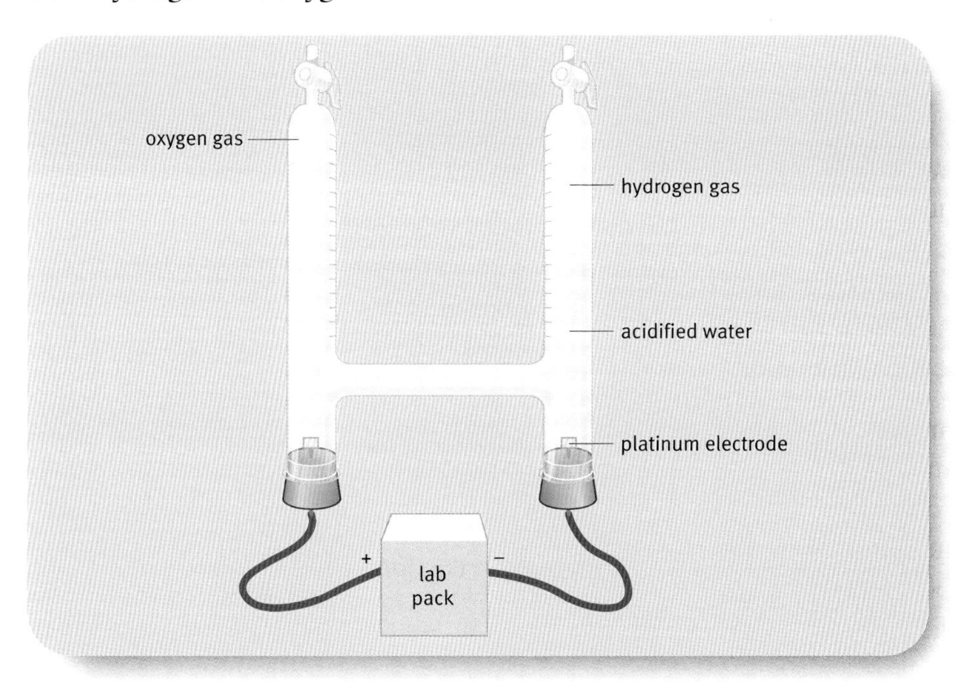

In the Hoffman voltameter, electrical energy splits the compound water into its elements.

1 Copy and complete using words from the Language bank:
Compounds can undergo a ______ to form new compounds, or even to form ______. When a gas flame heats a pan, the ______ are methane and oxygen and the ______ are water and carbon dioxide.

2 Which elements make up:
a zinc sulphide **b** silicon dioxide **c** calcium oxide?

3 Name the products that form when the following react, and write a word equation for each:
a magnesium and oxygen **b** copper and sulphur.

4 Look at the diagram above. Why is more hydrogen than oxygen formed when water is split up?

5 Iron and sulphur react to form a compound. Name it and find out how the reactants and product differ. Suggest a formula for the compound.

Language bank 

chemical reaction
chloride
compounds
elements
oxide
products
reactants
sulphide
word equation

Checkpoint

1 About matter

Match up the beginnings and endings to write four sentences.

Beginnings
Atoms are
You might find molecules
In an element,
Compounds contain

Endings
atoms of different elements chemically combined.
the atoms are all the same.
the smallest particles of matter.
in an element or in a compound.

2 Match the symbols

Match up each symbol with its element.
Underline the metals and circle the non-metals.

Symbols	Elements
O	aluminium
Fe	mercury
Al	helium
He	carbon
Na	oxygen
H	sodium
Hg	iron
C	hydrogen

3 Organising the elements

Copy and complete these sentences, unscrambling the words.

a We group all the elements in the **diporcie balet**.

b Elements have different **tipperroes**. Some are metals and some non-metals. They are different **surcool**. Some are **loisds**, some **squildi** and some **sesag** at room temperature.

c Elements with similar properties are grouped **theretog**. **Slatem** are on the left and **non-slatem** are on the right.

4 True or false?

Decide whether the following statements are true or false. Write down the true ones. Correct the false ones before you write them down.

a Water is an element.
b Water is a liquid at room temperature.
c Water contains hydrogen and nitrogen atoms.
d Water is made up of molecules.

5 Reactions and equations

Copy and complete these sentences, choosing the correct ending. Use a different colour to write each sentence.

Beginnings
In a chemical reaction,
We use word equations
The products are
The reactants

Endings
formed in the reaction.
the atoms combine in new ways.
combine together in the reaction.
to represent reactions.

6 Burning methane

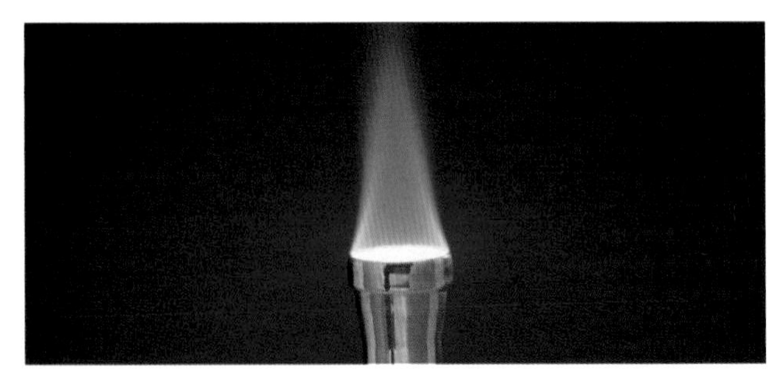

Here is a word equation for burning methane:

methane + oxygen ⟶ water + carbon dioxide

Copy the equation. Underline the reactants and then circle the products.
List the elements and the compounds.

Compounds and mixtures

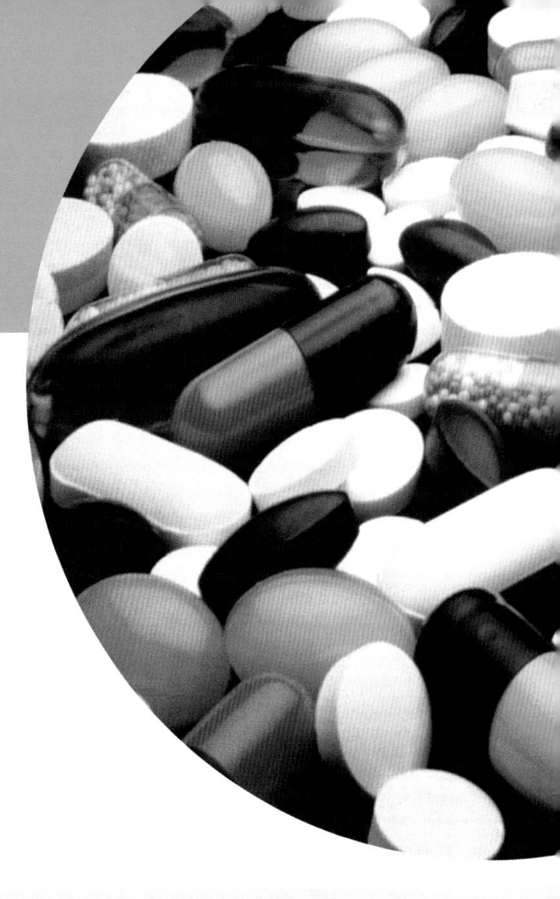

Before starting this unit, you should already be familiar with these ideas from earlier work.

- The particle model says matter is made up of particles. Atoms are the simplest particles. What particles are made when atoms join?
- In an element, the atoms are all the same. About how many elements are there? List five of them.
- A compound contains atoms of different elements combined together. Think of three compounds you have studied.
- A chemical reaction is a permanent change that makes a new material. Bubbles show that a chemical reaction is happening. What other telltale signs help you spot a chemical reaction?
- A mixture can be separated because it contains more than one substance. Can you remember how to separate pure salt out from rock salt?

You will meet these key ideas as you work through this unit. Have a quick look now, and at the end of the unit read them through slowly.

- In a **compound**, the different elements are present in fixed amounts. Think of carbon monoxide – there is always one carbon atom for every oxygen atom. But in a **mixture** you could have any ratio of carbon and oxygen.
- The elements in a compound cannot easily be separated because they are chemically combined. But in a mixture the substances are not combined so can be separated, such as pure water from sea water by distillation.
- To represent a compound, we write the symbols of its elements together in a **formula**. The formula shows not only which elements are in the compound but also the ratio of their atoms. For example, the formula CO_2 shows that carbon dioxide contains carbon and oxygen, and that there are twice as many oxygen as carbon atoms.
- Elements and compounds are changed in chemical reactions as their atoms join together in new ways. We can often predict which substances will be formed in a reaction, and write their formulae.
- Pure elements and compounds always change state at the same temperature – they have fixed **melting points** and **boiling points**.
- The particle model helps us see what goes on when reactions take place, and what happens in changes of state.

8F.1 Element or compound?

- How are elements and compounds different?

The cards below show information about some materials. Some of them are elements and some are compounds.

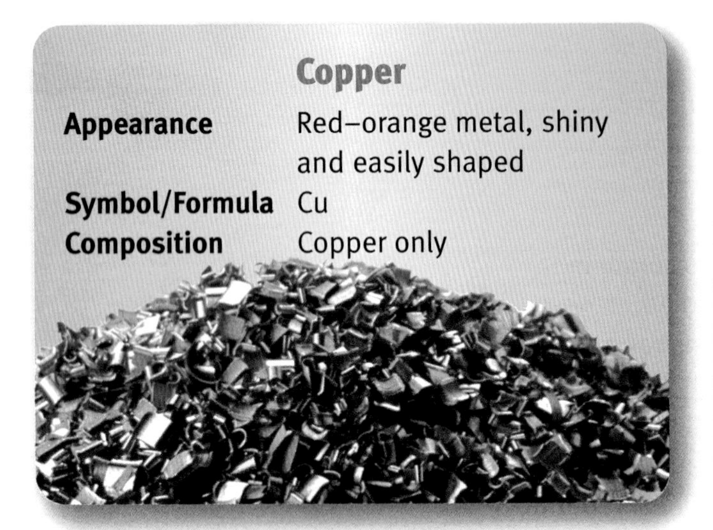

Copper

Appearance	Red–orange metal, shiny and easily shaped
Symbol/Formula	Cu
Composition	Copper only

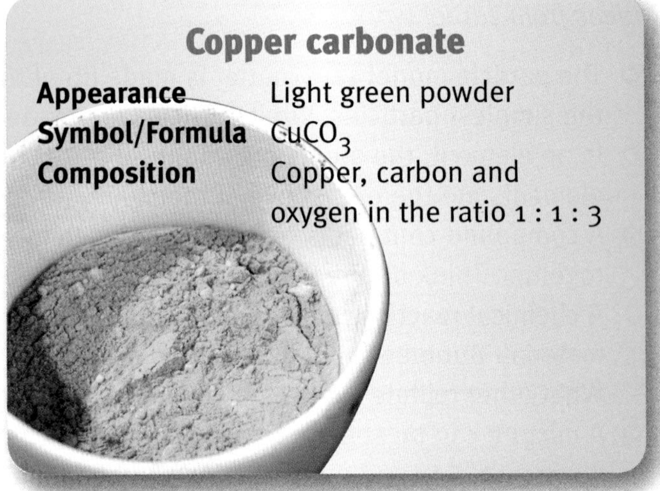

Copper carbonate

Appearance	Light green powder
Symbol/Formula	$CuCO_3$
Composition	Copper, carbon and oxygen in the ratio 1 : 1 : 3

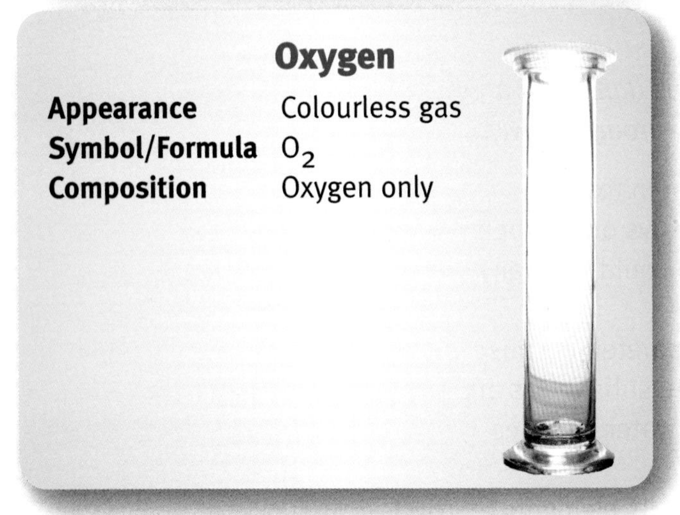

Oxygen

Appearance	Colourless gas
Symbol/Formula	O_2
Composition	Oxygen only

Carbon

Appearance	Black powder
Symbol/Formula	C
Composition	Carbon only

Copper oxide

Appearance	Black solid
Symbol/Formula	CuO
Composition	Copper and oxygen in the ratio 1 : 1

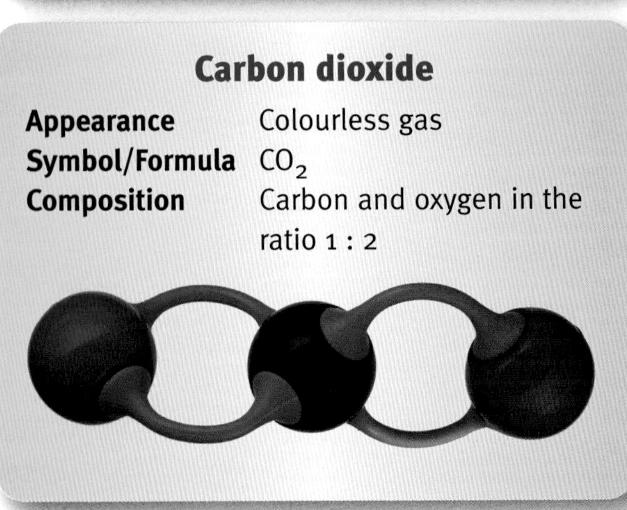

Carbon dioxide

Appearance	Colourless gas
Symbol/Formula	CO_2
Composition	Carbon and oxygen in the ratio 1 : 2

Elements and compounds

Remember
Elements have **atoms** of only one kind. **Compounds** contain atoms of more than one element chemically joined.

Copper is an element – it contains only copper atoms. Copper oxide is a compound – it contains copper atoms joined to oxygen atoms.

Elements cannot be broken down into anything simpler. Compounds can be broken down into their separate elements. To do this we need to carry out a **chemical reaction**.

Formula

Atoms of different elements join up to make a compound. We show this by combining the **symbols** of the elements to make the **formula** of the compound. This is just a shorthand way of showing the elements present, and in what ratio (that is, how many of each).

CuO

Cu is copper *O is oxygen*

There are no little numbers, which means there is one copper and one oxygen.

For every copper atom there is one oxygen atom.
Ratio: 1 Cu : 1 O *'One copper to one oxygen'*

$CuCO_3$

Cu is copper *C is carbon* *O is oxygen*

The little '3' means there are three oxygens.

For every copper atom there is one carbon atom and three oxygen atoms.
Ratio: 1 Cu : 1 C : 3 O *'One copper to one carbon to three oxygen'*

1 Copy and complete using words from the Language bank:
Elements contain particles or _____ of one kind. _____ contain atoms of two or more different _____ chemically joined together. To separate a compound into its _____, you have to carry out a _____.

2 **a** Classify the cards opposite, as elements or compounds.
b Which information was most useful for your classification?

3 Write a 'Composition' line like the ones on the cards for these:
a magnesium oxide, MgO **b** copper sulphide, CuS
c chlorine, Cl_2 **d** titanium dioxide, TiO_2

4 What does the formula O_2 for oxygen tell you about the particles in oxygen gas?

Language bank 

atoms
chemical reaction
chemically joined
composition
compounds
elements
formula
molecules
ratio
symbol

Elements to compounds

M

- How do compounds differ from the elements from which they are made?

Making iron sulphide

If you mix the elements iron and sulphur, you won't see any noticeable change. However, if you gently heat the mixture with a Bunsen burner, the elements react. They change into a new substance: a compound called iron sulphide. Iron sulphide contains the elements iron and sulphur, but it has very different properties from the mixture.

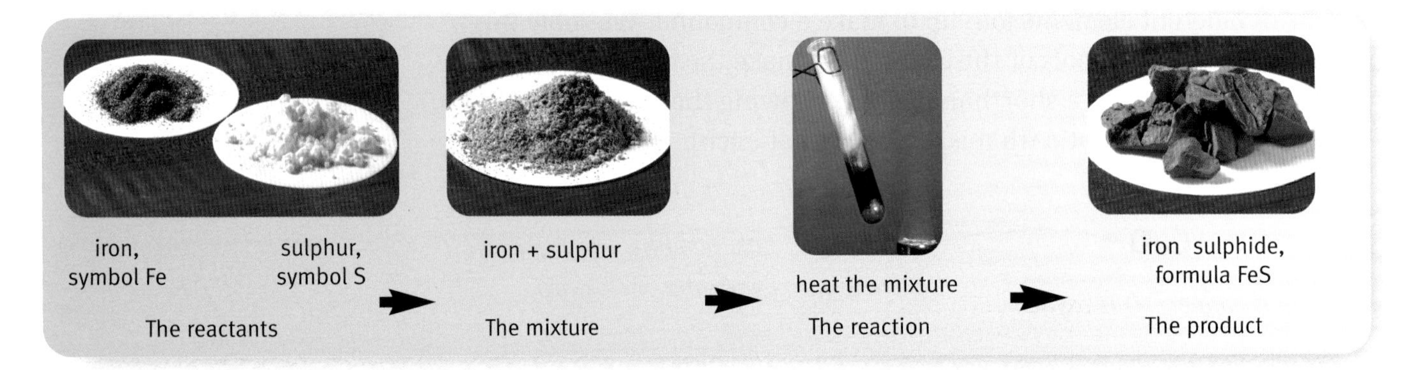

Here is a word equation for the reaction: **iron + sulphur ⟶ iron sulphide**

How is iron sulphide different from iron and sulphur?

Iron sulphide is very different from the reactants that formed it. We can do some simple tests to show that iron sulphide is a new substance with its own unique properties.

Test 1: Appearance before, during and after the reaction

The reactants, the iron and sulphur in the mixture, change in appearance as the reaction takes place. This tells us that a chemical change has happened. The reactants carry on glowing after the Bunsen burner is removed, showing that heat is given out as the product forms. This is another sign that a reaction has happened.

Test 2: Magnetic or not?

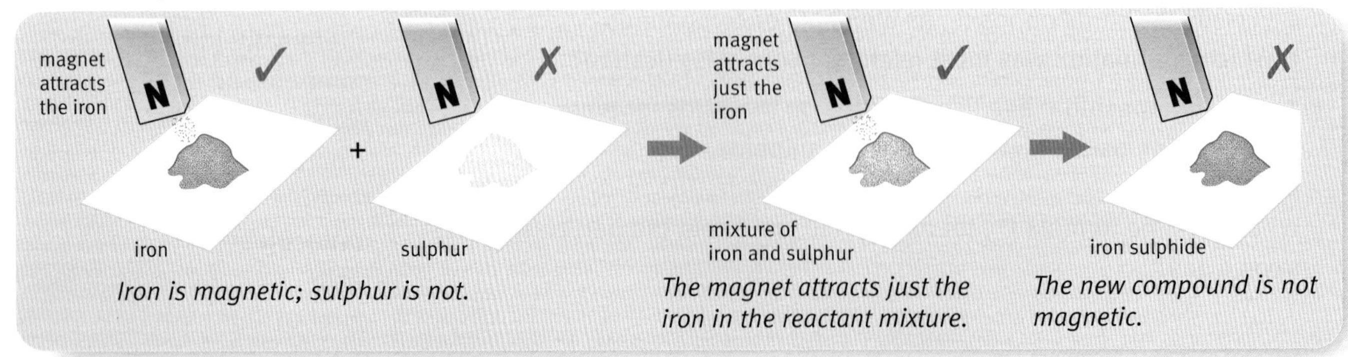

Iron is magnetic; sulphur is not.

The magnet attracts just the iron in the reactant mixture.

The new compound is not magnetic.

Test 3: Reaction with hydrochloric acid

Bubbles of gas are given off by the iron and hydrochloric acid.

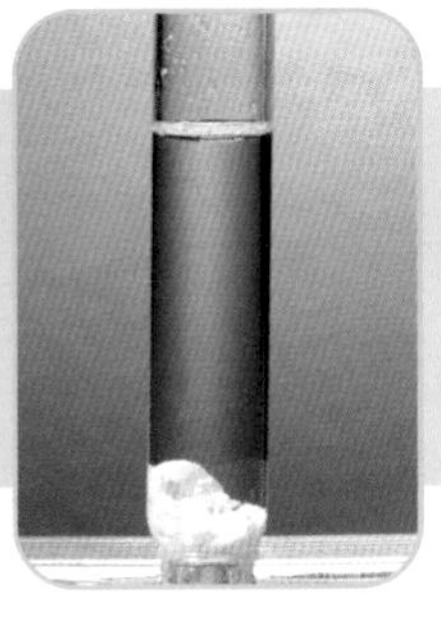

There are no bubbles with sulphur.

In the mixture, bubbles come off the iron filings only.

The bubbles with iron sulphide are not hydrogen.

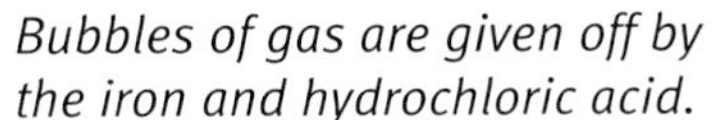

Hydrochloric acid reacts with iron to produce hydrogen gas. But hydrogen is not produced with sulphur or with iron sulphide. The chemical properties of iron change as it turns into iron sulphide.

Remember
Compounds are different from their constituent elements, in other words, the elements that make them up.

Picture the particles

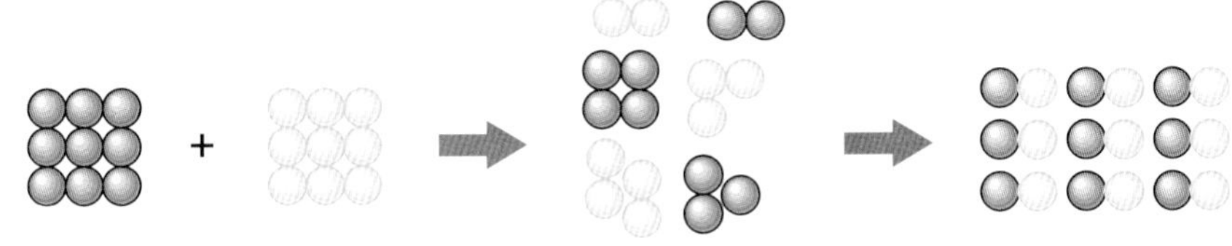

Iron particles are atoms of iron. Sulphur particles are atoms of sulphur.

The mixture contains atoms of sulphur and iron. Any amount of iron or sulphur could be in the mixture.

The atoms of iron and sulphur are chemically joined. They are in a fixed ratio. There is one iron atom for every sulphur atom.

Guess what?

Elements combine in fixed ratios to make some amazing compounds. Carbon, hydrogen, nitrogen and oxygen combine to form the explosive TNT, which has the formula $C_7H_5N_3O_6$.

1 Copy and complete using words from the Language bank:
The ______ of a compound are different from those of the ______ which make it up. This is because in a compound, the elements are ______.

2 Give two differences between the particles in a mixture of iron and sulphur and the particles in the compound iron sulphide.

3 Which elements are present in these substances, and in what ratios? (The periodic table on page 55 will help you.)
a zinc sulphide, ZnS **b** sodium fluoride, NaF
c ammonia, NH_3 **d** iodine, I_2.

4 Draw the particles to represent:
a magnesium oxide (one magnesium atom for every oxygen atom)
b hydrogen chloride (one hydrogen atom for every chlorine atom)
c hydrogen sulphide (two hydrogen atoms for every sulphur atom).

5 Write the formula for each compound in question **4**.

Language bank 

chemical reaction
chemically joined
compound
elements
fixed ratio
formula
mixture
product
properties
reactants
symbol

Compounds and chemical reactions (M)

Do compounds react chemically?

Elements can react to make compounds, such as iron and sulphur reacting to make iron sulphide. But it is not only elements that react. Compounds can also take part in chemical reactions and change into new substances. The photos show some examples.

Compounds reacting

Hydrochloric acid reacts with magnesium carbonate, producing bubbles of carbon dioxide gas.

hydrochloric acid + magnesium carbonate → carbon dioxide + water + magnesium chloride

Clear sodium carbonate solution reacts with pale green iron chloride solution, producing a solid. This sinks to the bottom of the test tube as a solid **precipitate**.

sodium carbonate + iron chloride → iron carbonate + sodium chloride

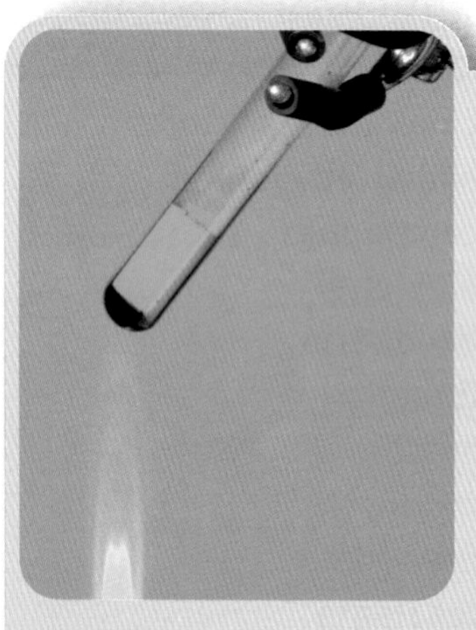

If you heat green copper carbonate, it changes colour and forms black copper oxide. Carbon dioxide gas escapes into the air.

copper carbonate → copper oxide + carbon dioxide

If you heat white sucrose (sugar) it darkens, eventually turning black.

sucrose → carbon + water

Signs of a chemical reaction

In a chemical reaction, the atoms in the reactants rearrange and join in different ways to form the products. Telltale signs that this is happening include the sorts of changes shown in the photos. The word wall shows some observations that tell us a chemical reaction is happening.

Unfortunately, some reactions show very little change, so they are hard to spot. To confuse things further, some materials change colour when you warm them, but they are not actually undergoing a chemical reaction! The photo opposite shows an example.

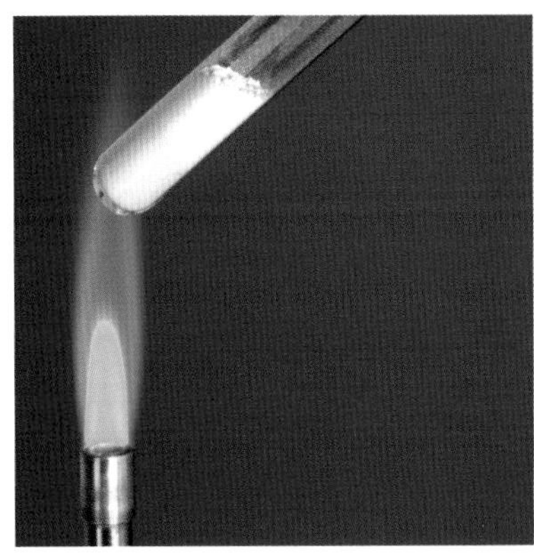

Zinc oxide changes from white when cold to yellow when hot. On cooling, it goes white again. The atoms have not been rearranged, so it is still zinc oxide.

Summary concept map

This concept map connects what you have learned about elements, compounds and reactions. Try drawing your own version. You will probably have your own way of linking these ideas.

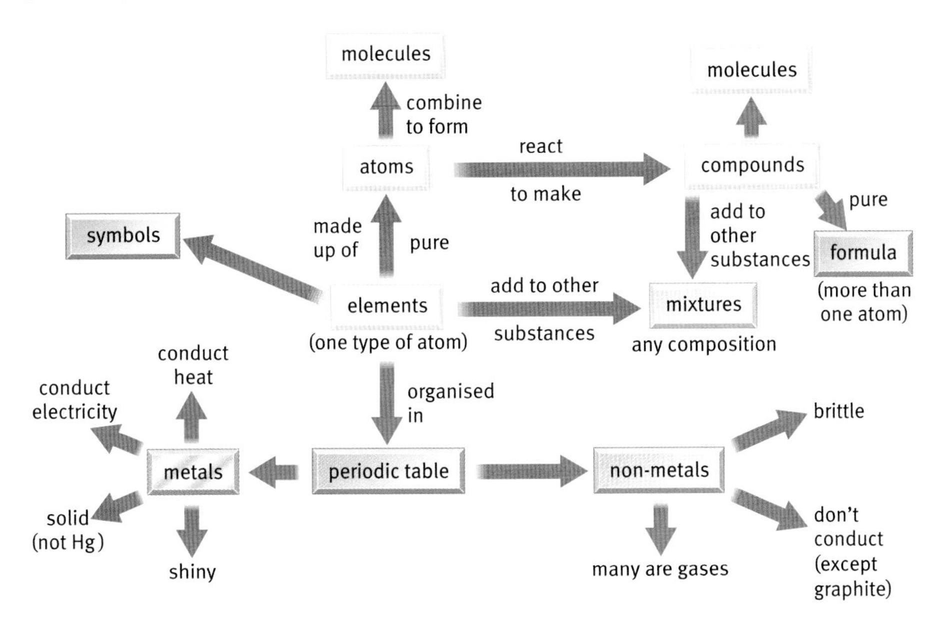

So a chemical reaction has happened if you observe a change that isn't easily changed back.

1 Copy and complete using words from the Language bank:

Compounds may undergo _____ and change into new substances. These products will have different properties from the _____ that formed them. There are certain signs that a chemical reaction has happened, such as giving off _____ of gas or forming a solid _____.

2 List five changes that show that a reaction has happened.

3 The photo shows ammonia solution and copper sulphate solution being mixed. Do you think the two substances are reacting? Give your reasons.

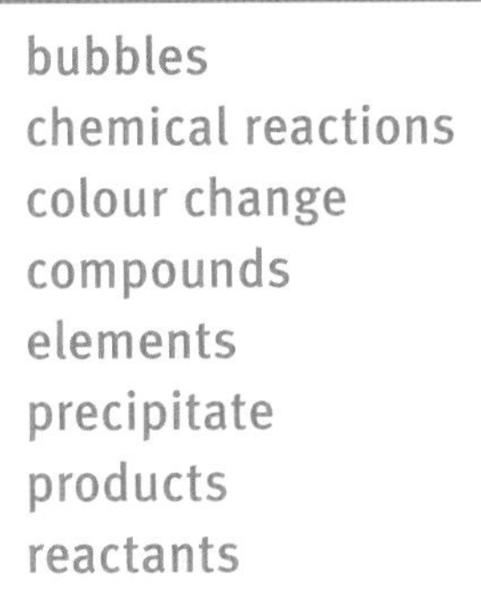

Language bank

bubbles
chemical reactions
colour change
compounds
elements
precipitate
products
reactants

Mixtures

O Are there other sorts of materials besides elements and compounds?

OFFICIAL ANALYSIS	mg/l		mg/l
CALCIUM	55	SULPHATE	13
MAGNESIUM	19	NITRATE	<0.1
POTASSIUM	1	IRON	0
SODIUM	24	ALUMINIUM	0
BICARBONATE	248		
CHLORIDE	37	DRY RESIDUE AT 180°C	280

p.H. AT SOURCE.....7.4

STORE IN A COOL DRY PLACE AWAY FROM

Scottish Spring Water

TYPICAL ANALYSIS	mg/l		mg/l
Calcium	60	Chloride	155
Magnesium	15	Sulphate	1
Sodium	46	Nitrate	5
Potassium	2.2	Fluoride	0.1
Carbonate(CaCO3)	145	Total Dissolved Solids	453

Pure water contains nothing but water. Mineral water is impure, but it is safe to drink!

A **pure** substance is not mixed with anything else. If you had a gas jar of oxygen that was not mixed with anything else, you would have pure oxygen. Compounds can be pure too. For example, copper oxide is pure if it dosen't contain anything except copper oxide.

Mixtures

A material with more than one substance in it is **impure**. A **mixture** contains more than one substance mixed up, but not chemically joined. So mixtures are impure.

The labels shown come from two different brands of mineral water. The **composition** of each bottle of water is different, because the water comes from two different places with different rock types. The mineral content is therefore different. Both mineral waters are impure, because they contain a mixture of compounds, one of which is water.

A mixture can be made from any combination of substances with any composition. Compounds always have a fixed composition – they have a known ratio of elements which is shown in their formula. Because mixtures do not have a fixed composition, they do not have a formula.

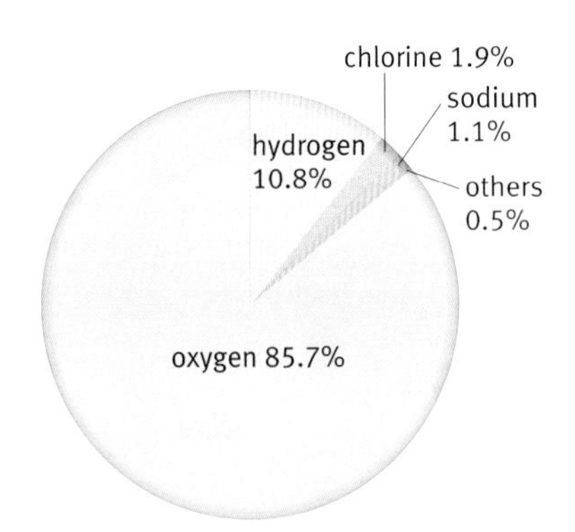

A typical composition of sea water. The constituents and their ratio change depending from which beach you take your sample.

Everyday mixtures: sea and air

Sea water is another mixture of water and minerals, but its salt and mineral **constituents** make it undrinkable.

Air is a mixture. Look at the picture of the particles in air. The particles are different, showing that there is more than one substance. Some of them are elements and some are compounds. Some of the particles are atoms and some are molecules.

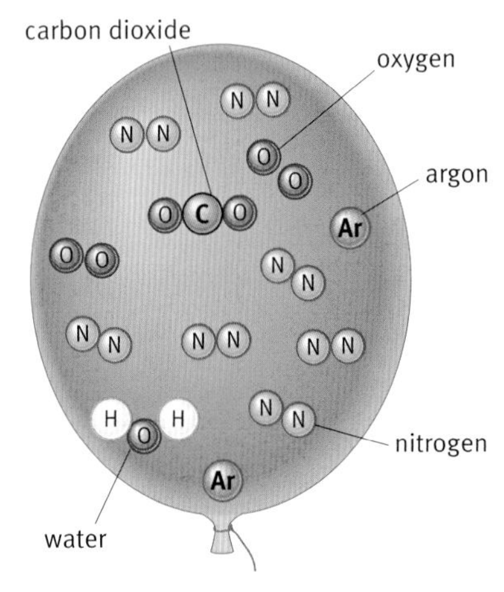

The particles in air.

Changing composition

The exact composition of air varies considerably depending where you are. For example, on a rainy day, the water content of air is much higher than on a sunny day.

The air you breathe out has more carbon dioxide in it than the air you breathe in. This is because you produce carbon dioxide in **respiration**, and breathe it out. The table on page 24 shows some more differences between the air you breathe in and the air you breathe out.

Using air

We think of air as a gas, or a mixture of gases. But if air is **pressurised** (squashed) and then allowed to quickly expand, it cools and turns to a liquid.

If this liquid air is then slowly warmed, the components of the mixture boil off at different temperatures. The gases can be collected and separated from each other. This is known as **fractional distillation** of liquid air. The photo shows a factory where air is separated in this way.

People use the separated gases from air for many things.

- Oxygen is used for people to breathe, for example if they are ill and need extra oxygen, or for scuba diving.

Liquid air is separated here by fractional distillation.

- Nitrogen fills some food packages such as crisp packets. It provides an inert atmosphere where chemical reactions don't happen, including the ones that make the crisps go soggy.
- Carbon dioxide puts the bubbles in fizzy drinks.

Sealed inside a submarine, the carbon dioxide you breathe out builds up. Some aeroplanes and submarines have 'carbon dioxide scrubbers', which remove carbon dioxide from the air. This prevents the people inside from suffocating.

1 Copy and complete using words from the Language bank:

Some materials are pure elements or ______. Many materials are not pure, but are a ______ of substances. Mixtures are different from ______, as they do not contain elements in fixed proportions. The ______ of a mixture can change. Air is a mixture of gases which can be separated by ______ of liquid air.

2 Look at the particle picture of air. Name:

a a compound **b** an element made up of single atoms

c an element made up of molecules.

3 Look at the table on page 24.

a Sketch a pie chart to show the main gases in air.

b Apart from producing carbon dioxide, what else does your body do to change the composition of the air that you breathe out?

4 Holly is going scuba diving for the first time. She's worried about breathing gas from a cylinder as she thinks it won't be pure like the air. Write to Holly to put her mind at rest.

Language bank 

composition
compounds
constituents
elements
formula
fractional distillation
impure
liquid air
mixture
pressurised
pure

Mixtures and changing state

- Are there other sorts of material besides elements and compounds?

Remember

Scientists can separate mixtures using simple lab methods such as:
- filtering to remove solid bits from a liquid
- chromatography to separate substances with different solubilities
- distillation to separate a solvent from a solution.

Changing state

When pure water changes state, it always changes at the same temperature. Frozen water always melts at 0 °C. Liquid water always boils at 100 °C. We say that water has a **melting point** of 0 °C and a **boiling point** of 100 °C.

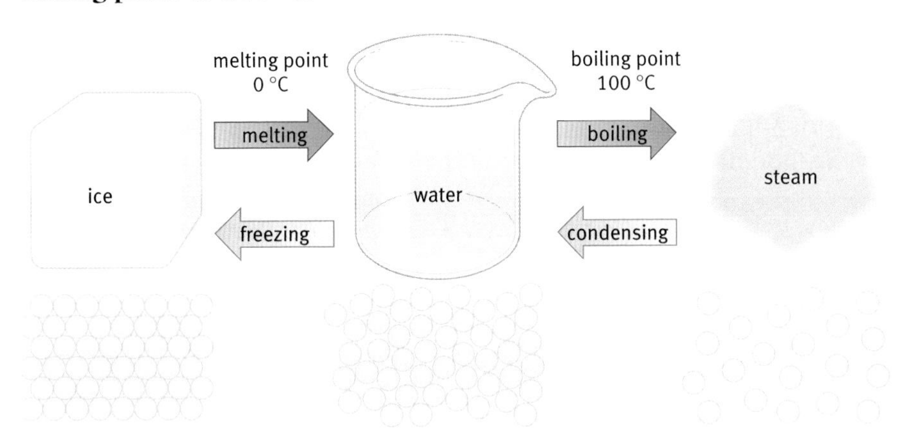

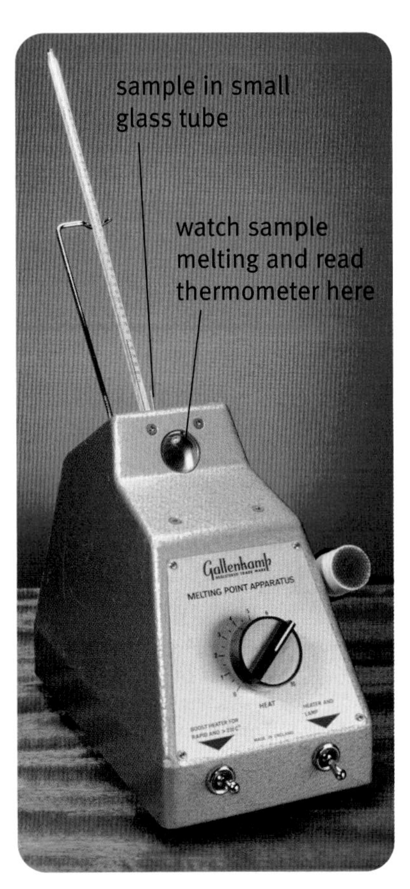

This apparatus measures the melting point accurately. You put a small amount of your substance inside in a glass tube. The apparatus heats it up and you can watch the temperature as it melts. You compare this with the temperature in the data book.

Like water, all pure substances have fixed melting and boiling points. The melting points or boiling points have all been checked by scientists and they are published in data books. So if we think we have some pure copper sulphate, for example, we can measure its melting point and check it against the data book.

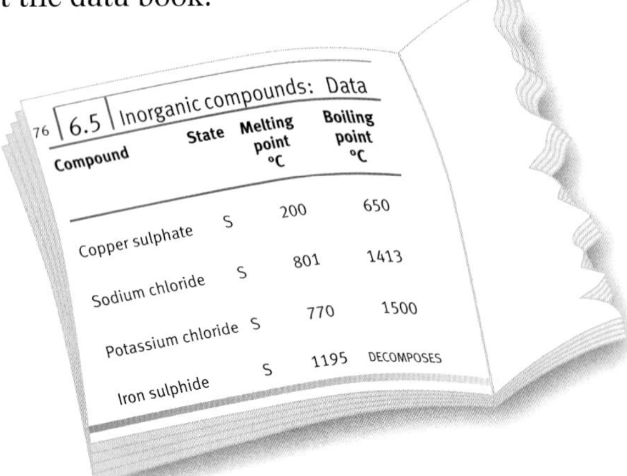

76 | 6.5 | Inorganic compounds: Data

Compound	State	Melting point °C	Boiling point °C
Copper sulphate	S	200	650
Sodium chloride	S	801	1413
Potassium chloride	S	770	1500
Iron sulphide	S	1195	DECOMPOSES

Mixtures change the melting and boiling points

If you have an impure substance (a mixture), the melting and boiling points change depending on the composition. Impurities tend to raise the boiling point and lower the freezing point. So if you have water with dissolved impurities, it will boil above 100 °C and freeze below 0 °C.

Type of water	Boiling point (°C)
deionised	100.2
tap	100.8
salty	102.5

Which water is the purest?

So we put salt on roads in winter to melt the ice.

No, the salt lowers the temperature at which the salty water will freeze. So at minus 4, if there's enough salt, the mixture is still a liquid.

How pure?

How do we know if a substance we have is pure or not? The greater the amount of impurity there is in a substance, the more its melting or boiling point differs from the value in the data book. Checking the melting or boiling point gives some idea of how pure a substance is.

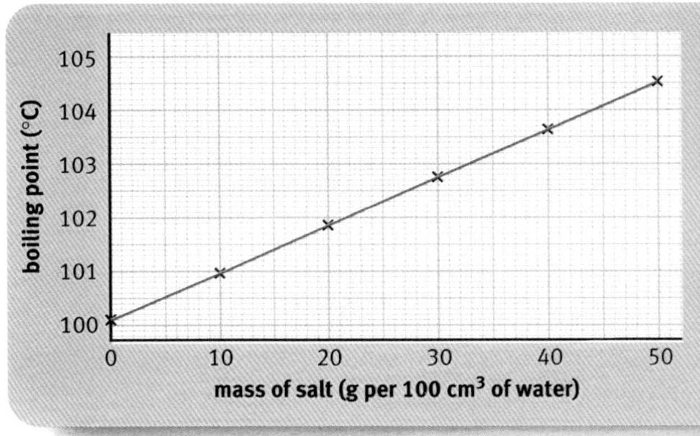

As you dissolve more salt in water, the boiling point gets higher (up to a limit).

Another check is that pure substances tend to melt suddenly at a particular temperature. Impure substances are more likely to melt gradually over a range of temperature.

1 Copy and complete using words from the Language bank:
   A ______ element or compound has a fixed melting point and ______.
   If there are ______, the ______ is generally lower and the boiling point is higher.
2 When you do a melting point test on an unknown white solid, it melts suddenly at between 799 and 802 °C. Look at the data opposite. What do you think the solid is?
3 Look at the table showing three types of water. Which sort of water do you think would freeze at the lowest temperature?
4 Look at the graph. Harry has some salty water that boils at 103 °C. How much salt does it contain?
5 Write a paragraph to explain why salt is put on roads in winter.

Language bank

boiling point
changing state
composition
impure
impurities
melting point
mixtures
pure

Checkpoint

1 Comparing compounds and mixtures

Copy the table below. Complete it by writing 'yes' or 'no' in the empty boxes.

Properties	Compounds	Mixtures
contain atoms		
contain more than one element		
constituents can easily be separated		
constituents are chemically combined		
elements are always present in the same ratio		
elements may be present in any ratio		

2 Match the formulae

Match up each formula with its compound. Beside each one, write down how many atoms in total the formula shows.

Formulae

CuO
CO_2
H_2O
$CuCO_3$
$NaCl$
CO

Compounds

water
sodium chloride
copper oxide
copper carbonate
carbon monoxide
carbon dioxide

3 Missing labels

George and Baljit made notes in their science lesson. George drew a particle diagram and Baljit noted down the labels. Later they couldn't remember which label went with which diagram. Copy the diagram and write each label under the correct part.

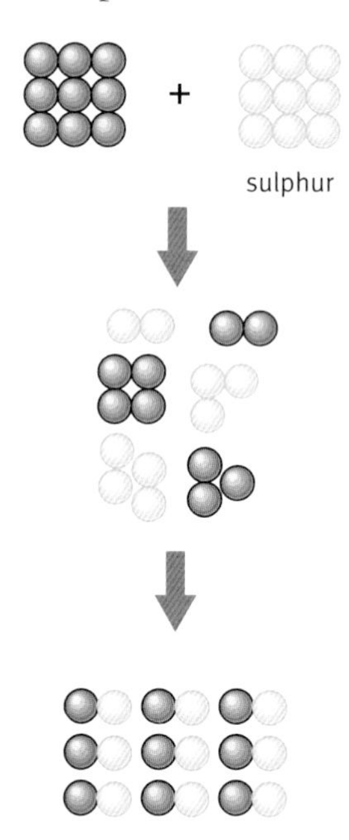

Labels

mixture of iron and sulphur
S
iron sulphide, FeS
iron, Fe

4 True or false?

Decide whether the following statements are true or false. Write down the true ones. Correct the false ones before you write them down.

a Pure substances have fixed melting and boiling points.

b Water always boils at 200 °C.

c Water with dissolved impurities boils at a higher temperature than pure water.

d We can find out how pure a mixture is by checking its melting point.

Rocks and weathering

Before starting this unit, you should already be familiar with these ideas from earlier work.

- You might see rocks in a cliff face or mountainside, but there are also rocks under the ground. Marble is one type of rock. Name two more.
- Soil forms from rocks. Does water flow more quickly through sandy soil or clay soil?
- Particles are arranged differently in solids and in liquids. Summarise these differences in a couple of sentences.
- The pH scale describes how acidic or alkaline a solution is. Neutral solutions have pH 7. What sort of pH does a weak acid have?
- If you leave bowl containing a solution of a salt in water, the water disappears, leaving the salt behind. Where has the water gone?

You will meet these key ideas as you work through this unit. Have a quick look now, and at the end of the unit read them through slowly.

- A **rock** is a mixture of substances called **minerals** that occur naturally in the Earth's **crust**.
- Rock have different **textures** depending on how their mineral particles are arranged. Some rocks are **porous** – they have little spaces in their structure which can hold water.
- Rocks can be worn away or **weathered** by conditions in the environment. **Physical**, **chemical** and **biological processes** wear away rocks. Changes in temperature can weather rocks physically. The acid in rainwater can react with rocks and wear them away chemically.
- Weathered fragments of rock are transported away from where they fall. **Sediment** carried by water can be dropped or **deposited** many miles away.
- Layers of sediment may be deposited on top of each other and become **cemented** together to form new **sedimentary rock**. The remains of dead organisms may fall to the bottom of a sea or lake and form part of the rock. Water evaporating from a lake can also leave behind sedimentary rock, formed from the minerals that were dissolved in it.

Rocks

What are rocks made of?

What do you know about the Earth, apart from being the planet where you live? For a start it's very old, around 4600 million years. It has a central part called the **core** which is made of iron and a bit of nickel. The core is very hot indeed. Around the core is a hot semi-liquid rock layer called the **mantle**. Covering this is the cooler solid surface layer that we live on. This is the **crust**, made of rocks and minerals.

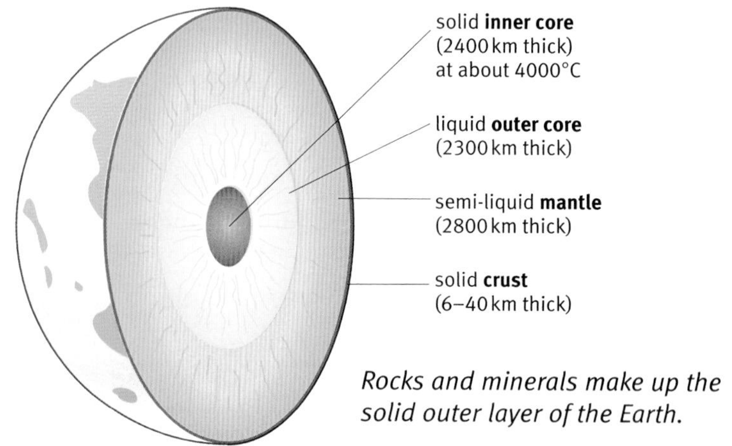

Rocks and minerals make up the solid outer layer of the Earth.

What is a mineral?

Minerals are the solid substances that make up the Earth's crust. Minerals have a definite composition, a regular structure and are often a single colour. Most minerals are compounds, though a few are elements. The table shows some minerals.

Mineral name	Chemical name	Photo
haematite	iron oxide	
malachite	copper carbonate	
diamond	carbon	
quartz	silicon dioxide	

What is a rock?

A **rock** is a mixture of minerals. The minerals are in little pieces called **grains**. In some rocks the grains are large and you can see them with the naked eye. If a rock has a mixture of grains, it might look multi-coloured or speckled.

Other rocks are crystalline. They have smooth faces which reflect light and so appear shiny. The grains have formed crystals that fit together so you can't see the individual grains.

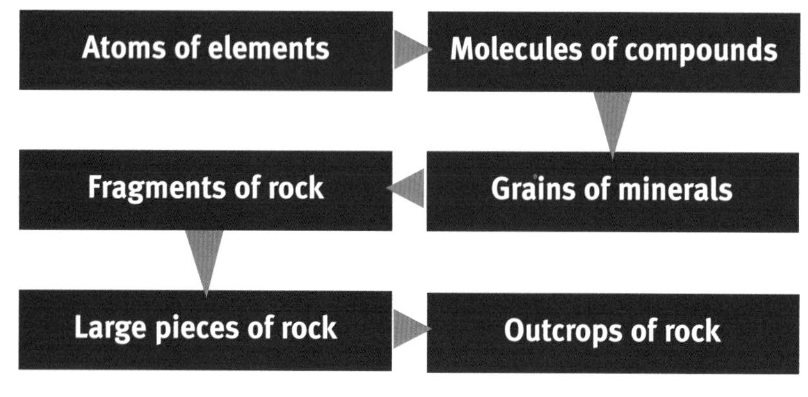

So are grains particles?

No, grains are pieces of minerals. Particles are tinier – atoms and molecules, too small to see.

Classifying rocks – the rock kingdoms

Geologists identify rocks by looking at properties such as colour, hardness, texture, how they split up when hit (cleavage) and their chemical behaviour. Rocks can be made up of many different minerals, so their properties can vary.

The easiest way to classify rocks is by where they have come from. This splits the rock world into three different rock types:

Guess what?

*A **geologist** studies the Earth and its structure, a **seismologist** studies earthquakes and a **palaeontologist** studies fossils.*

Igneous rocks are formed when the molten rock inside the Earth cools and solidifies.

In this piece of granite you can see the interlocking grains of minerals – white feldspar, light grey quartz and dark mica.

Sedimentary rocks are formed from material that is laid down in layers.

*In this sandstone you can see the small rough grains that have settled out from water, loosely **cemented** (joined) together.*

Metamorphic rocks are formed when high temperature and pressure change other rocks.

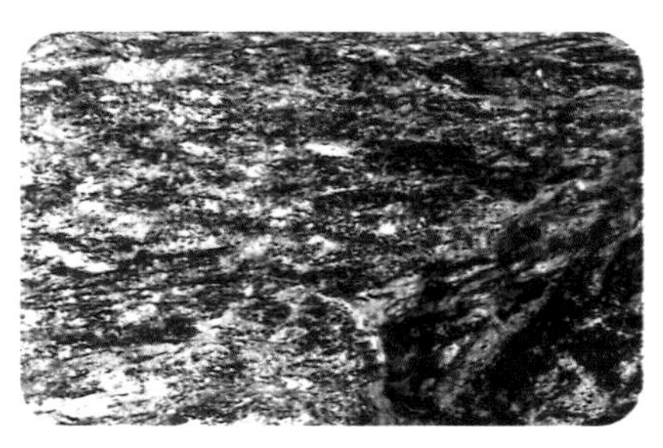

This schist has a glittering surface, banded layers and small crystalline grains.

Investigating texture

Hannah put a sample of granite into a beaker of water and a sample of sandstone into another beaker of water. The table shows her observations.

Rock	Observation	Inference (conclusion)
granite	no bubbles	Granite does not absorb water.
sandstone	bubbles	Sandstone does absorb water.

Sandstone has a more **porous** texture than granite. In sandstone, the grains do not fit closely together (they do not **interlock**) so there are small gaps which fill with water. Grains interlock more closely in glassy and crystalline rocks than in rough-textured ones.

Language bank 

cementedcomposition
compounds
crust
elements
grain
igneous
interlock
metamorphic
minerals
porous
rock
sedimentary
texture

1. Copy and complete using words from the Language bank:

   The Earth's _________ is made up of rocks. A rock is formed from a mixture of _________. Minerals are usually chemical _________ which have a definite _________. The main rock types are _________, _________ and _________.

2. List these in order of size, smallest first:

   rock fragment, atom, molecule, grain.

3. Hannah's two rock samples were the same size and she put each into the same volume of water. After half an hour she noticed the water level in the sandstone beaker was lower. Explain why, including sketches of the grains in your answer.

BG2 Weathering

- How does rain cause rocks to weather?

Gravestones of limestone (left) and slate (right).

These limestone and slate gravestones are about the same age. They don't look it! The writing is less clear on the left-hand gravestone because the limestone has been worn away. **Weathering** is the name we give to the slow breakdown of rocks into smaller fragments.

There are three types of weathering:

- **physical weathering**, also called mechanical weathering, caused by physical factors such as temperature changes
- **chemical weathering**, caused by chemical reactions such as the action of rainwater on certain minerals in a rock
- **biological weathering**, for example, digging animals or growing plant roots can make cracks in rock bigger until bits of rock fall off.

A closer look at chemical weathering

Rocks such as limestone contain the minerals calcite (calcium carbonate) and dolomite (magnesium carbonate). Carbonates react with acids. This is how chemical weathering happens:

1. Rainwater is naturally acidic. This is because carbon dioxide in the air reacts with the rainwater to make a weak solution of carbonic acid. This acid reacts with the carbonate minerals in rocks:

   calcium carbonate + carbonic acid → calcium hydrogencarbonate

2. Rainwater can become more acidic because of pollutants in the air. For example, burning fossil fuels can produce sulphur dioxide and oxides of nitrogen. These dissolve to form sulphuric acid and nitric acid, which react quickly with the carbonate minerals in rocks:

   calcium carbonate + nitric acid → calcium nitrate + carbon dioxide + water

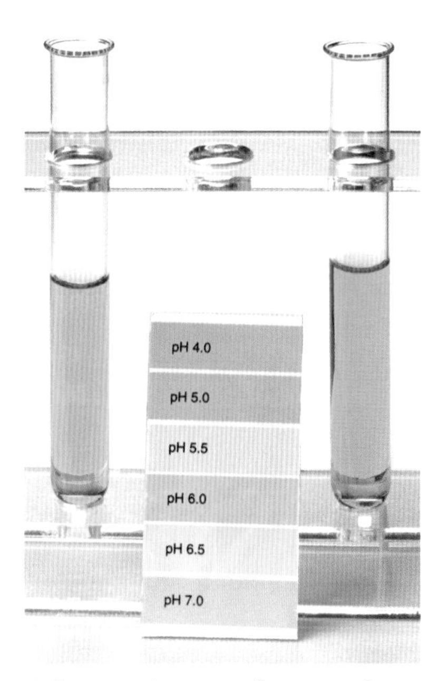

Rainwater is naturally around pH 6, but acidic pollutants from burning fossil fuels lower its pH to make acid rain.

Investigating chemical weathering

Studying the effects of rainwater on rocks could make you very wet and very fed up. Instead we can model the effect of rainwater on rock in the lab by placing a piece of granite in acidic, oxygen-rich water, as shown in the pictures. Chemical weathering of this kind has most impact in warm and wet areas which are heavily polluted.

> **Guess what?**
>
> *The total amount of weathered rock on the Earth is estimated to be 3×10^{24} kg. (That's 3 with 24 zeros after it – a lot of weathered rock.)*

Granite before (left) and after (right) being left in acidic hydrogen peroxide solution. If you look at the edges you can see it has been weathered. Some of the minerals in the rock, the feldspar and mica, react with the solution. This weakens and softens the structure of the rock.

Why is weathering important?

If rocks were not weathered, there would not be any soil for plants to grow in. The picture shows why.

Weathered rock particles, decayed plant and animal matter, water and air mix to form the soil that sustains life on Earth.

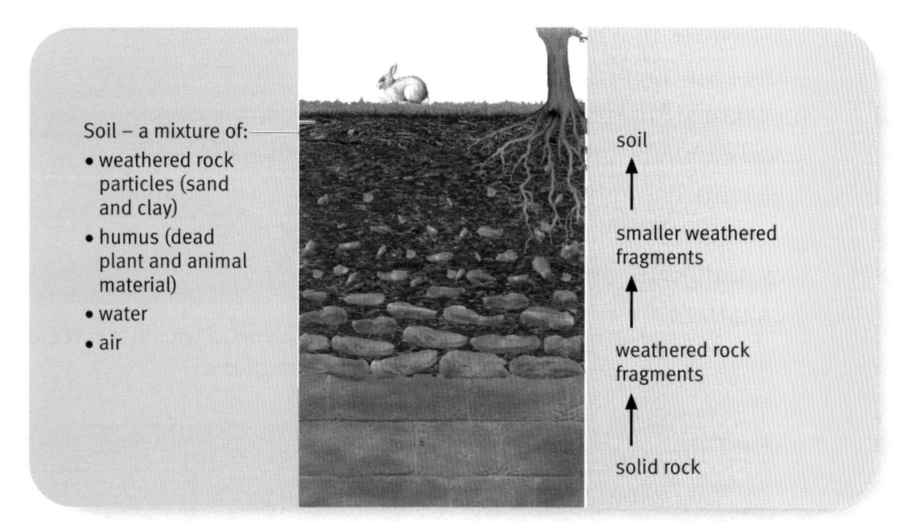

The structure of soil varies depending on the rock type that formed it.

1 Copy and complete using words from the Language bank:
   ___________ is the breakdown of rocks into smaller ___________.
   There are three type of weathering: ___________, chemical weathering and biological weathering.

2 **a** Why is rainwater naturally acidic?
   b What makes rain more acidic?

3 **a** Find out the names of two rocks that can be chemically weathered by natural rainwater.
   b Would they be weathered more quickly in a warm moist country or a cold dry country?

4 Briefly describe how soil is made.

Language bank

acid
biological weathering
carbonates
chemical weathering
fragments
grains
minerals
physical weathering
pollutants
soil
weathering

Temperature changes and rocks

O How do changes in temperature cause rocks to weather?

Climbing at night reduces the risk of rock fall, which is more likely as the day warms up.

Through each day and night the temperature changes in a natural pattern, which can help to weather rocks into small fragments. This is physical weathering, and there are two types:

- **freeze–thaw weathering**, caused by water freezing and thawing again
- **exfoliation**, caused by the rock heating up and cooling down.

Freeze–thaw weathering

This happens when water is frozen at night and then thaws during the day. When water freezes, it expands. If it is enclosed and can't expand freely, it exerts huge forces on its surroundings. We can see this if we fill a bottle with water and put it in a freezer overnight.

If water finds its way into small cracks or **fissures** in a rock, the same thing can happen. When the temperature falls the water freezes and expands, and the forces are large enough to make the crack bigger. If this happens every day and night, eventually the rock shatters.

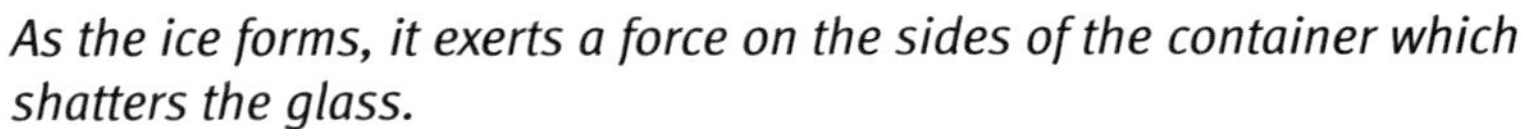

As the ice forms, it exerts a force on the sides of the container which shatters the glass.

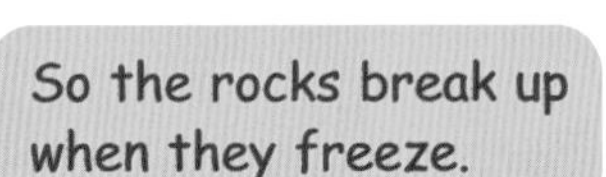

No, it's the water freezing and expanding then melting again, time after time, that does the damage.

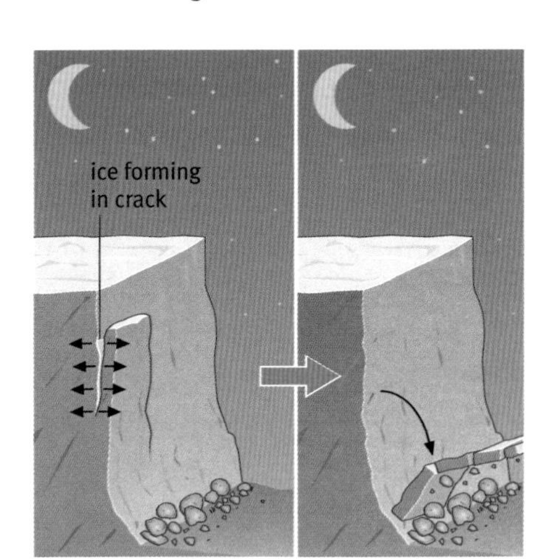

At night the ice makes the crack bigger. During the day more water fills it, and the next night this freezes and makes it even bigger. Eventually the rock breaks up.

Guess what?

The forces exerted when water freezes are so strong that they can split open copper or iron pipes. This is why we insulate water pipes and turn off the water to outside taps in winter.

Exfoliation

Exfoliation, or onion skin weathering, is another form of physical weathering caused by changing temperatures. Rocks expand when heated by the Sun through the day, and they contract when cooled through the night. If this happens repeatedly to a rock, it can cause the surface to flake and fall off, like peeling an onion.

In exfoliation the surface of the rock breaks up into little pieces, forming scree.

The Screes is a well known scree slope by Wast Water in the Lake District. It has formed by the exfoliation of the rock face above.

Investigating exfoliation

If you heat a sample of granite in a Bunsen burner flame and rapidly cool it in water several times, the rock loses its strength. It is easily broken up by tapping it with a hammer.

Why does the rock break up when it is heated and cooled? It contains grains of different minerals. Each mineral expands and contracts a different amount. This causes forces within the rock which break it up.

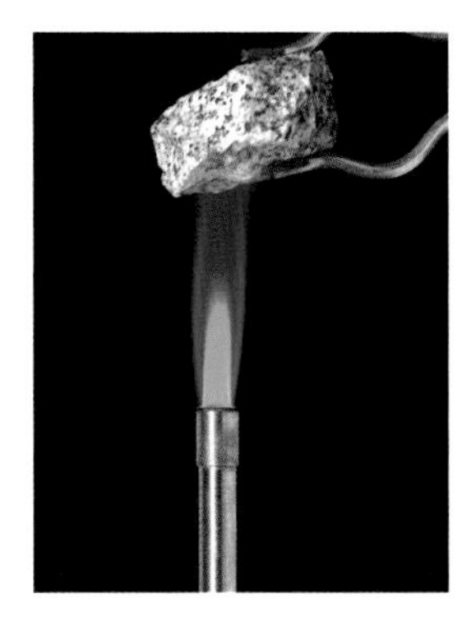

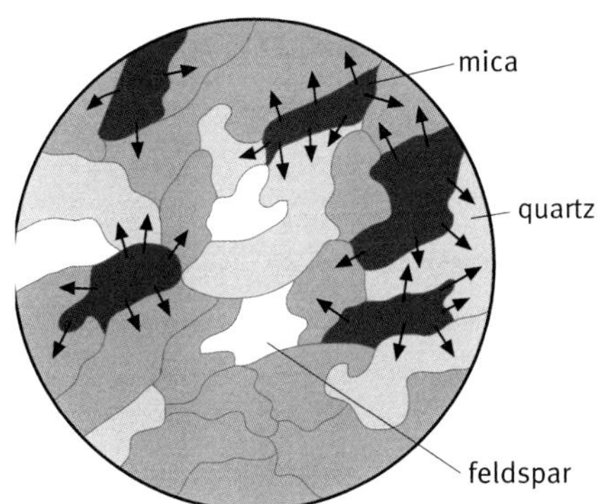

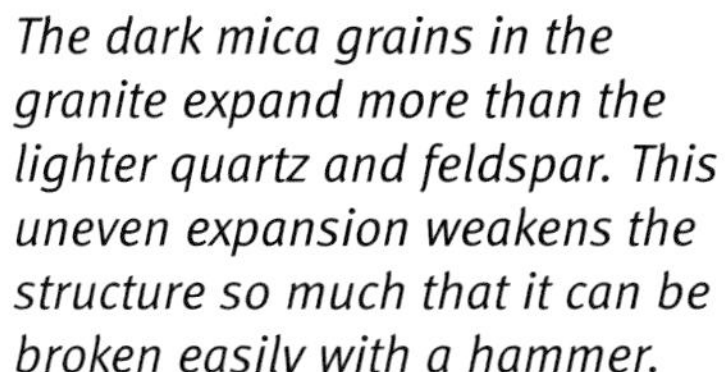

The dark mica grains in the granite expand more than the lighter quartz and feldspar. This uneven expansion weakens the structure so much that it can be broken easily with a hammer.

1 Copy and complete using words from the Language bank:
   ________ changes throughout the day and night can weather rocks. ________ weathering happens when water in small cracks repeatedly freezes, which makes it ________. Rocks on the Earth's surface are heated and cooled, which causes them to expand and ________. This results in ________ skin weathering, also called ________.
2 What is scree and how does it form?
3 In country A the weather is mild and wet. In B it is dry and warm during the day, but very cold at night. In C it is very wet and the temperature can be very high or very low. What kind of weathering will break up the rocks most in A, B and C?
4 Use the particle theory to explain why rock surfaces expand during the day and contract at night.

Language bank

contract
exfoliation
expand
fissures
fragments
freeze–thaw weathering
grains
minerals
onion skin weathering
physical weathering
scree
temperature

Transportation

- What happens to weathered pieces of rock?

The Grand Canyon in Arizona, USA, has been formed by the Colorado River cutting through the rock layers. The sides of the canyon show a 2 km deep sediment bed which is over 250 million years old. But how did the sediment get there?

Rivers move rocks

Weathering results in fragments broken off a rock. But this is not the end of the story. The fragments can be carried away from where they were formed, and dropped somewhere else. Here they may form new sedimentary rocks.

Water is especially good at transporting rock fragments, or **sediment**. Rivers can:

- **weather** rocks, as in the Grand Canyon
- pick up sediment and **transport** it to other places
- drop or **deposit** the sediment.

Weathering a rock and transporting away the pieces is called **erosion**.

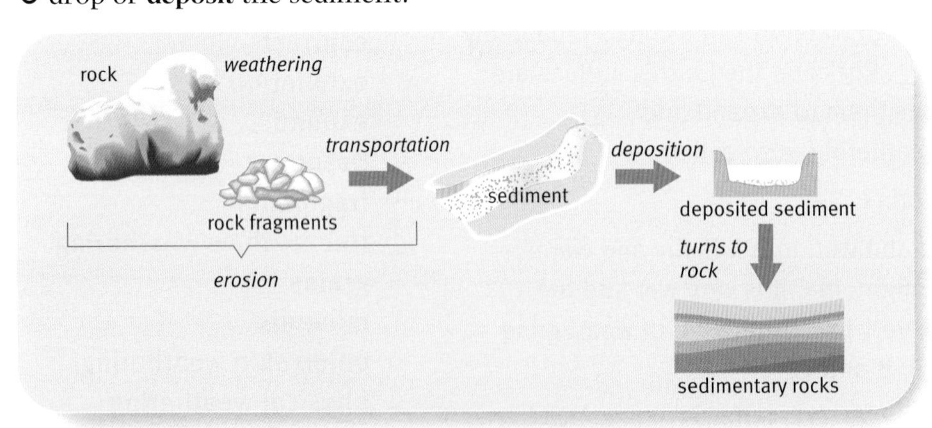

It's not just rivers that carry sediment. It can also be transported by **glaciers** (huge frozen rivers), or by the wind, as in a sandstorm.

More about transportation and deposition

How much sediment can a river hold? That depends on how fast it is flowing, or how much energy it has. The more energy the river has, the more it erodes rocks around it, and the larger the load of sediment it carries. Downstream its energy gets less and it can't hold so much sediment, so it deposits it.

While the sediment is being carried in the river, it becomes even more weathered. The pieces jostle and hit each other. Their sharp corners are knocked off and they gradually get smoother, rounder and smaller.

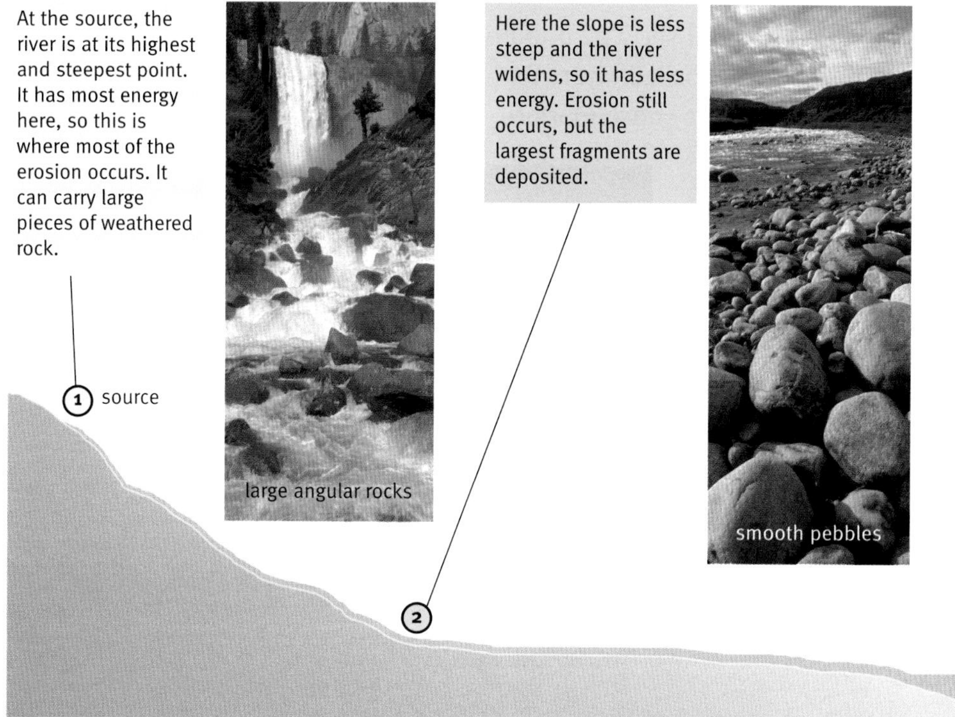

A river deposits the larger rocks and pebbles first, and nearer the mouth the small stones, sand and then silt fall to the bottom. The fragments become smoother and more rounded the nearer they get to the mouth. The river is like a giant sieve, sorting the sediment into different sizes along its length.

1 Copy and complete using words from the Language bank:

______ of rock results in rock fragments. These can be carried away by a river as ______. They get rounder and smoother in the river. Downstream the river has less ______ and it drops the sediment. This is called ______.

2 **a** Why are rock fragments in a river more rounded the nearer they are to the mouth?

b Why do you find larger rock fragments deposited higher up a river, and smaller ones deposited lower down?

3 What do you think would happen to any dissolved materials that are carried in river water when they reach the mouth?

4 In times of heavy rain and flood, what do you think happens to the normal pattern of sediment deposition by a river?

Language bank 

deposition
energy
erosion
fragments
glaciers
rivers
sediment
sedimentary rock
transportation
weathering
wind

Sedimentary rocks

- Why do sediments form layers?
- How are sedimentary rocks formed?

A river deposits layers of sediment such as sand and silt. The building up of the sediment is called **accumulation**. The deposited layers fix together to form sedimentary rock. This is known as **consolidation**.

There are many types of sedimentary rock, formed from the consolidation of different sediments.

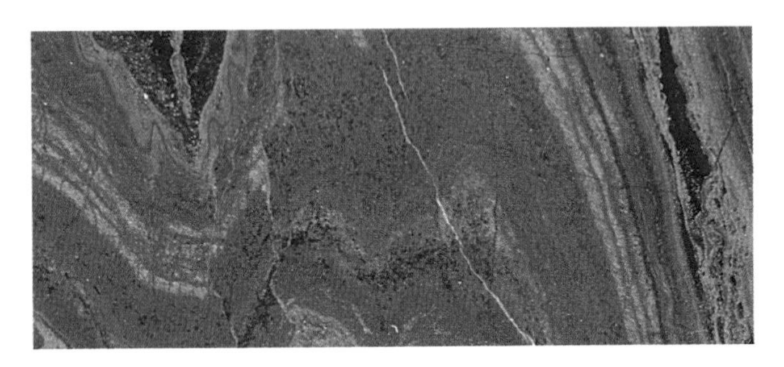

How does sedimentary rock form?

Sedimentary rocks may be laid down in layers or **strata**. Each new layer is formed from new sediment laid down on top of an older layer. Minerals dissolved in the water cause the sediment grains to join together. This is called **cementation**.

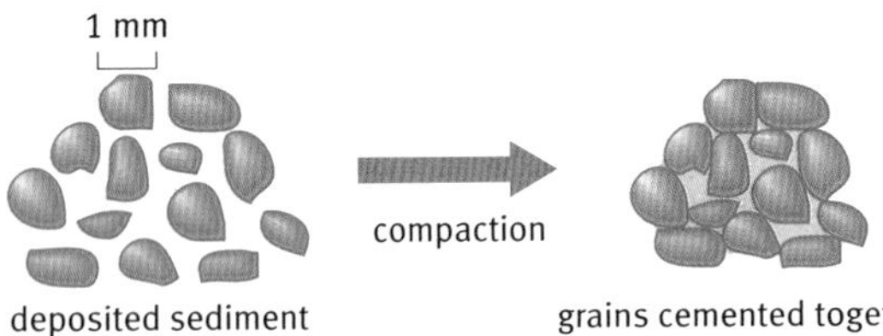

Minerals come out of solution under the pressure of the sediment layers above and form cement.

The older, lower beds can be warped and eroded and then newer beds laid down on top of them. Sandstone forms this way.

Other sedimentary rocks are formed by the evaporation of water. For example, a lake with lots of dissolved minerals might dry up. This leaves mineral deposits known as **evaporites**. Gypsum is an example.

Gypsum is used to make plaster of Paris, a material used for sculpture.

Sedimentary rocks can form from organic material that was once living. Shelly limestone is an example.

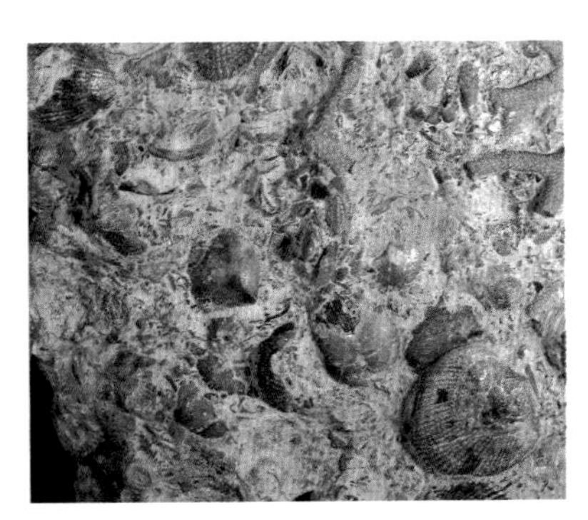

The shells of dead sea creatures became compacted to form this shelly limestone rock.

How fossils form

Fossils are the remains of dead plants or animals preserved in rock. They came to rest at the bottom of the sea, for example, and became buried by the accumulation of sediment. We usually see fossils in sedimentary rocks, but they can be present in metamorphic rocks.

Ammonites, ancient sea creatures, left shell-like fossils. The ancient fern had ridged plant cells which helped it to make a well defined fossil.

Fossilisation happens when the hard parts of the organism are further hardened by minerals in the sediment. The picture opposite shows this. Sometimes body parts leave a mould or impression in the sediment, which is then filled by minerals, creating a cast of the organism.

Using fossils to find out about sedimentary rocks

Sedimentary rocks can tell us much about what has happened to the Earth during its long history. Geologists have analysed rocks from both sides of the Atlantic Ocean to find out which bits of land were once joined up. If the strata are similar on both sides, and contain similar fossils, they were probably once all the same land mass.

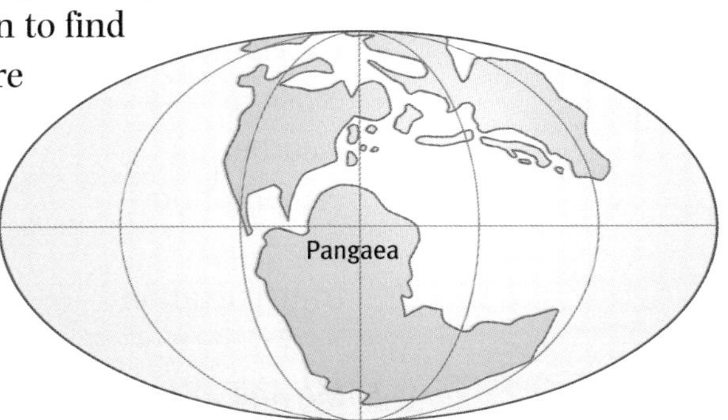

The world as geologists think it was in the Triassic period, about 200 million years ago. There were no maps then (or people)! Geologists have studied rocks and fossils to work out which land masses used to be joined.

1. Copy and complete using words from the Language bank:
   Sedimentary rocks are usually formed in layers or ________ .
   Deposited ________ is cemented together by minerals in solution.
   Some sedimentary rocks are called ________ , formed when water evaporates and leaves behind the dissolved ________ .
2. What are fossils and why are they important?
3. The continents have moved to their present positions because of plate tectonics. Find out more about plate tectonics, for example: What is it? Who proposed the idea? Does it affect human life?

Guess what?

The rhyme 'She sells sea shells on the sea shore' is about Mary Anning. She was born in Lyme Regis in 1799 and lived until 1847. She collected and sold fossils on the beach to the tourists of the time. Her fossils helped start a new science – palaeontology.

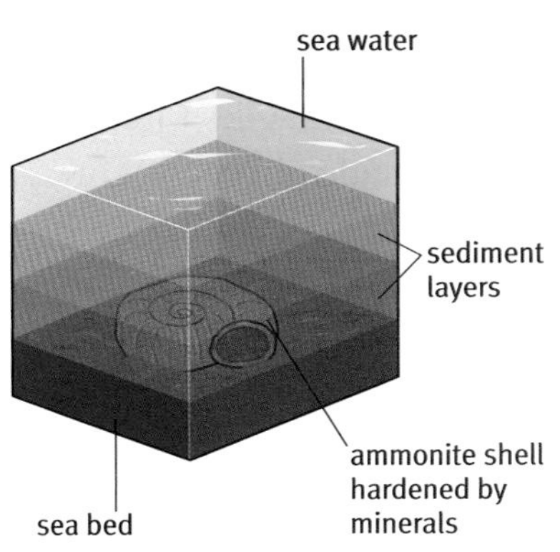

The sediment layers turn to rock, and the ammonite shell forms a fossil as minerals harden it.

Language bank

accumulation
cementation
consolidation
deposited
evaporites
fossils
minerals
sediment
sedimentary rocks
strata

Checkpoint

1 Where in the Earth?

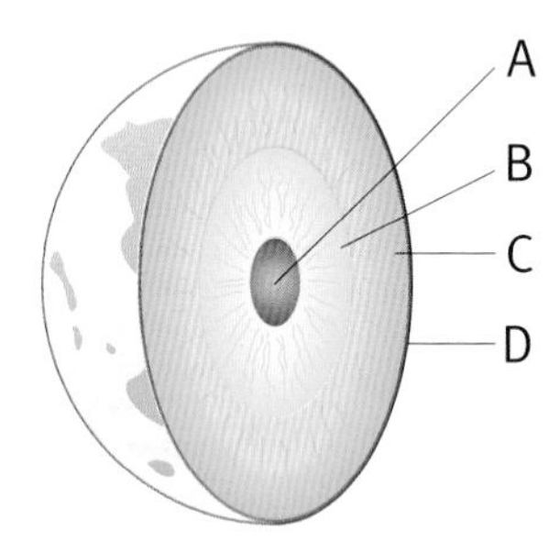

Look at the diagram. Match up each letter A to D with the labels below. Draw a circle round the one that is solid. Put a square box around the one made of rocks.

Labels
outer core
mantle
inner core
crust

2 Match the meaning

Match up each word with its definition.

Words
rock
minerals
texture
grains
porous

Definitions
the size of the grains and how closely they fit together in a rock
a mixture of minerals
compounds and elements that make up the Earth's crust
having spaces between the grains
little pieces of minerals in a rock

3 Types of weathering

Copy the following processes and write P if it is physical weathering, C if it is chemical weathering and B if it is biological weathering.

a Acidic rainwater reacts with carbonate minerals in a rock.
b Water in cracks freezes at night and expands, then melts during the day, eventually causing rock pieces to break off.
c Tree roots grow into cracks in a rock and cause it to break up.
d The surface of a rock expands in the Sun and contracts at night more than the inside does, causing stress in the rock.

4 Forming sedimentary rock

Sketch this diagram and choose the correct label below for A to E.

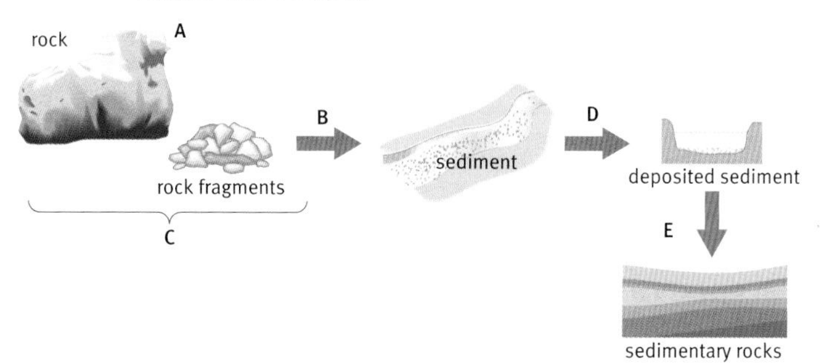

Labels
erosion
weathering
cementation
deposition
transportation

5 Moving around

Copy and complete these sentences, unscrambling the words.

Sediment can be carried by water in **svirre** or glaciers.
How much sediment a river can hold depends on how fast it is **niflwog**. A fast river has more energy and can hold more **stemdine**.
As the river **swols nowd** it has less energy and deposits the sediment.

The rock cycle

Before starting this unit, you should already be familiar with these ideas from earlier work.

- Materials are recycled on Earth in processes that can take millions of years. During these processes the particles of matter become combined in different ways. Do you think matter is destroyed when materials change like this?
- Different rocks have different textures. Which is more porous, sandstone or granite?
- Weathered fragments of rock are transported as sediment and deposited to form new sedimentary rock. Can you think of three ways the original rock might have been worn away into fragments?

You will meet these key ideas as you work through this unit. Have a quick look now, and at the end of the unit read them through slowly.

- **Sedimentary rocks** are formed from sediments laid down in layers. The pressure causes minerals to come out of solution and **cement** the grains together. Limestones are formed this way, and there are many different types depending on the mixture of minerals and the environmental conditions where they formed.
- **Igneous rocks** are formed when **magma** or molten rock inside the Earth cools and solidifies. If the cooling happens slowly, the particles have more time to come together and crystallise before the rock solidifies. So slow cooling results in rocks like granite with large crystals; quicker cooling gives rocks with much smaller crystals, such as basalt.
- **Metamorphic rocks** are formed when high temperature and pressure change other rocks deep in the Earth. For example sedimentary limestone may be changed to marble by heat and pressure.
- These three types of rock have different properties. Some have big crystals or grains; others are glassy or have small crystals. Some are porous and some are denser than others. Some have fossils and some have bands or layers in the rock. These characteristics help us decide what type of rock it is and how it formed.
- All these rocks are constantly being recycled and changed from one form to another over millions of years in the **rock cycle**. Energy is transferred in the rock cycle.

Limestone

Are all limestones different?

You know that there are different sedimentary rocks, such as limestone or sandstone. Sedimentary rocks may be formed in one of three ways:

- from the cementation of sediment layers – **detrital rocks**
- minerals left behind when water evaporates (evaporite rock) – **chemical rocks**
- from once-living materials – **organic rocks**.

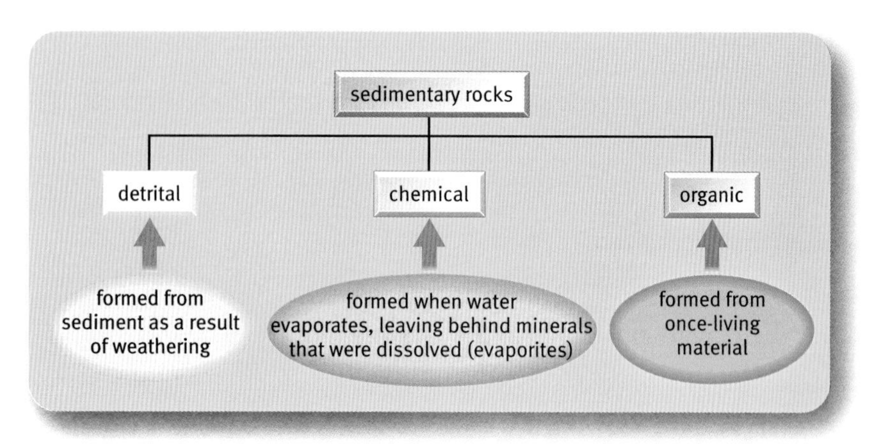

Looking at limestones

There are lots of different types of limestone. Limestone rock can be formed in any of the three ways listed above, so limestone can have a variety of properties. Like all rocks it is a mixture, and its composition will vary depending on how it was formed.

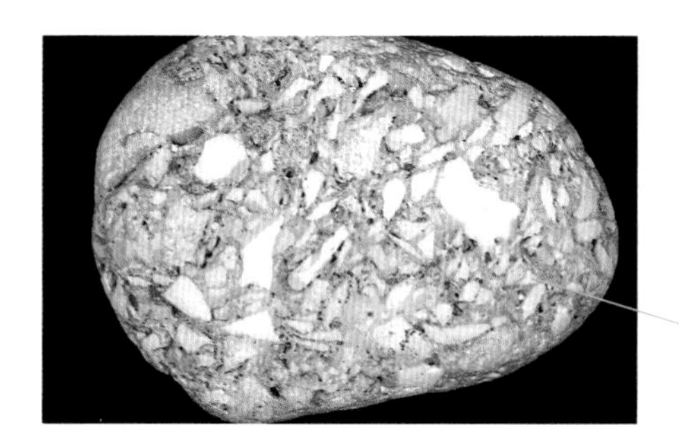

Limestone breccia forms from fragments of other rocks (it is a detrital limestone). It is found near areas of weathering such as the base of a cliff.

angular fragments of limestone, finer matrix of calcite (calcium carbonate)

Pisolitic means 'like a pea'.

Pisolitic limestone is a chemical sedimentary rock. The rounded structures form when calcite ***precipitates*** *from water (when it falls out of solution). This kind of limestone is formed in shallow seas which provide ideal conditions for precipitation to occur.*

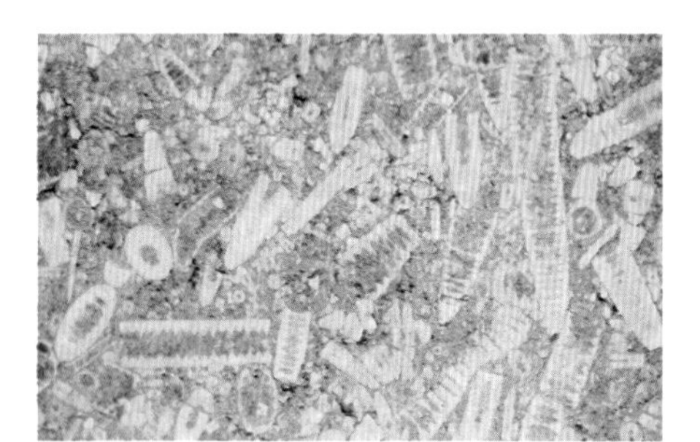

This crinoidal limestone was formed in ancient seas from sea creatures rather like starfish and sea urchins. It is therefore an organic limestone. The remains of sea creatures are in a matrix of calcite.

Crinoidal?

The little sea creatures that formed it were called crinoids.

Chalk is another organic sedimentary rock. It is powdery with very fine grains. Chalk formed from the remains of micro-organisms, so it often contains fossils. It is very pure, and probably formed at a time when the land was dry and there was little erosion by water.

How much carbonate is in limestone?

Limestone contains calcium and magnesium carbonates, which react with acid. The more carbonate there is in a rock sample, the more acid it will react with. There might be sediment made from sand (silicon dioxide) in limestone, and this does not react with acid.

- George and Perminder ground up three different types of limestone. They placed 10 g of each into separate beakers.
- They added hydrochloric acid from a measuring cylinder until they couldn't see any more bubbles of carbon dioxide.
- They then filtered the mixture to collect any unreacted rock. They left this overnight to dry and weighed it the next day.
- They used their results to work out how much of each original rock sample was carbonate.

Limestone sample	Acid used (cm^3)	Mass of rock left over that didn't react with acid (g)
A	98	0.2
B	95	0.5
C	92	0.8

Which rock sample contained the most carbonate?

Language bank

calcite
calcium carbonate
carbon dioxide
cementation
chemical rocks
detrital rocks
evaporite
hydrochloric acid
limestone
magnesium carbonate
matrix
organic rocks
precipitate
sediment

1 Copy and complete using words from the Language bank:

Limestones can be made from ______ , from a solution evaporating or from organic material. They contain metal carbonates including ______ carbonate and ______ carbonate. These react with acid to produce ______ gas.

2 Name the three different types of sedimentary rock.

3 Calculate the percentage of carbonate in each limestone sample A, B and C above.

Igneous rocks

Where do igneous rocks come from?

Imagine being inside an erupting volcano at temperatures over 1000 °C, as it throws red-hot molten rock or **magma** high into the air. This is what happens when igneous rocks are formed.

The word igneous comes from the Latin word meaning 'fire', as igneous rocks form from cooling magma. When magma reaches the Earth's surface it is called **lava**.

Mount Pinatubo in the Philippines erupts, blasting lava and ash from its mouth. The ash settles and the lava cools and solidifies, forming new igneous rocks.

Types of igneous rock

Sometimes magma cools below the Earth's surface. This might happen in a volcano's side-vent (**dyke**). Sometimes liquid magma flows between rock strata and solidifies there, forming a **sill**.

> **Guess what?**
> Most volcanoes run on a belt on the Pacific Ocean called the Ring of Fire.

The molten rock is deep in the Earth, insulated from the cooler surface. This means it cools slowly. As it gradually solidifies, the mineral crystals have time to grow large before the rock becomes totally solid. Rocks formed like this are called **intrusive igneous rocks**.

Other igneous rocks are formed on the surface of the Earth, so the lava cools quickly. There is no time for large crystals to form so these rocks have very small crystals or a glassy type of structure. Rocks formed like this are called **extrusive igneous rocks**.

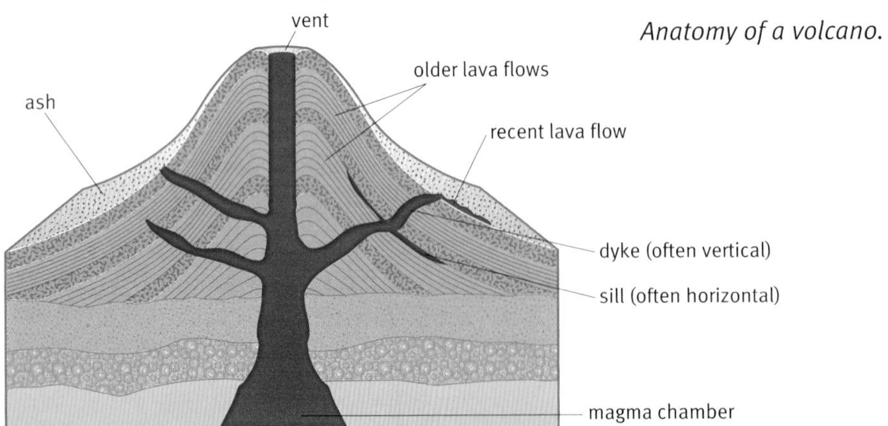

Anatomy of a volcano.

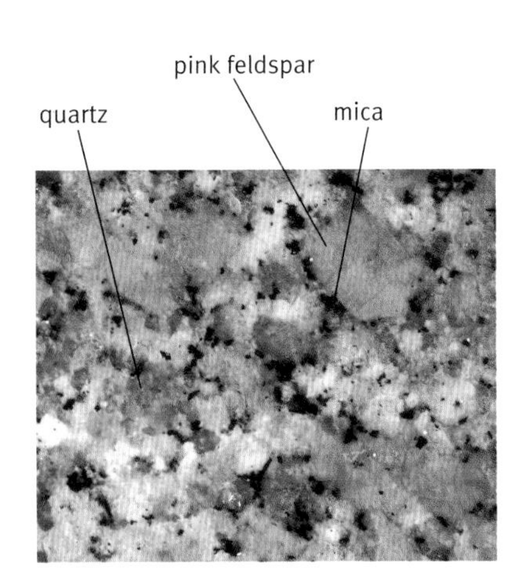

This sample of pink granite was formed slowly, deep in a dyke. It has large crystals, up to about 5 mm.

Obsidian is glassy; no crystals visible.

Pumice: gas bubbles, visible.

Basalt: very fine crystals.

Investigating cooling rocks

We can model slow and fast cooling using salol (a waxy solid). We melt it and put some on a hot slide and some on a cold slide to cool.

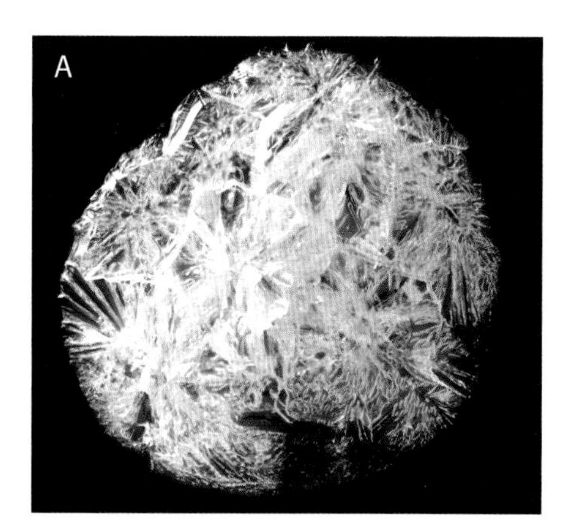

The salol cooled more slowly on the warm slide (A). Here the particles had more time to come together to form large crystals before it all turned solid. The crystals are smaller on the cold slide (B).

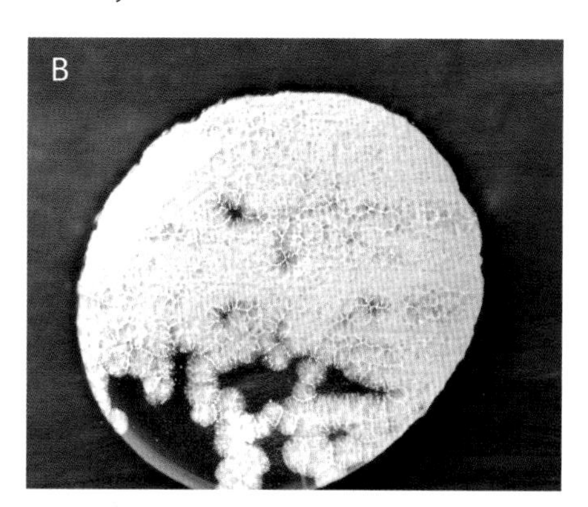

Different densities

Igneous rocks have different compositions depending on the rock that melted to form them. For example, granites are usually rich in minerals that contain silica. Gabbros have more iron-containing minerals.

Silica-rich rocks have a lower density than iron-rich rocks. To identify an unknown igneous rock, finding its density gives some clues.

1) Weigh the rock to find its mass.

2) Find its volume:

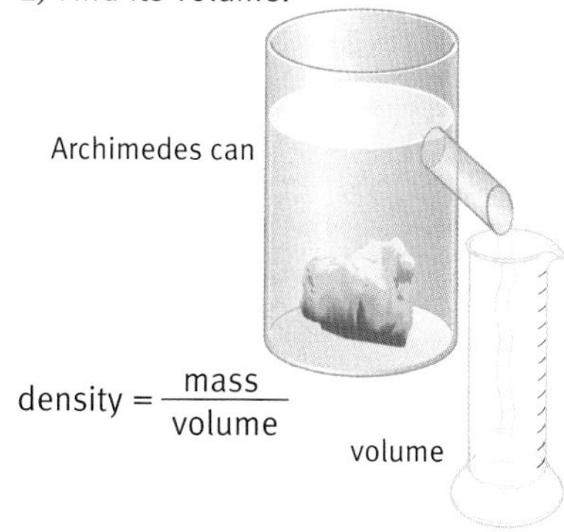

$$\text{density} = \frac{\text{mass}}{\text{volume}}$$

Divide the mass of a rock by its volume to find the density. This gives a clue to the minerals inside.

1 Copy and complete using words from the Language bank:
Igneous rocks form from cooling ______ or lava. They can be ______, which means they formed on the surface of the Earth, or ______, which means they formed underneath the Earth's surface.

2 Explain the difference between magma and lava. Which one cools to form extrusive igneous rock?

3 Why do intrusive igneous rocks have larger crystals than extrusive ones? Use the word 'particle' in your answer.

4 Typical rock densities: granite 2.75 g/cm^3; gabbro 3.0 g/cm^3.

a Jo measured the mass and volume of a rock: mass 364 g, volume 120 cm^3. Is it granite or gabbro?

b Explain this difference in density between granite and gabbro.

Language bank

- crystals
- dyke
- erupt
- extrusive igneous rocks
- igneous rocks
- intrusive igneous rocks
- lava
- magma
- salol
- sill
- volcano

8H.3 Changing rocks

What is different about metamorphic rocks?

You might think that once igneous or sedimentary rocks have formed, they stay there. But heat and/or pressure can change these solid rocks into new forms, called **metamorphic rocks**. The baking and squeezing may change the rock only slightly, or if conditions are extreme the rock may become quite different.

*The wavy bands or **foliation** shown in this metamorphic rock have been caused by conditions of high pressure. This can happen when some parts of the Earth's crust collide or move past each other.*

Comparing rock types

The table shows the main differences between sedimentary, igneous and metamorphic rocks.

Rock type	Sedimentary	Igneous	Metamorphic
Structure	platy or layered, with grains that may be poorly held together	crystalline with interlocking minerals firmly held together	often sugary, particles may be aligned or random
Fossils present?	fossils very common	no fossils present	remains of fossils possible, but rare
Bedding	flat beds often present unless rock has been folded	random arrangement of crystals	often have wavy bands called foliation
Porosity	often porous	non-porous	varies, but often less porous than sedimentary rocks

Examples of metamorphic rocks

Generally, the higher the temperature and pressure, the larger are the grains in the metamorphic rock.

Slate forms from sedimentary shale or clay in conditions of low temperature and low pressure. The fine grains in slate are too small to be seen by the naked eye.

Slate forms from ...

... shale.

In slate the grains are fine and the layers are more defined and less flaky than in shale.

Marble forms from sedimentary limestone and chalk. Blue marble is almost completely calcite (calcium carbonate) but it may contain dolomite (magnesium carbonate). It forms when limestone is strongly heated at low pressure.

Metaquartzite forms from sedimentary sandstone. When sandstone is heated its appearance becomes paler and more sugary, with a finer and more even texture. Metaquartzite is not as porous as the sandstone that formed it.

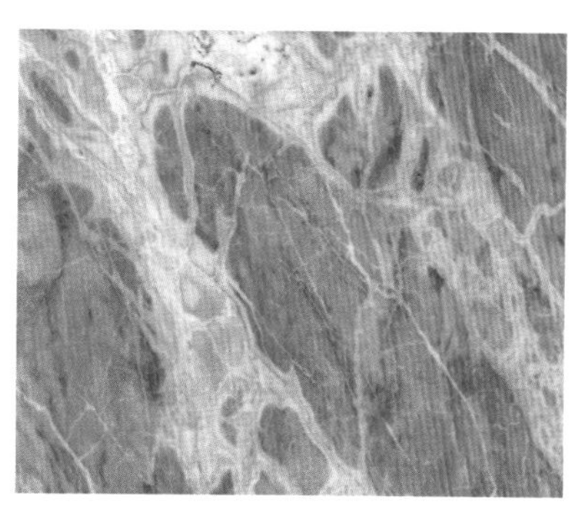

Marble forms from ...

... limestone.

The heat destroys the original limestone structure and gives the rock a new texture.

Metaquartzite forms from ...

... sedimentary sandstone.

In metaquartzite the grains are large and held together loosely.

Where do metamorphic rocks form?

How do these conditions of heat and pressure that change rocks come about? Hot magma can find its way up into cracks in the crust, wedging them open to form an **igneous intrusion**. The heat may cause rocks in contact with it to metamorphose, for example, shale forming slate and limestone forming marble.

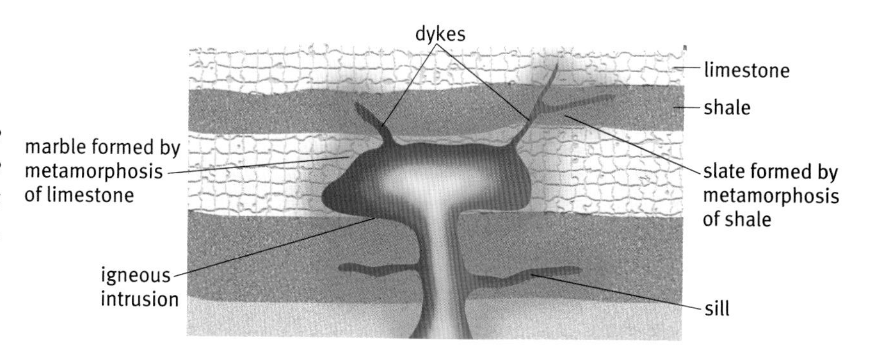

The deeper the rocks, the more pressure they are under, from all the rock above them. Rocks may be heated by an igneous intrusion nearby.

1 Copy and complete using words from the Language bank:

Conditions of ______ and ______ can cause some rocks to change even though they may be solid. The rocks formed are called ______ rocks. These rocks may have wavy bands called ______.

2 Write out the correct statements below about metamorphic rocks.

a They are formed of distinct layers or bands.

b Their crystals may be aligned.

c They are less porous than the sedimentary rock that formed them.

3 Why are fossil samples found in metamorphic rocks often distorted?

4 Gneiss forms under high pressure and temperature. What kind of grain structure will it have? Explain your answer.

Language bank

dyke
foliation
fossils
heat
igneous intrusion
limestone
marble
metamorphic rocks
pressure
shale
sill
slate

3H.4 The rock cycle

What is the rock cycle?

Metamorphic rock may form from igneous or sedimentary rock, but even this is not the end of the story. There is a continual process in which rocks are recycled over many years into new rocks. The three types of rock are linked together by processes that constantly supply and transform the Earth's materials. These processes are summarised in the **rock cycle**.

The rock cycle.

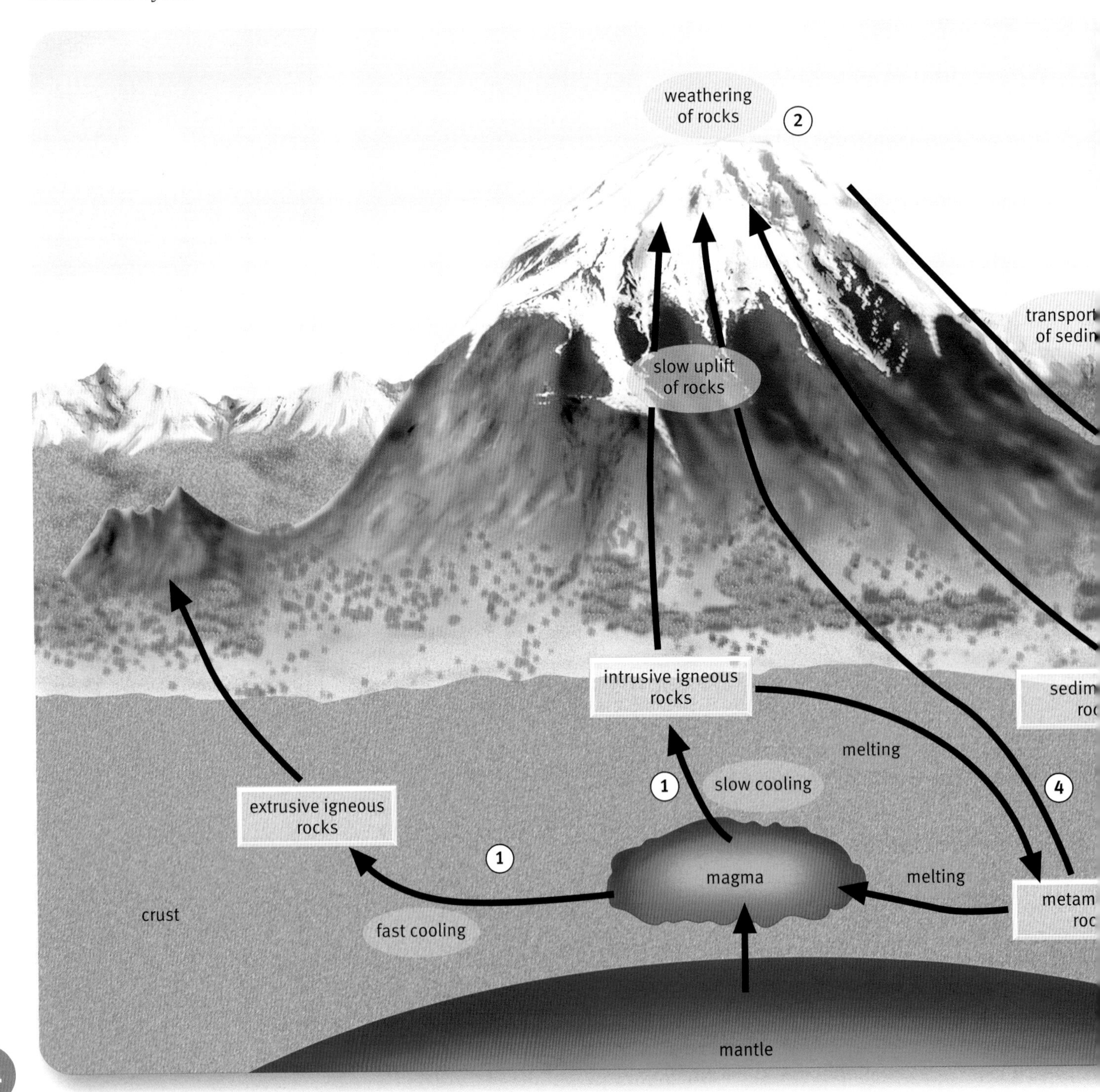

The important processes of the rock cycle are these:

① Magma cools to form both intrusive and extrusive igneous rocks.

② All rock types may be weathered, by physical, biological or chemical means. The weathered sediment may be transported by wind, water or ice. It may later form sedimentary rock.

③ Sedimentary rocks form from deposited sediment or from solutions. They are usually compressed and the particles cemented together.

④ Metamorphic rocks can form from all rock types, especially igneous and sedimentary, when they are changed by heat or pressure or both.

Language bank

cementation
compression
continual process
cooling
deposition
formation
melting
rock cycle
sediment
transportation
uplift
weathering

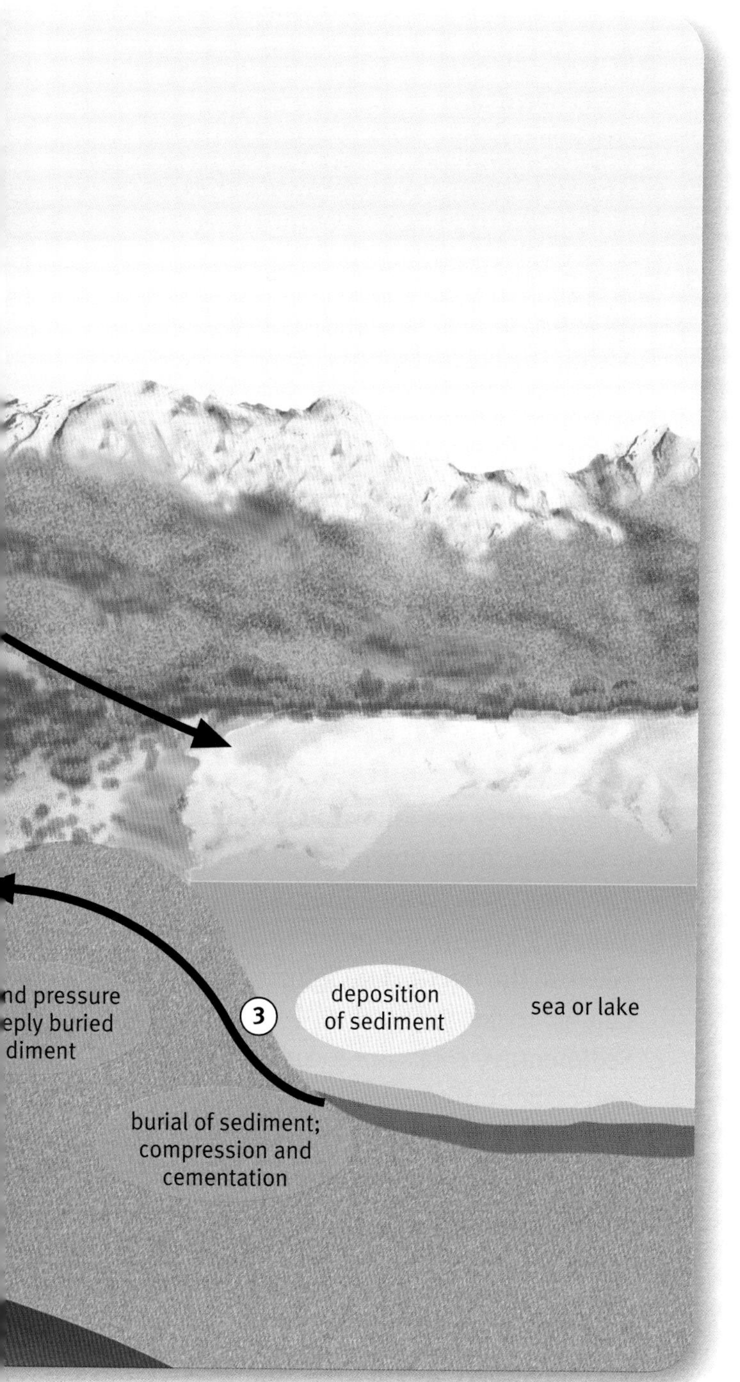

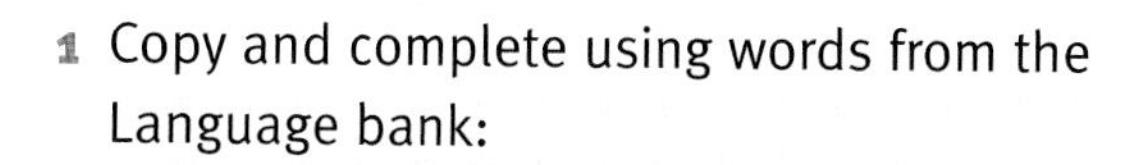

1 Copy and complete using words from the Language bank:

The ______ cycle links together the processes that form and change rocks. It is a ______ process in which old rocks are transformed into new ones.

2 Copy the flow chart below and write labels for A to G. Use the large rock cycle to help you.

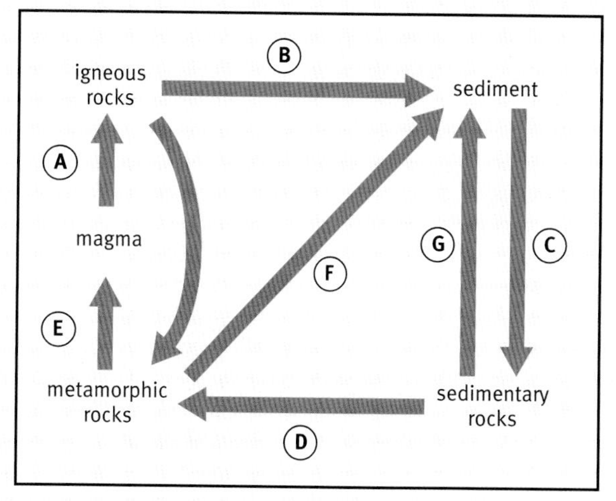

3 Weathering erodes rocks into small fragments or sediment. Why then has the Earth's surface not been weathered until it is completely flat?

4 The Earth is sometimes described as being 'dynamic'. What do you think this means in terms of rock formation?

Checkpoint

1 How much carbonate?

Look at this experiment to find out how much carbonate is in a type of limestone.

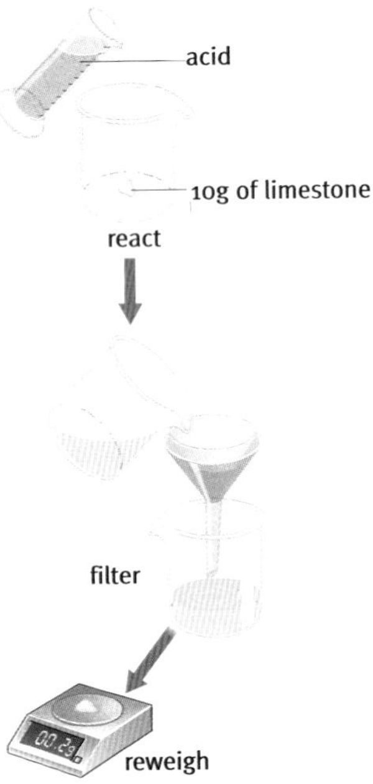

Choose the correct description and result below for this experiment.

Descriptions

The acid reacted with carbonate in the rock to give off carbon dioxide.

The acid reacted with oxide in the rock to give off carbon dioxide.

The acid reacted with carbonate in the rock to give off hydrogen.

The acid dissolved the rock but no gas was produced.

Results

The mass of rock did not change during the experiment because rocks cannot be destroyed.

The mass of rock was greater after the experiment because carbon dioxide had been added.

The mass of rock was less after the experiment because the carbonate had reacted with the acid.

The mass of rock was less after the experiment because acid is like rainwater.

2 Forming igneous rocks

Match up the beginnings and endings to make complete sentences. Use a different colour to write each sentence.

Beginnings	Endings
Magma is ...	... molten rock on the Earth's surface.
Lava is ...	... slowly inside the Earth.
Intrusive igneous rocks form ...	... molten rock inside the Earth.
Extrusive igneous rocks form ...	... quickly on the Earth's surface.

3 It's your choice

Copy and complete the following sentences, choosing the correct words.

Deep in the Earth, heat and/or pressure can change existing rocks into new **metamorphic** / **igneous** / **intrusive** rocks.

Rocks may be heated by nearby hot **magma** / **slate** / **lava** finding its way into cracks underground.

Marble / **sandstone** / **shale** is a metamorphic rock that is formed from limestone or chalk.

4 True or false?

Decide whether the following statements are true or false. Write down the true ones.

a The rock cycle formed the rocks we see today.

b The rock cycle is no longer happening because the Earth is no longer hot enough to change rocks.

c Sedimentary rocks are formed by deposition and cementation.

d Igneous rocks can be weathered to form sediment and so can end up as part of sedimentary rocks.

e Metamorphic rocks are only formed from lava.

Heating and cooling

Before starting this unit, you should already be familiar with these ideas from earlier work.

- The particle model explains differences in behaviour between solids, liquids and gases, and explains changes of state.
- We use a thermometer to measure temperature, or how hot an object is. What units do we use to measure temperature?
- Some materials conduct heat and electricity well. Name an example.
- If you leave a liquid, it will evaporate (change into a gas). What could you do to make a basin of water evaporate more quickly?

You will meet these key ideas as you work through this unit. Have a quick look now, and at the end of the unit read them through slowly.

- **Temperature** measures how much heat energy an object has. This depends on how quickly its particles are moving.
- Heat energy is transferred wherever there is a temperature difference.
- Heat energy may be transferred by **conduction**, **convection**, **evaporation** or **radiation**. In conduction, convection and evaporation, the particles of a material transfer the heat.
- Solids are good **conductors** – the heat energy is transferred along through them. Solids expand when heated.
- **Convection** happens in liquids and gases. **Convection currents** carry away the heat energy.
- **Evaporation** happens at the surface of a liquid.
- **Radiation** does not need a **medium**, so it does not depend on the movement of particles.
- We use **thermal conductors** when we want heat transfer to be efficient. For example, the base of a saucepan might be made of copper to conduct the heat quickly through to the food.
- **Thermal insulators** prevent heat escaping. Insulating materials contain air spaces so do not conduct heat well, and if the air spaces are small this prevents convection currents being set up. A silvered surface reflects radiated heat back .
- The forces of attraction between particles in a solid are weakened during melting. They are completely broken during boiling or evaporation, and the particles are free to move in the gas.

Temperature

What's the temperature?

The coldest place on Earth is Antarctica, where temperatures as cold as –89 °C have been recorded. At the other extreme, the hottest place is the El Alzizia desert in Libya where temperatures have soared to 58 °C. But what exactly do we mean by hot and cold?

Can you trust your senses?

Try holding one hand in hot water (not too hot!) and the other in cold water. Then put them both into warm water. You'll probably find something strange. The cold hand sends messages to your brain saying that the warm water feels hot. To the hot hand it feels cooler. The fact is that our senses are not always very accurate. We can't always trust them, which is why we use thermometers.

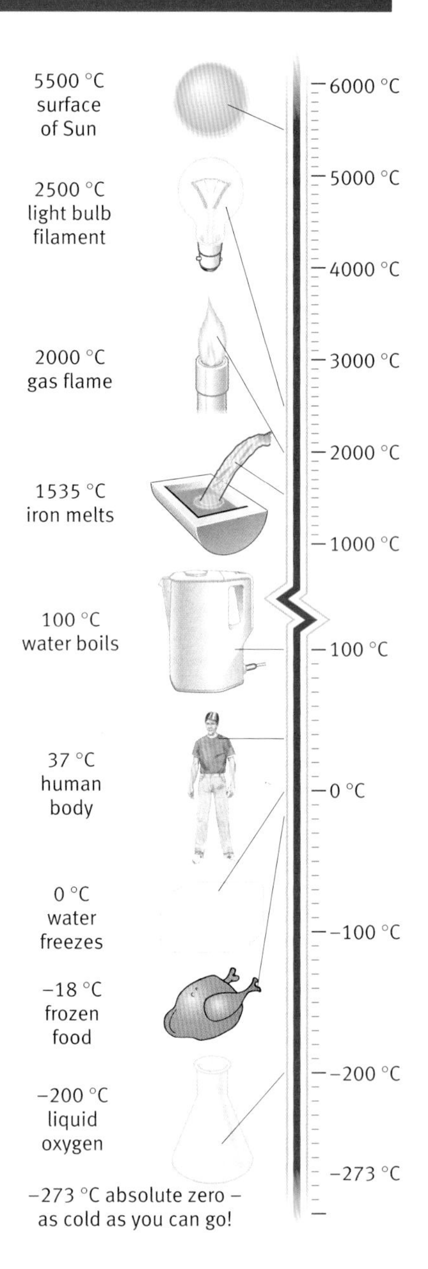

The Celsius temperature scale

We measure the **temperature** to tell us exactly how hot or cold something is. To do this we use a **thermometer**, which has a scale on it. The **Celsius** temperature scale is based on two fixed points, the melting point of ice (water) and the boiling point of water at normal atmospheric pressure. The melting point of water is called 0, and the boiling point is called 100. There are 100 divisions or **degrees** between these two points.

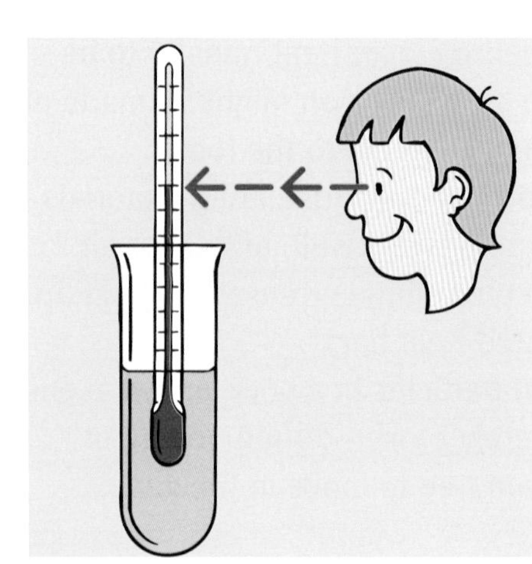

What's the temperature?

Look at the picture to see how to read a thermometer and find the temperature accurately.

Guess what?

Anders Celsius (1701–44), inventor of the temperature scale that takes his name, actually had the boiling point of water as 0 and the melting point as 100. This was later changed round after his death.

Make your own thermometer scale

If you had a thermometer without a scale, you could make your own scale. Dip it in melting ice for a few minutes and mark off the reading: this is 0 °C. Then put it in boiling water and mark off this reading: 100 °C. Then divide the distance between your two fixed points into 100 equal units.

You say 'thirty-seven degrees Celsius' — *This stands for degrees* — *You say 'minus fifty- four degrees Celsius'*

37°C –54°C

For temperatures above zero the + sign is often left out — *This stands for Celsius* — *minus sign means below zero*

The right thermometer for the job

There are different thermometers for different jobs. For example, your body temperature is 37 °C but the temperature in a freezer might be –20 °C. You need different thermometers to measure these temperatures accurately. Each thermometer measures a **range** of temperatures, from the hottest to the coldest on its scale.

Some thermometers have a liquid in a bulb. The liquid expands when it becomes warm, and the level moves up the tiny capillary tube inside. You read where the top of the liquid has got to on the scale. But not all thermometers are like this – there are lots of different kinds. Digital thermometers show you the reading in numbers.

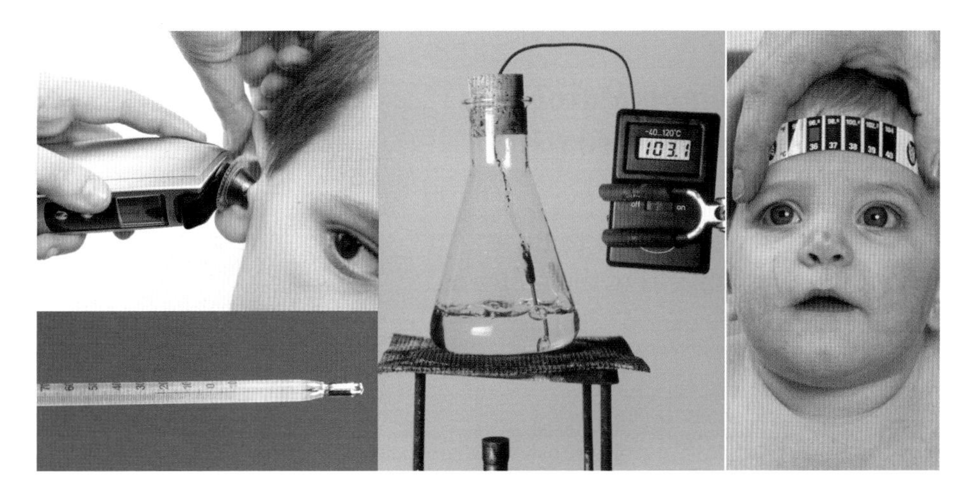

An oven thermometer has a range of 120 to 220 °C, whilst the range of the clinical thermometer is only 35 to 40 °C. This makes any small rise in your body temperature easy to see. Paper thermometers are safe and unbreakable. Laboratory thermometers often show –10 to 110 °C.

1. Copy and complete using words from the Language bank:

   We use a _____ to measure how hot something is, because our senses are not always very _____. The scale we usually use is called the _____ scale, with the symbol _____. Thermometers are designed for the job they do. For example, the _____ is used to measure body temperature.
2. Why do we need a temperature scale?
3. Choose a type of thermometer and describe how it works.
4. Human body temperature is 37 °C. What would this have been on Celsius's original temperature scale?

Language bank 

°C
accurate
bulb
capillary tube
Celsius
clinical thermometer
degrees
digital thermometer
range
scale
temperature
thermometer

Hotter and colder: conduction

How do things get hotter or colder?

Fuels are stores of chemical energy. We burn them to release heat energy (and light energy). Look at the chip pan on the stove. The heat energy from the flame is transferred to the oil in the pan. The temperature of the oil rises as heat is transferred to it.

The flame is hotter than the pan. This is why the heat energy is transferred from the flame to the metal pan, and then to the oil.

What's the difference between heat and temperature?

Heat is a type of energy. We call it **heat energy** or **thermal energy**. Like other forms of energy, it is measured in **joules** (J).

Heating is the transfer of thermal energy. Heat flows from one thing to another when there is a temperature difference. It flows from the hotter thing to the cooler thing.

Aren't heat and temperature the same?

No, heat is thermal energy. The temperature measures how much heat energy there is.

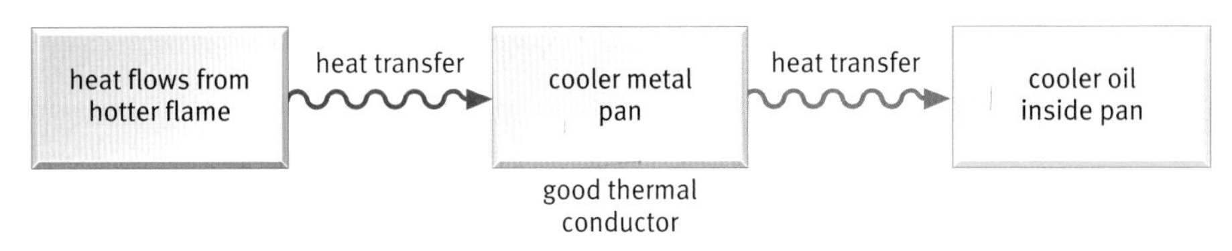

The oil gets hotter because it is supplied with thermal energy. As a result, its temperature rises. If you stopped heating the oil, thermal energy would flow away from it, into the cooler air around it. Then the oil would get colder again and its temperature would fall.

The thermal energy is transferred to the oil through the metal pan. It is transferred by **conduction**. 'Conducting' means transferring. Heat is conducted through any kind of material, but some materials are better conductors than others. Metals are good **thermal conductors**.

Good conductor or insulator?

The polystyrene cup and the aluminium can in the photo are both at room temperature, 25 °C. This is cooler than your hand, which is about 37 °C. But the cup feels warm to the touch and the can feels cold. Why? The can is aluminium, a metal, so it conducts the heat from your hand away from you. It feels cold. The polystyrene cup is a poor thermal conductor (a **thermal insulator**), so it does not conduct the heat away from your hand so quickly. It feels warm.

- Good conductors (poor insulators) feel cold to the touch. These include metals such as copper used for pans and in central heating systems.
- Good insulators (poor conductors) feel warm to the touch. These include wood used for table mats and plastics used for pan handles. The Space Shuttle has insulating ceramic tiles on it, which stop it burning up on re-entry to the atmosphere.

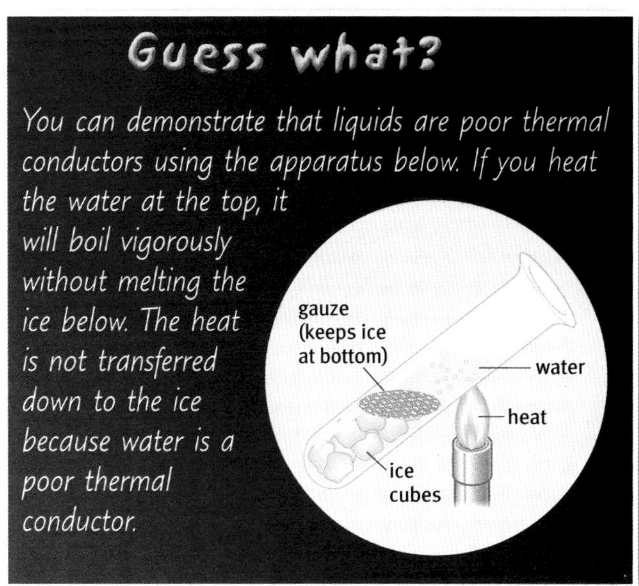

Guess what?

You can demonstrate that liquids are poor thermal conductors using the apparatus below. If you heat the water at the top, it will boil vigorously without melting the ice below. The heat is not transferred down to the ice because water is a poor thermal conductor.

Do clothes make you warmer?

Some solids are good conductors. But liquids and gases are poor conductors. Materials with air trapped in them, such as loft insulation, are insulating materials.

Birds' feathers trap air like loft insulation does. This is why duvets are often filled with eiderdown, fluffy feathers from the eider duck. Clothes and duvets do not make you warmer, they simply stop thermal energy moving away from your skin.

1. Copy and complete using words from the Language bank:

   Heat is a form of _____, so it is measured in _____. The temperature is a measure of the amount of _____, which changes when heat energy is _____.

   Solids, especially metals, are good _____. Liquids such as water and gases such as air are poor thermal conductors. They are good _____.
2. What is the difference between heat and temperature?
3. Some quilted jackets and sleeping bags contain feathers. Explain why these are good at keeping you warm.
4. Classify these materials as good thermal conductors or good thermal insulators: aluminium, copper, wool, down, air, polystyrene, water. Add three more materials to each list.

Language bank 

conducting
conduction
energy
heat energy
heating
insulating
insulation
joules (J)
temperature
thermal conductors
thermal energy
thermal insulators
transferred

Convection

○ How do materials change when they are heated and cooled?

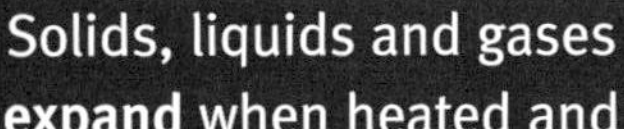

Remember
Solids, liquids and gases **expand** when heated and then **contract** when cooled. This is because their particles move faster when they are heated, which makes them move apart. The particles themselves do not change size.

Bigger and hotter

The photos below show solids, liquids and gases expanding when you heat them.

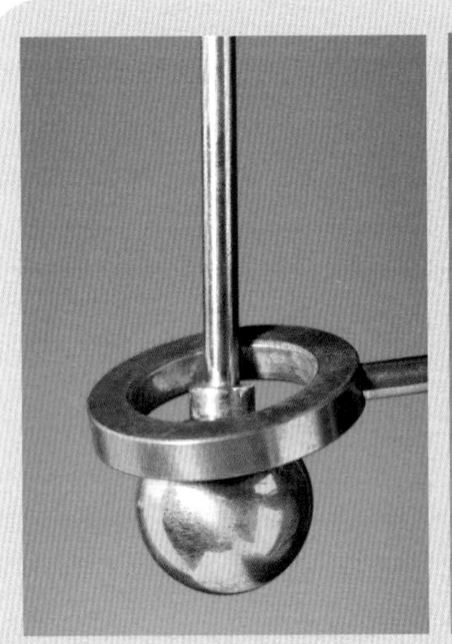

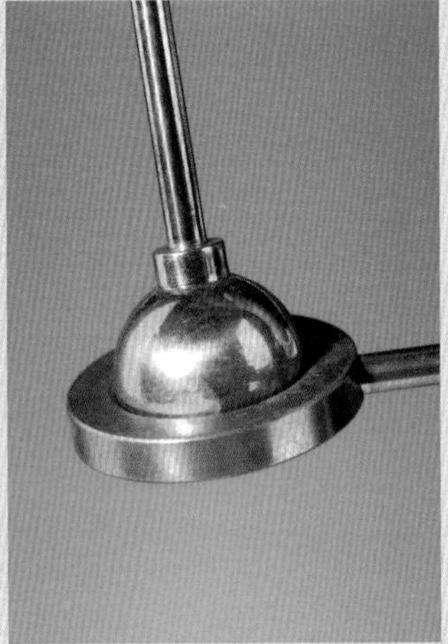

The solid metal ball will easily fit through the ring at room temperature, but if you heat it, it expands in all directions and will not fit through the ring.

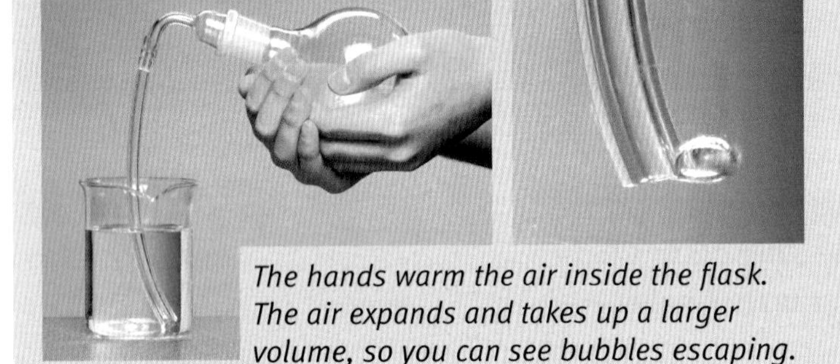

The hands warm the air inside the flask. The air expands and takes up a larger volume, so you can see bubbles escaping.

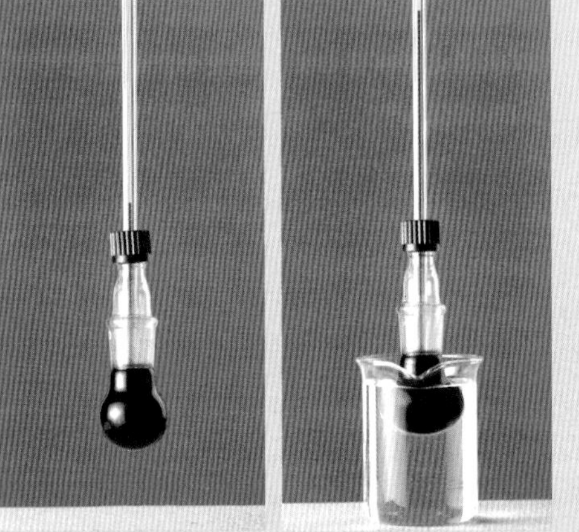

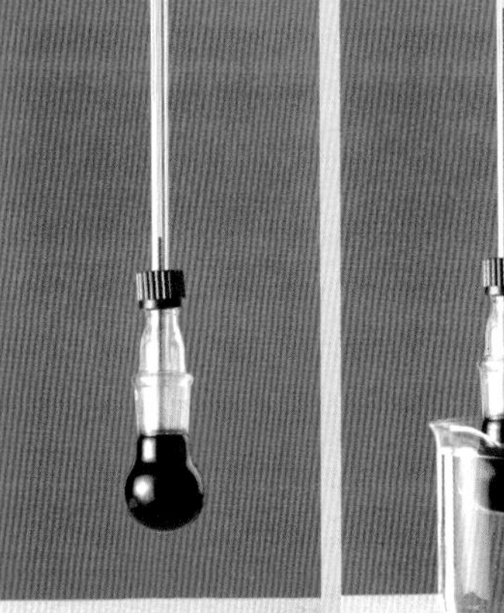

As the liquid in the flask is heated, it expands and rises up the thin capillary tube. The liquid in a thermometer rises in the same way.

Seeing the trails

If you put purple potassium manganate(VII) crystals into water and heat one side of the tube, you will see a trail of colour falling down the cool side and rising up the warm side as it dissolves in the water.

purple potassium manganate(VII) crystals dissolve

cooler water falls

hotter water rises

convection current

Why does this happen? The photos above show that when solids, liquids and gases are heated they expand. If they expand, their density will fall:

$$\text{density}\downarrow = \frac{\text{mass}}{\text{volume}\uparrow}$$

If the volume gets bigger (due to expansion) ...

the density must decrease

This explains why warmer water rises. If you put a table tennis ball at the bottom of a bath of water, the ball would rise to the top of the water and float, because it is less dense than water. The water provides enough upthrust to allow the ball to float.

The same thing happens to the warm water at one side of the tube. It is less dense than the cold water above it, so the warm water rises and cold water from the other side of the tube takes its place.

This movement of water caused by heat is called a **convection current**. It transfers thermal energy from one part of the water to another by **convection**. Convection will transfer thermal energy in any **fluid** (a fluid is a liquid or a gas).

> **Guess what?**
> *How does a hot air balloon rise up in the air? A burner heats the air inside the balloon. The hot air inside is less dense than cold air, so the balloon floats in the cold air around it.*

Convection in action

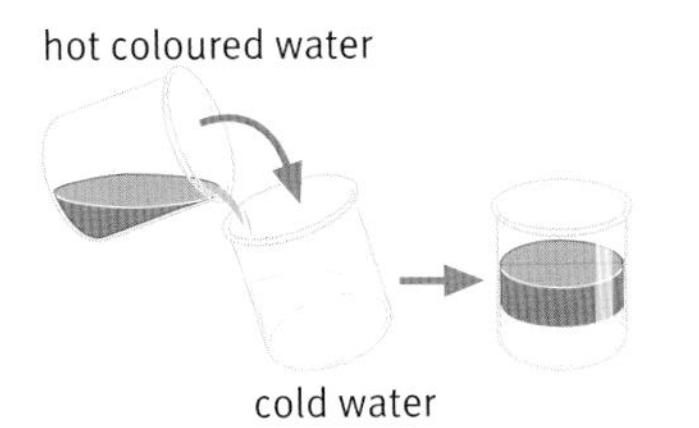

The hot coloured water is less dense than the cold water, so it stays at the top when you pour it in.

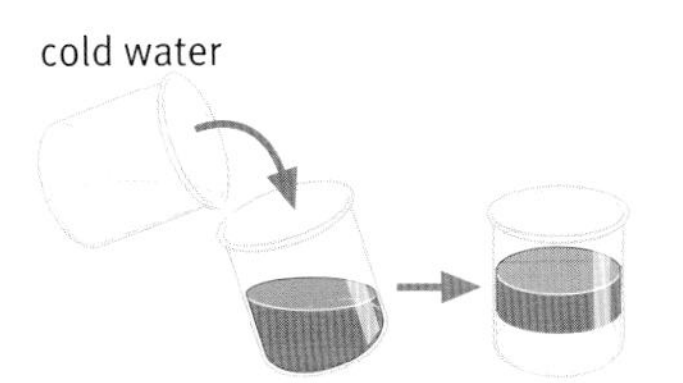

The cold water is more dense than the hot coloured water, so it sinks to the bottom.

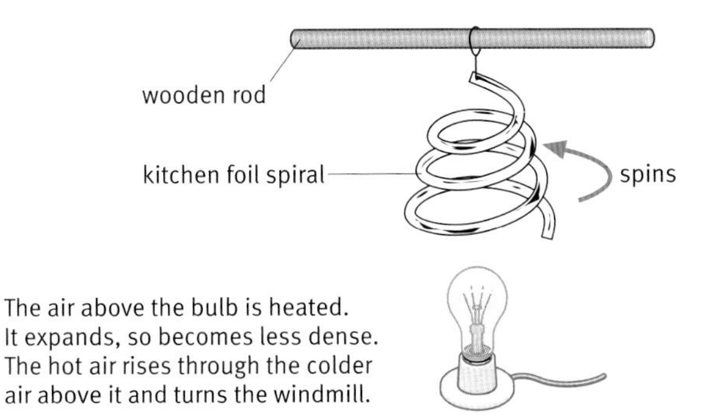

The air above the bulb is heated. It expands, so becomes less dense. The hot air rises through the colder air above it and turns the windmill.

Sea breezes

During the day, the Sun warms up the land and the sea. The land gets warmer than the sea, so air above the land warms up and rises. The cooler air over the sea moves towards the land to replace it, causing an onshore breeze.

At night, the land cools quicker than the sea, so the opposite happens – the breeze is offshore.

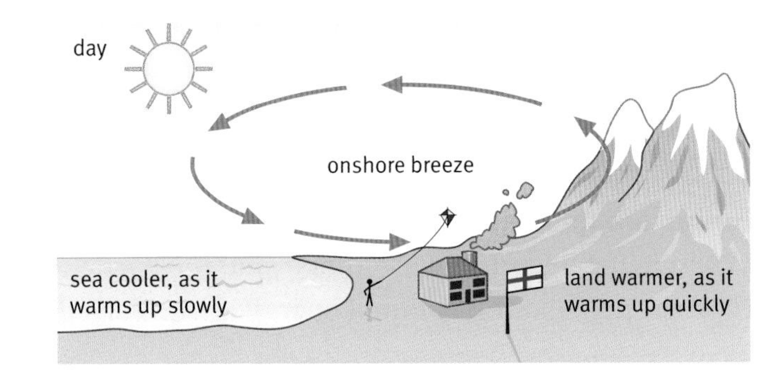

1 Copy and complete using words from the Language bank:

_____ is the way that heat is transferred through a _____, which means any _____ or gas. Convection _____ are set up because hot fluids rise and cold fluids sink to take their place. This happens because materials _____ when they are heated, so their _____ becomes less.

2 Why would it be dangerous to heat a completely sealed container of a liquid or a gas?

3 How does warming a liquid cause a convection current to form?

4 Many heating systems use convection to heat up rooms. Explain in detail how a central heating radiator warms a room by convection.

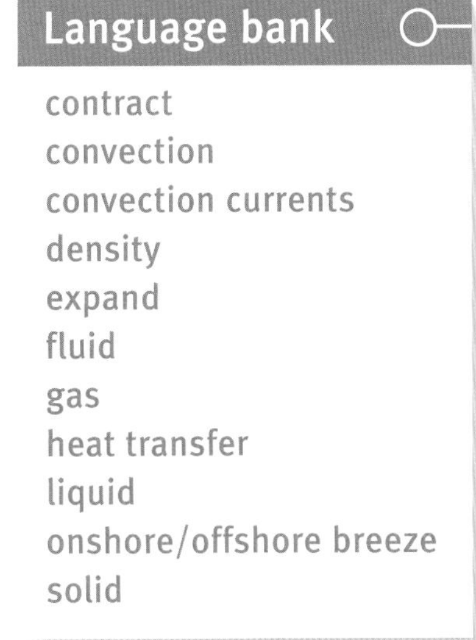

Language bank

contract
convection
convection currents
density
expand
fluid
gas
heat transfer
liquid
onshore/offshore breeze
solid

Particles and heat transfer

- How do things get hotter or colder?
- How do materials change when they are heated and cooled?

Particles again

Why are solids good conductors, and why do convection currents form in fluids but not in solids? We can use the particle model to explain this. Look at these diagrams to remind yourself.

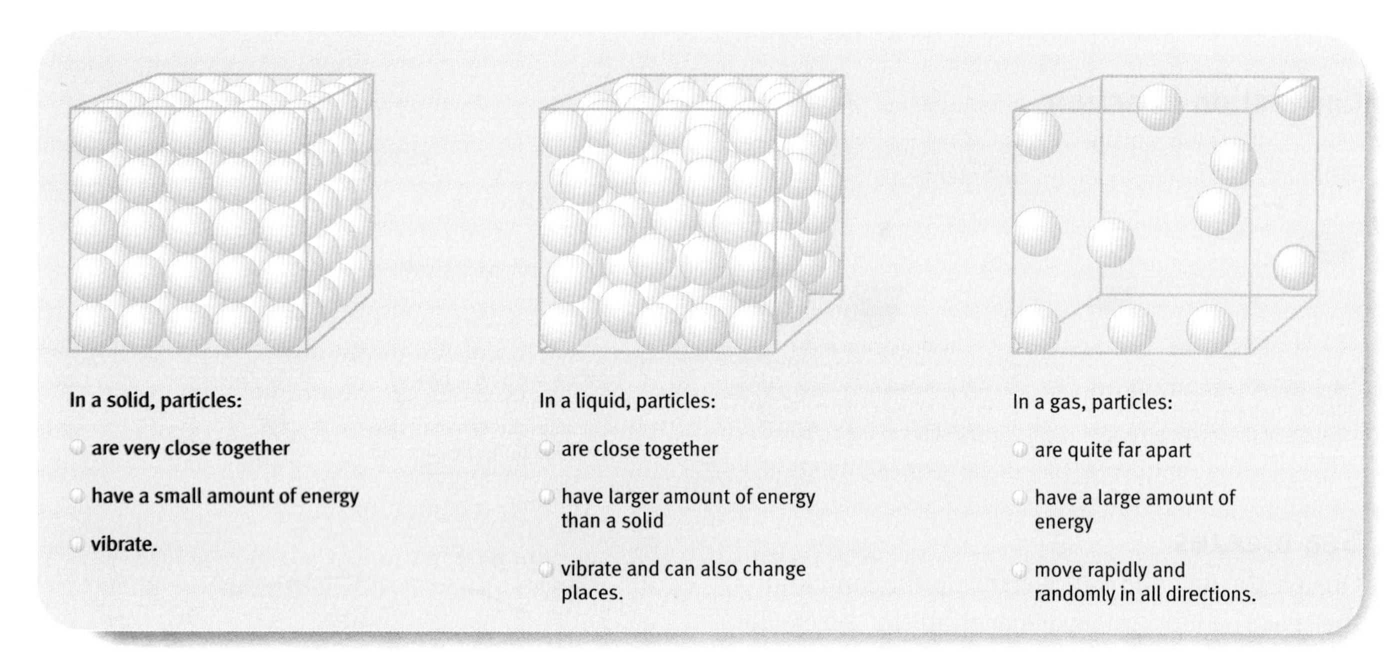

Solids are good conductors

When a metal bar is heated at one end, the particles vibrate more and hit their neighbours. Thermal energy is transferred along the bar.

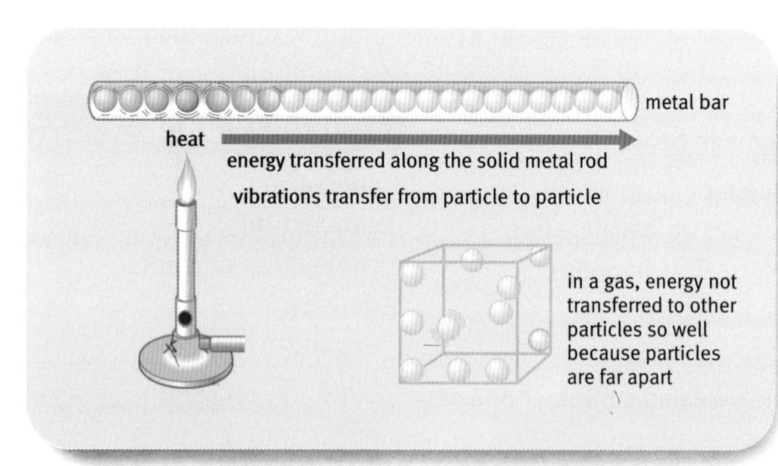

In conduction, movement (kinetic) energy is transferred from one particle to the next. The energy is transferred all the way along the solid. On the other hand, convection works in fluids because their particles are free to move independently, unlike the particles in solids.

A model for conduction

The closer you are, the more quickly the shaking passes down the line. Try it with your friends!

Convection works in fluids

In a fluid, the particles are not held so closely together with their neighbours. The vibration of one particle is not transferred to its neighbours, so fluids are poor conductors.

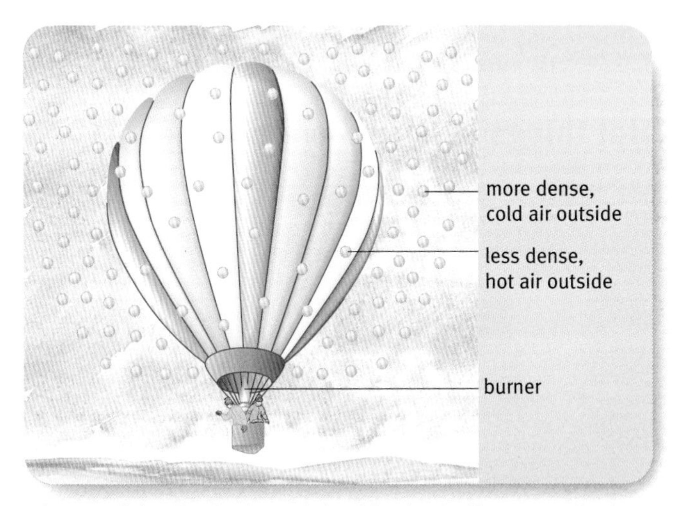

The particles in the hot air inside the balloon are further apart than the particles in the cold air outside. The hot air is less dense than the cold air, so it rises, making the balloon float.

Transferring heat energy without particles

Conduction through a solid and convection through a fluid both need a material or **medium** – they need particles to transfer the thermal energy. There is a third way of transferring heat energy, called **radiation**. Radiation can transfer heat without a medium.

1 Copy and complete using words from the Language bank:

Solids are good at transferring heat energy by _____. This is because their _____ are very close together. In a _____, the particles do not touch so a gas is a poor conductor. Fluids transfer heat energy by _____ because their _____ are free to move.

2 Explain with particle diagrams why conduction in a solid and convection in a fluid need a medium for heat to be transferred.

3 Look at the model for conduction at the top of the page. Explain what the model shows, and what A, B and C represent.

Language bank

conduction
conductors
convection
fluid
gas
heat energy
liquid
medium
particles
radiation
solid

Radiation

- How do things get hotter or colder?
- How do materials change when they are heated or cooled?

Conduction and convection need a medium – moving particles transfer the heat energy. But **radiation** transfers heat energy without a medium. The heat from the Sun travels to Earth through the vacuum of space and needs no particles to help it move.

The Sun's heat washes over the Earth, warming the new day.

Hot things radiate thermal energy

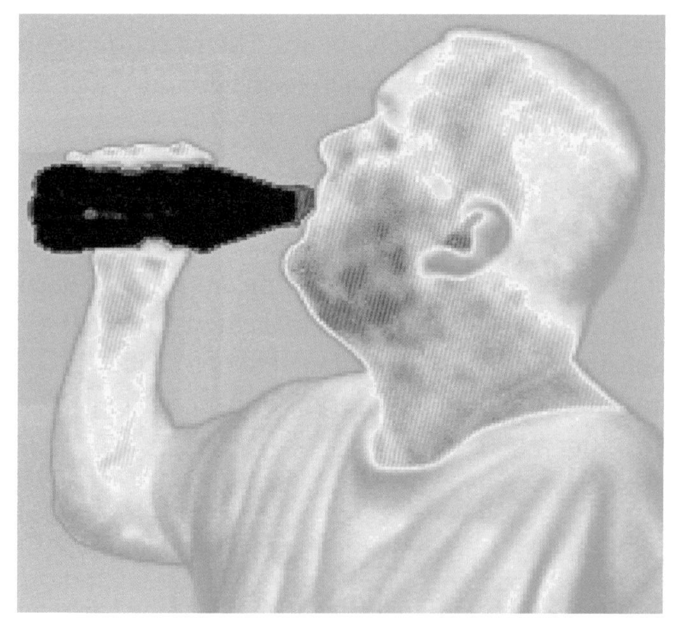

In these thermograms, the camera detects radiated heat. Red is warmest, then yellow, green and blue (coldest).

All warm things give out thermal energy as invisible **infrared radiation**. The hotter something is, the more it radiates **thermal energy**. The man is warmer than the room so heat radiates out from him in all directions. The blue colour of the drink shows that it is cold. In the house, the roof is well insulated, while the walls and windows are losing heat.

Aagh, radiation sounds like radioactivity.

That's a different kind of radiation. This is thermal radiation.

Like light

Infrared radiation is a type of light. Like light, it travels in waves from one place to another. It also reflects off shiny surfaces. This is why the back of an electric fire is mirrored, like the one shown opposite.

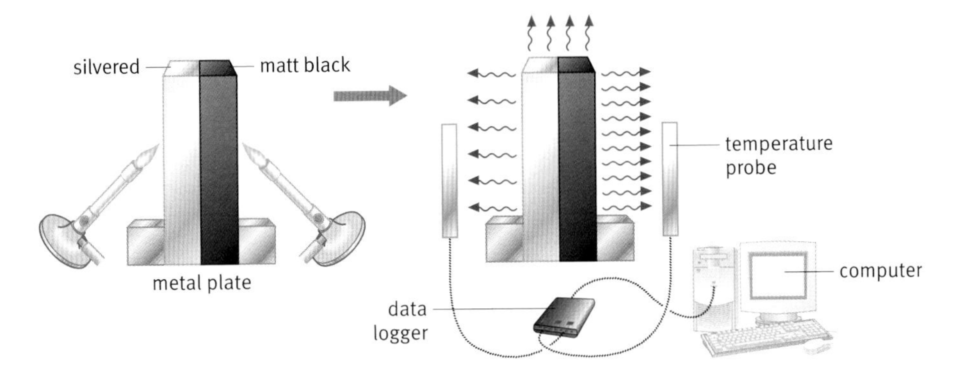

But dark colours radiate heat better than shiny or bright colours. In the diagram above, the metal plate has a dull black side and a shiny side. If you heat it, both sides are the same temperature, but the black side radiates the heat better than the shiny one.

These night vision goggles let the soldier see where he is going in the dark. They amplify any light that is present, and also detect heat as infrared (IR) radiation.

Using infrared radiation

When you change channel using the remote control, you are sending infrared (IR) radiation to the TV. Many laptops have an IR link to a mobile phone or personal organiser.

1. Copy and complete using words from the Language bank:

   Heat energy can be transferred in three main ways, by ______, conduction and ______. Heat transfer by radiation does not need a ______. So thermal radiation, also called ______ radiation, can pass through a vacuum. This is why we can feel the warmth of the Sun through the ______ of space even though it is millions of miles away.
2. Explain why radiation does not need a medium to transfer heat energy.
3. Why should central heating radiators be painted black, not white, to be most effective?

Language bank 

conduction
convection
fluid
gas
infrared radiation
liquid
medium
particles
radiates
radiation
reflects
solid
thermal energy
vacuum
wave

Saving it

- How can we reduce energy waste?

In our homes, we use insulators to slow down the transfer of thermal energy from the warm inside to the cold outside. This helps us to:

- save money, as we don't have to use as much fuel to heat our houses
- save the world's energy resources, as we reduce the use of fossil fuels
- reduce pollution, as power stations produce less electricity and we burn less fuel in our central heating boilers.

Insulate it all!

Loft insulation

We put insulation material in the loft. It has large pockets of air, which is a poor conductor of heat, so it reduces heat loss by conduction through the roof. Because the pockets are separated from each other, convection currents can't transfer heat through the material.

Guess what?

Scandinavian houses are very well insulated. As a result they use around 30% less energy than ours do, even though it's often a lot colder.

Double glaze it

Double glazing means having two sheets of glass in the windows. There is an air gap of about 16–20 mm between them. As in loft insulation, the air helps reduce heat transfer to the outside. Some glass also has a thin coating of metal, which helps to reflect heat radiation back into the house.

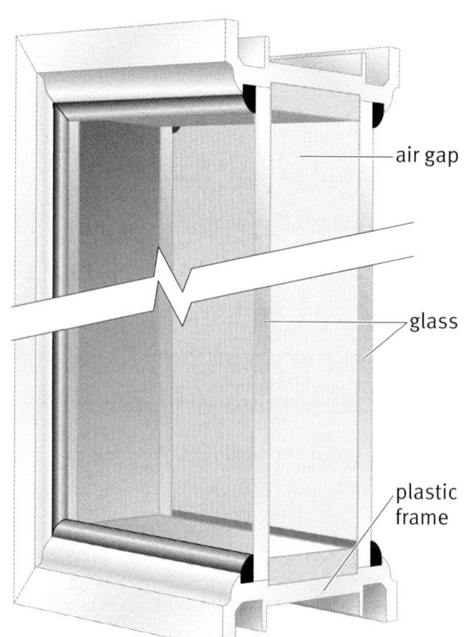

Cavity wall insulation

Houses built after around 1930 have a gap or **cavity** between the outer bricks and the inner walls.

This gap helps prevent heat loss by conduction. Often it is filled with an insulating material such as foam, polystyrene beads or mineral wool. This also helps prevent convection currents setting up and so reduces heat loss even more.

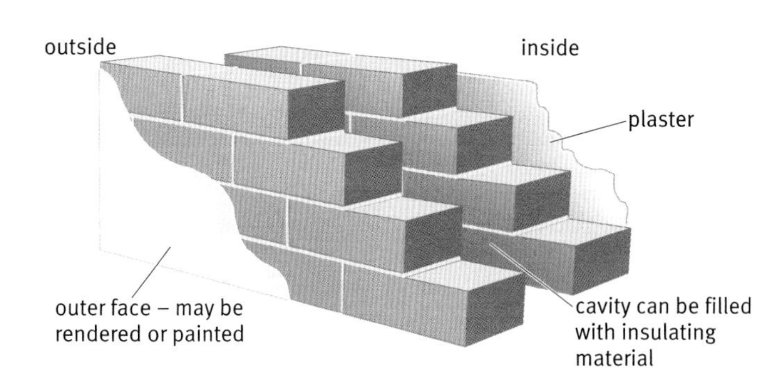

Draught excluders

Strips of PVC stuck around windows and doors prevent cold draughts entering the house.

Darught excluders are a cheap way of saving on fuel bills.

Lag it

Lagging the hot water tank means fixing a thick insulated jacket around it. The jacket is quilted and contains a lot of air. This is a cheap and efficient way of reducing heat loss.

Insulation method	Money saved per year (£)	Carbon dioxide pollution saved in using less fossil fuels (party balloons of CO_2)
loft insulation (installing from scratch)	157	77 643
loft insulation (making it thicker)	40	19 807
double glazing	34	16 850
cavity wall insulation	70	34 393
draught excluders	8	3 965
lagging hot water tank	11	5 452

Language bank 

cavity wall insulation
conduction
convection
double glazing
draught excluders
energy resources
heat energy
insulators
lagging
loft insulation
pollution
radiation

1. Copy and complete using words from the Language bank:
   Insulation stops heat _____ transferring from our homes to the colder outside. This saves money, saves the world's energy _____ and reduces _____. Simple methods of insulating a house include _____ insulation, _____ glazing, cavity _____ insulation, draught _____ and _____ the hot water tank.
2. Which method of insulation saves the most money per year?
3. Why is it important that we do not waste energy?
4. Double glazing might cost £2000 to install, and loft insulation might cost £120. Which method of insulation pays for itself more quickly?

A detailed look at changes of state

How can we explain change of state?

Changing state

What happens to the particles during changes of state?

If you heat a solid, the particles stay the same but they vibrate more. As a result they move slightly further apart, so the solid expands. If you carry on heating, the forces of attraction that hold the particles together in a solid are weakened, and the solid melts and becomes a liquid. This change happens at the **melting point**.

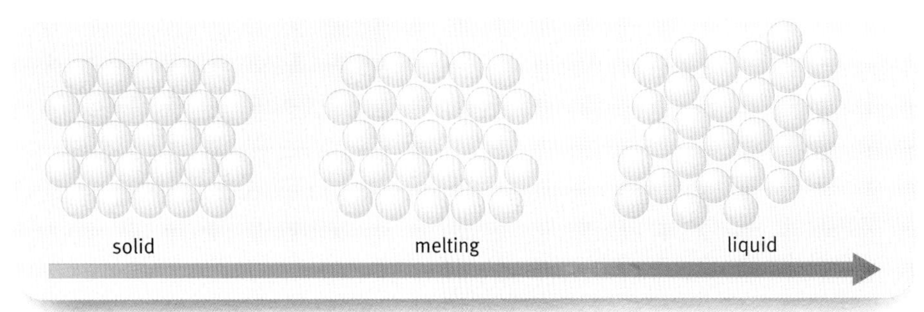

In a liquid, the particles are still held together but not so strongly as in a solid. They can move around independently.

If you carry on heating the liquid, the particles move around more quickly. As it gets hotter, the forces of attraction holding the particles together in the liquid break, and the particles are free. The liquid boils and becomes a gas. This change happens at the **boiling point**.

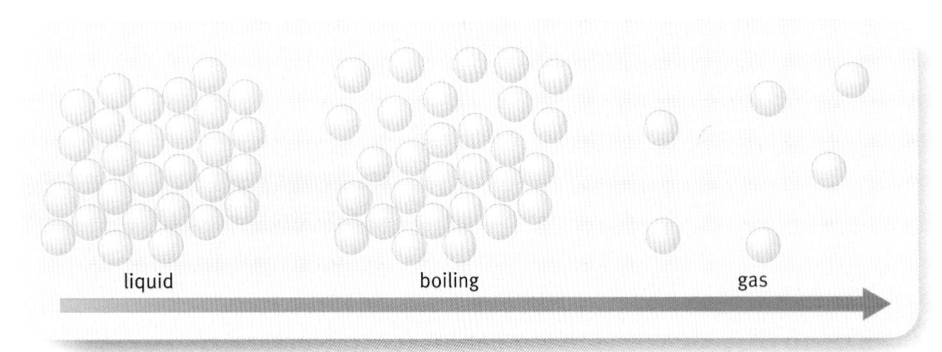

In a gas, the particles are not held together at all.

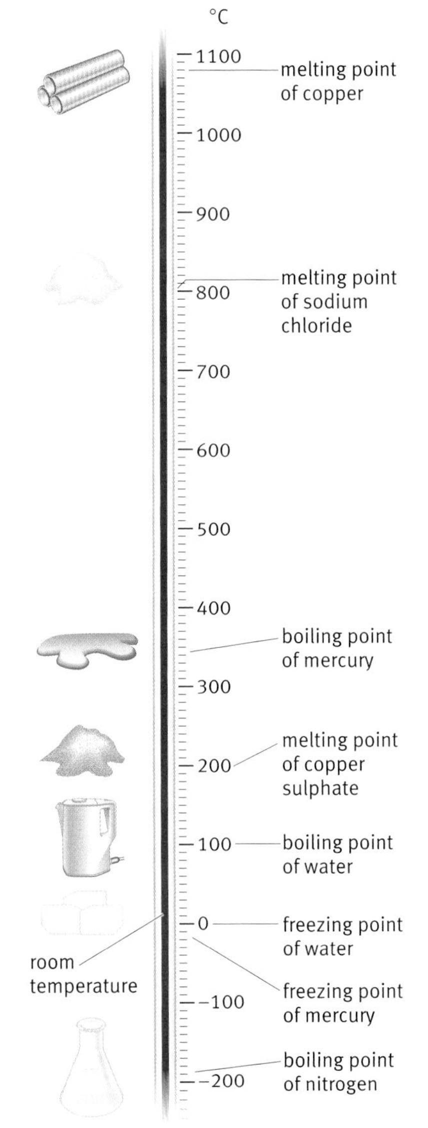

Melting and boiling points

Pure substances always melt and boil at certain fixed temperatures. The melting point of pure water is 0 °C, and the boiling point is 100 °C. Room temperature is between these two points, so water is a liquid at room temperature. Look at the thermometer diagram to see why copper is a solid at room temperature, and why nitrogen is a gas.

How the temperature changes as you heat a solid

Salol is a waxy substance that melts at a convenient temperature for us to measure in the lab. The graph shows how the temperature of some salol changes as it is heated.

The temperature of the solid rises steadily. But when the temperature reaches the melting point of salol, the graph flattens out.

The salol is still being heated, but its temperature does not go up. The heat energy is being used to weaken the forces of attraction between the particles in the solid.

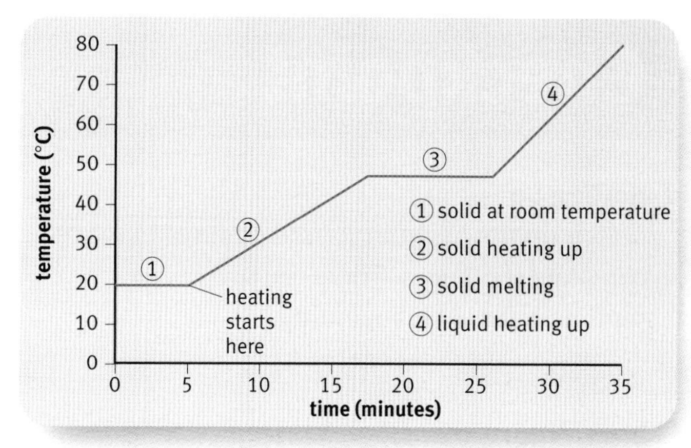

While the salol is melting (3), forces of attraction between the particles are being weakened in the solid. The salol is taking in thermal energy but its temperature does not change.

Once the salol has all melted, the heat energy makes the liquid hotter and the temperature continues to rise.

A similar thing happens when a liquid boils. The forces of attraction are being broken to change from a liquid to a gas, and the temperature does not change while this happens.

Evaporation

In **evaporation**, a liquid turns to a gas at any temperature. The most energetic particles in the liquid escape and form a gas. The liquid loses heat energy to the air above it, which cools it down. So evaporation is another method of heat transfer. This is why sweating cools you down.

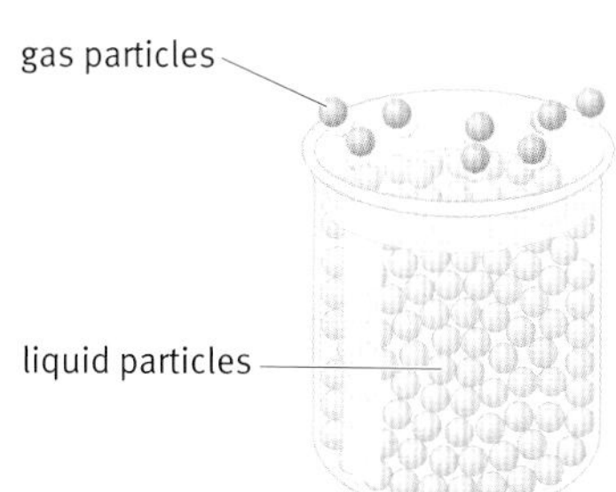

It is the most energetic particles that escape during evaporation, so the liquid cools down.

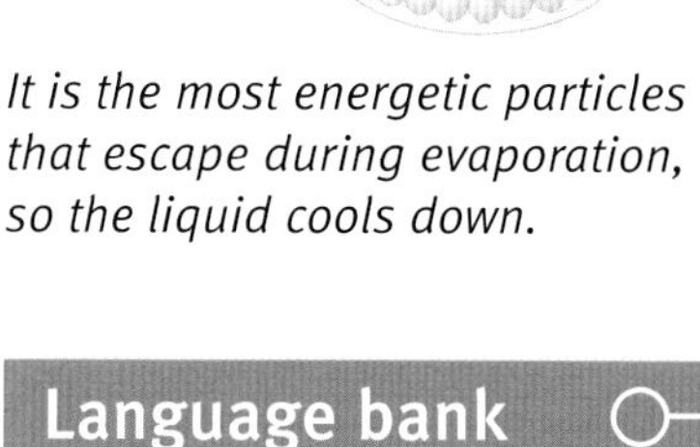

1 Copy and complete using words from the Language bank:

If you heat a ______, it melts. The forces of ______ between the particles are weakened and the solid turns into a ______. The ______ does not change while the solid changes state. The same thing happens when a ______ boils. Pure substances have fixed ______ and ______ points.

2 Explain why a hot metal rod contracts as it cools.

3 When a dog pants, water evaporates from its tongue. Explain why this cools the dog. Use the words 'energy transfer' in your answer.

4 At 300 °C, what state would these substances be?

a water **b** copper **c** nitrogen **d** mercury

5 Sketch a graph like the one above to show how the temperature would change if you had some steam at 150 °C and allowed it to cool to room temperature. Explain the shape of your graph.

Language bank

boiling point
boils
change of state
cooling
evaporation
forces of attraction
gas
liquid
melting point
melts
particle model
solid
temperature

Checkpoint

1 Hotting up

Match up the beginnings and endings to make complete sentences. There are two correct sentences for each beginning.

Beginnings

Heat is

Temperature is

Endings

measured in °C.

a measure of how much heat energy an object has.

a form of energy.

measured in joules.

2 How does it travel?

Copy and complete this table about ways of transferring heat energy. Choose from these words to fill the spaces.

evaporation

radiation

conduction

convection

Method of heat transfer	Does it need particles?	Where does it happen?	Example of use
	yes	in solids	to transfer heat through a frying pan to the food
	yes	in liquids and gases	sea breezes
	yes	in liquids	to cool you when you sweat
	no	wherever an object is warmer than its surroundings	to change channel

3 Up and away

The diagram shows a hot-air balloon. Why does it rise? Copy the correct explanation.

Explanations

The balloon acts like a greenhouse, letting the heat from the Sun warm the air inside.

The burner heats the air inside and the particles move apart, so the air inside is less dense than the cold air outside.

The burner heats the balloon fabric which expands, making the volume inside bigger so the air inside is less dense.

The air outside gets cooler in the evening, so the balloon rises up.

4 Changing state

Choose the correct label for A to D on this graph.

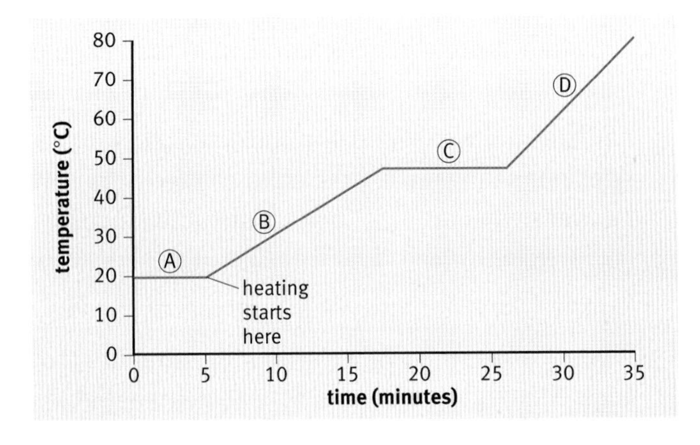

Labels

solid melting

solid at room temperature

liquid heating up

solid heating up

Magnets and electromagnets

Before starting this unit, you should already be familiar with these ideas from earlier work.

- A magnet attracts magnetic materials. Can you name a magnetic material?
- A magnet can attract or repel other magnets. What does 'repel' mean?
- Magnets are useful in everyday life. Think of a type of door held closed by a magnet.
- Electrical circuits need a power supply such as a battery. What's the important thing to remember when connecting up a circuit to make a current flow?

You will meet these key ideas as you work through this unit. Have a quick look now, and at the end of the unit read them through slowly.

- A magnet exerts a **force of attraction** on a magnetic material. Iron, cobalt and nickel are magnetic materials. A non-magnetic material does not feel a force of attraction from a magnet.
- A magnet's force of attraction acts through paper, wood and all other non-magnetic materials. However, a magnet will not act through a magnetic material such as iron. This is called **magnetic shielding**.
- There is a **magnetic field** around a magnet, and also around the Earth. This is the region where a magnetic material feels a force. **Magnetic field lines** show the strength of the magnetic force. They are closest together at the poles, where the field is strongest.
- We use the Earth's magnetic field to find our way around. A compass needle is a small magnet that swings to show us which direction is north.
- An **electromagnet** is a coil of wire carrying an electric current. It produces a magnetic field similar to the field around a bar magnet.
- The magnetic field lines become closer together when an electromagnet gets stronger. This happens if you put in a soft iron core, add more coils or increase the current.
- Electromagnets can be switched on and off, which makes them useful for cranes in scrapyards. They are also used as switches in cars, electric showers and many other devices, and they make electric bells carry on ringing.

Magnets

O What can a magnet do?

You know that a **magnet** can pull things towards it. It attracts some materials, which are called **magnetic materials**. A bar magnet has two ends called **poles**.

If a magnet can move, one pole points north. This is called the north pole (north-seeking pole). The other pole points south, and is called the south pole (south-seeking pole).

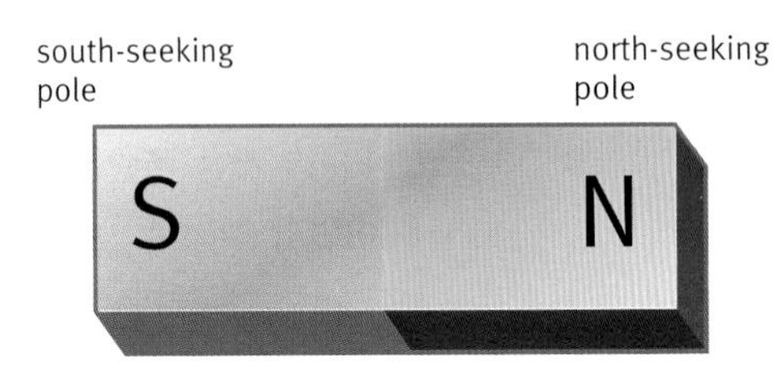

often made of steel (which contains iron)

Guess what?

Magnets are usually made from magnetic materials – iron, nickel or cobalt. Ceramic magnets are made from a pottery-like material containing iron oxide.

How a magnet behaves

The poles of a magnet attract some things and repel others.

The pole of a magnet will:

- *attract* magnetic materials, including iron, nickel, cobalt and materials that contain these metals

- *attract* the opposite pole of another magnet
- *repel* the like pole of another magnet

- *do nothing* to non-magnetic materials such as wood, plastic, copper – in fact any material that does not contain a magnetic metal.

Using magnets

You may have used magnets in games, or for sticking notes to the fridge. Magnets can pick all sorts of things up, from spilled pins to a whole car. The following pictures show that they have other uses too.

Pole	Pole	Effect
south	south	repel
north	north	repel
north	south	attract
south	north	attract

Like poles repel, and opposite poles attract.

The fridge door is kept shut using a magnetic strip.

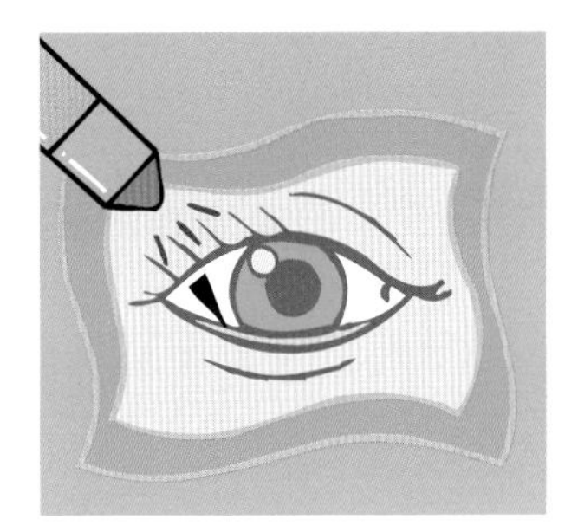

This powerful magnet is being used to remove an iron splinter from someone's eye.

The bicycle speedometer uses a magnet on the spoke. As the wheel turns, the magnet produces a voltage and this is converted into a reading on the speedometer.

The loudspeaker has a large magnet at the back, which makes the cone vibrate and produce sound waves.

Testing for magnetism

How do you know whether this nail is **magnetised** (whether it is a magnet)? The only way to prove it is by showing that the nail repels another magnet. Look at the picture opposite.

Attraction does not prove that the nail is a magnet, but repulsion does.

The nail is made of a magnetic material, so it will be attracted by the magnet even if it is not magnetised itself. The nail will also be attracted if it is magnetised, and has its opposite pole facing the magnet. So attraction does not tell us whether the nail is a magnet or not.

If the nail is magnetised and has its like pole facing the magnet, it will be repelled. It will not be repelled if it is not a magnet. So repulsion proves that the nail is a magnet.

1 Copy and complete using words from the Language bank:

Magnets attract magnetic materials such as _____, steel, nickel and cobalt, but not non-magnetic metals such as aluminium or tin. Wood, plastic and other materials are also _____ and are not affected by magnets. Like poles _____ and opposite poles _____. _____ is the only test for magnetism.

2 Which of these materials could be attracted to a strong magnet?

a an iron bar **b** a steel pin

c a gold ring **d** a 2p coin (made of copper and nickel)

3 Alnico is an alloy (a mixture of metals) which makes very hard and strong permanent magnets. Which metals could be in Alnico to give it its magnetic properties?

4 Find out and explain the difference between the following words: magnet, magnetic, magnetism.

5 Describe a situation where a magnet is used. Find an example that has not been mentioned on these two pages.

Language bank 

attract, attraction
cobalt
iron
magnet
magnetic
magnetised
nickel
non-magnetic
north (north-seeking) pole
pole
repel, repulsion
south (south-seeking) pole

More about magnets

- Can magnetism be stopped?
- Can magnets be made?

Stopping magnetism

You know that a magnet will attract a magnetic material such as a paper clip. What happens if you put something in between them? The magnet will still attract the paper clip through a non-magnetic material like plastic sheet. But if you put a magnetic material like a steel sheet in the way, the magnet no longer attracts the nail.

Blocking the action of a magnet by a magnetic material is called **magnetic shielding**.

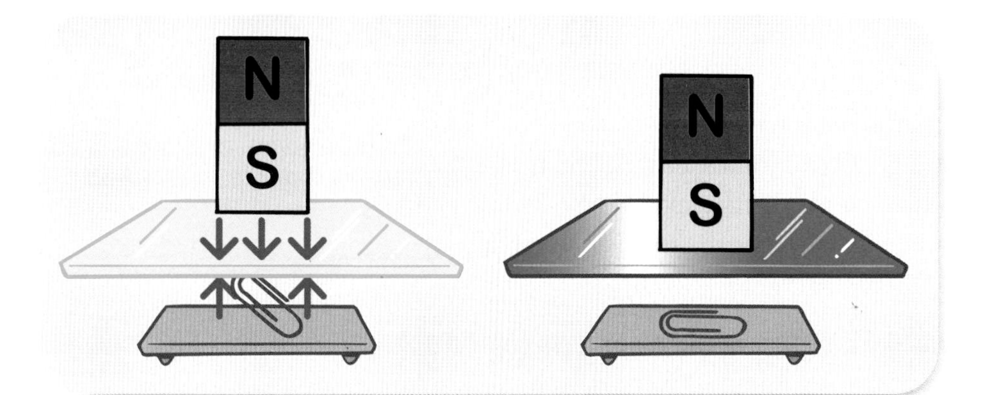

The magnet acts through plastic but not through steel.

In this toy theatre, the puppets are moved by magnets which act through the wooden stage.

If you bang a magnet, it can lose its magnetism. So never drop a magnet or hit it with a hammer. Magnets should be stored with covers on them, so that like poles of two magnets are not forced together for a long periods of time. This could make them lose their magnetism.

How do we make magnets?

A magnetic material can be **magnetised** (made into a magnet) by stroking it with the pole of another magnet.

You keep moving the magnet in a loop so it goes along the nail in one direction. The more strokes, the stronger the magnet becomes, until it can't get any stronger. It usually takes about 15 to 20 strokes to make a magnet.

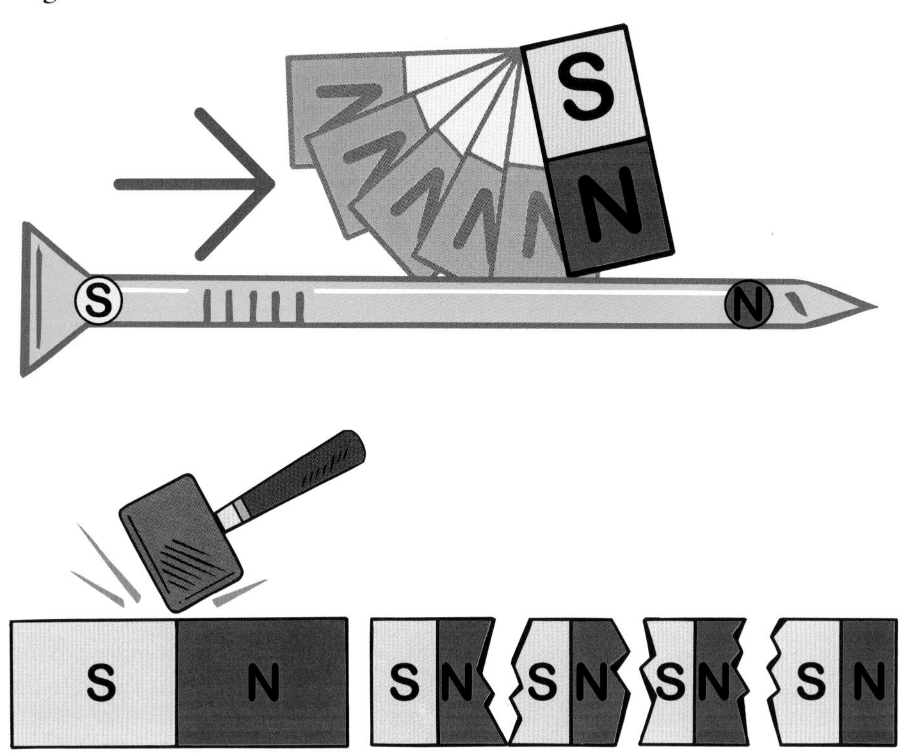

If a large magnet is broken up, it makes lots of smaller magnets.

We can also make magnets using electricity. You will find out more about this on page 120.

1 Copy and complete using words from the Language bank:
You can stop the effect of a magnet by shielding it with a _____ material. The magnetic effect can still be felt through _____ materials such as aluminium or plastic. Magnets are made by _____ a magnetic material in one direction a number of times.

2 Describe in detail how you could turn a steel pin into a small magnet.

3 A compass uses a floating magnet to help with navigation. Explain why it might be inaccurate to rely on a compass inside a car.

4 Suggest how you could accurately compare the strength of two magnets that you had made. Describe your test in detail.

Language bank 

magnetic
magnetised
magnetism
non-magnetic
shielding
stroking

BJ.3

Magnetic fields

What is a magnetic field?

Did you know rocks could be magnetic? **Lodestone** contains magnetic iron oxide. If you rest a piece of lodestone on a wooden block and float it in water, it points in a north–south direction. The same happens if you float a steel pin on water, or hang a bar magnet up in the air.

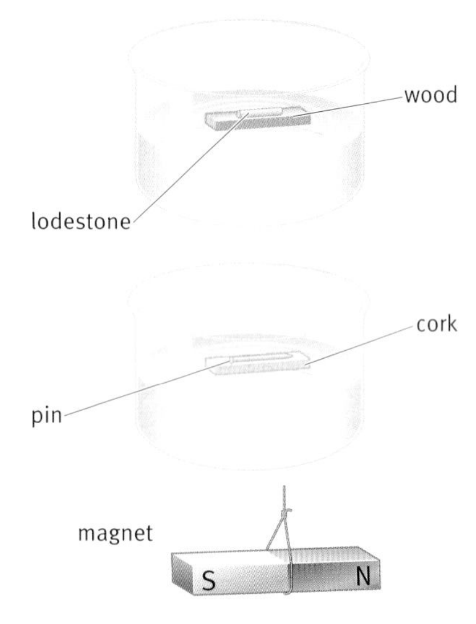

The Earth's magnetic field makes these magnetic materials line up in a north–south direction.

The Earth's magnetic field

The Earth contains molten iron at its core, which makes it act like a giant bar magnet. There is a **magnetic field** around the Earth, and around any magnet. This is an area around the magnet where a magnetic force can be felt.

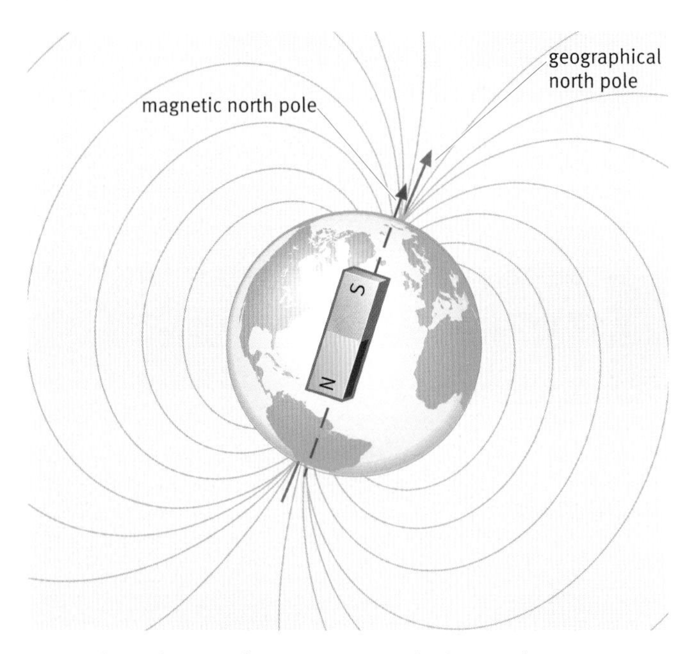

A north-seeking pole points towards the Earth's magnetic north pole.

We can't see the magnetic field around a bar magnet. But if we sprinkle iron filings around the magnet, they will show it to us. The magnetic iron filings feel a force when they are in the magnetic field. They align themselves along the lines of force, showing the **magnetic field lines**.

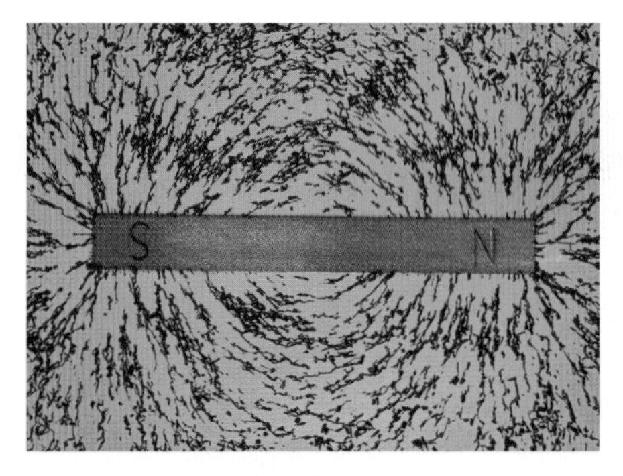

The filings are closest together at the poles. Here the lines of force are close together, and the magnetic field is strongest. It gets weaker further away from the magnet, where the lines of force are further apart.

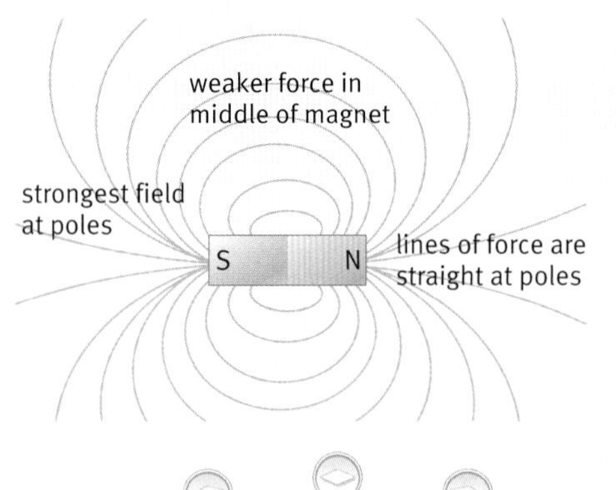

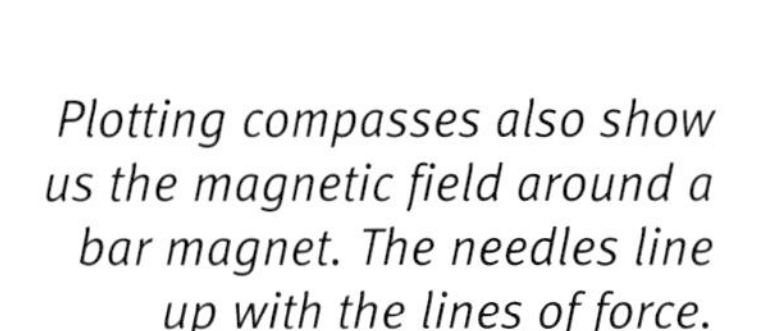

Plotting compasses also show us the magnetic field around a bar magnet. The needles line up with the lines of force.

S N

A little bit of history

William Gilbert (1544–1603) was physician (doctor) to Queen Elizabeth I. He also did experiments on electrical and magnetic effects, and wrote a book called *De Magnete* which was published in 1600. He discovered how to make magnets and was the first to use the term 'magnetic pole'. He was the first to show that the Earth had a magnetic field, by comparing its effect on compass needles with the effects of magnets. He argued that the Earth rotates on its own axis, which was unheard of at the time.

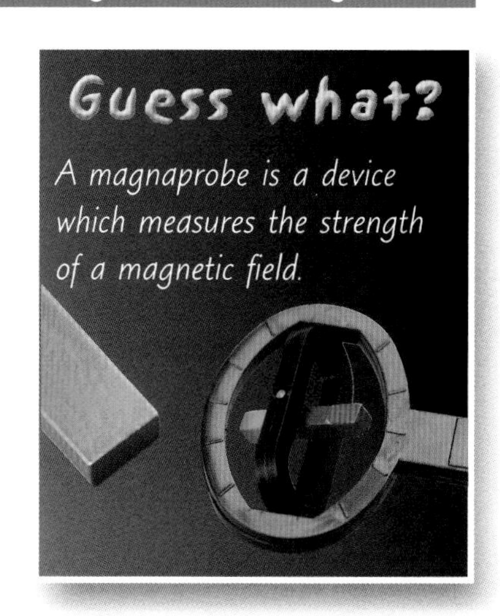

Navigation using magnets

We use a compass for **navigation** (finding which way to go). Inside the compass is a small magnet floating in alcohol. The Earth's magnetic field acts on the magnet, making it point to the Earth's **magnetic north pole**. This is not quite at the geographic north pole of the Earth, but we know the angle between the magnetic north pole and the gridlines on the map. To work out which way to go, we take a bearing.

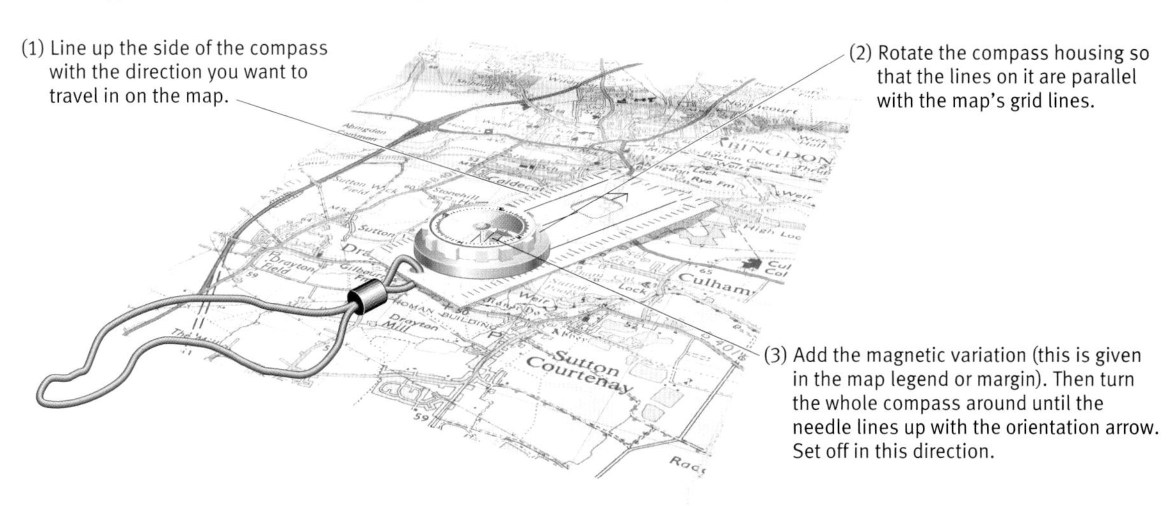

1 Copy and complete using words from the Language bank:

There is a magnetic ______ around the Earth, where a magnetic material feels a force. A freely moving ______ will come to rest in a north–south direction. The magnet's north-______ pole points towards the Earth's magnetic north pole. A compass uses the Earth's magnetic ______ to help with ______.

2 Which statements are true and which are false?

a The Earth's magnetic field pulls you towards the centre of the Earth.

b Copper filings show the lines of force around a magnet.

3 **a** If we can't see a magnetic field, how can we tell where it is strong and where it is weak?

b Where is the magnetic field around the Earth the strongest?

Language bank

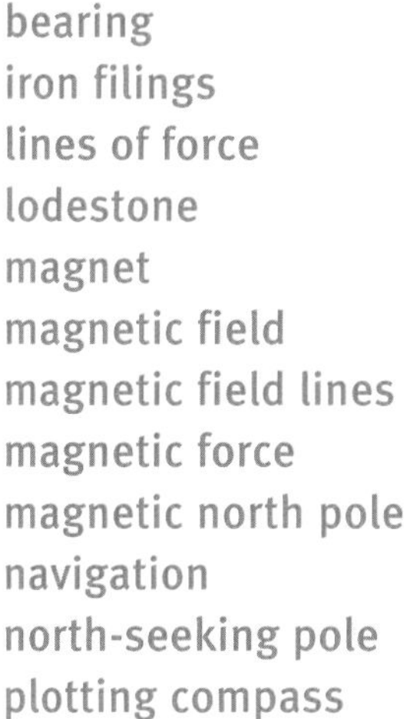

Electromagnets

How can electricity make a magnet?

If you pass electricity through a coil of insulated wire, something surprising happens. The coil, or **solenoid** as we call it, acts like a magnet – there is a magnetic field around it. If you put a magnetic material such as an iron nail into the centre or **core** of the solenoid, the magnetic field gets even stronger. You have made a magnet using electricity – we call it an **electromagnet**.

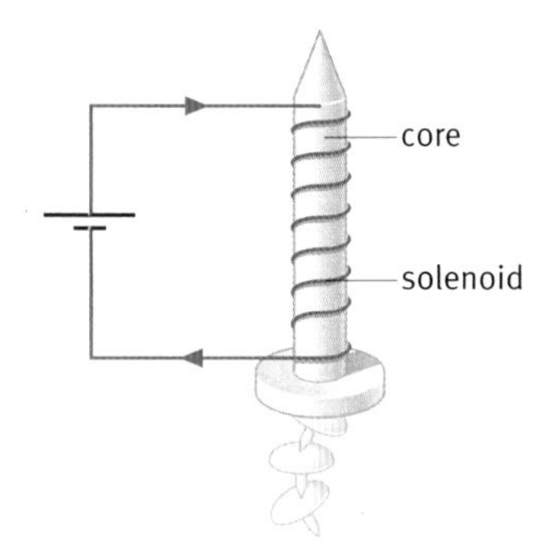

The electric current flowing in the coil of wire creates a magnetic field.

Using electromagnets

Electromagnets are very useful because unlike normal (permanent) magnets, they can easily be turned on and off.

The crane has a large electromagnet, which is turned on to lift scrap iron and steel, and turned off to drop it somewhere else.

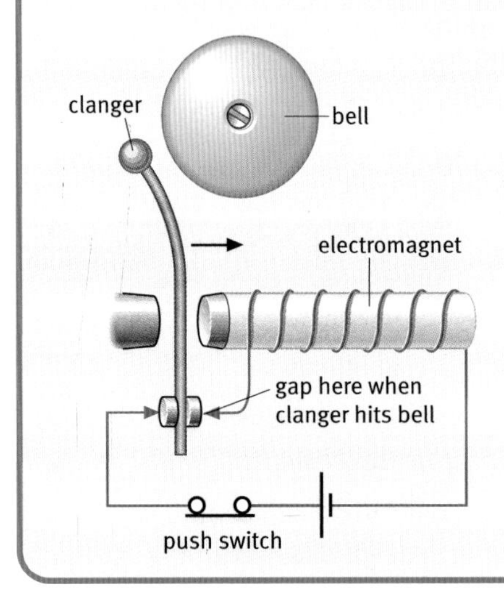

In an electric bell, the electromagnet attracts the arm of the clanger, making it strike the bell. The clever part is that in doing so, it breaks the circuit, which turns off the electromagnet. So the clanger goes back to its original position. This completes the circuit again, turning the electromagnet back on, which attracts the clanger, which strikes the bell.

This goes on and on and so the bell rings and rings and rings... until you take your finger off the switch.

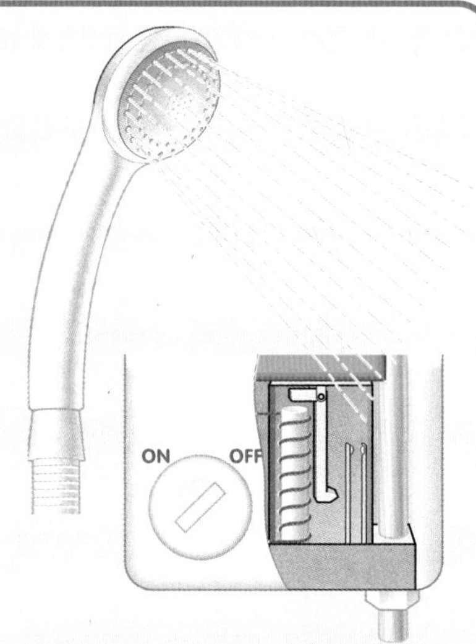

When you turn an electric shower on, you switch on a low-current circuit. An electromagnet moves a switch called a relay, and this turns on another much more powerful circuit which powers the water heater and pump. So you switch on a low-current circuit, which in turn switches on a higher-current circuit. This is safer than switching on the powerful circuit directly.

What determines the strength of an electromagnet?

You can compare how strong different electromagnets are by seeing how many paper clips or drawing pins they pick up. We have already seen that putting a core in an electromagnet makes it stronger. Electromagnets can also have:

- different numbers of coils
- a higher or lower current
- a different shape.

Changing the number of coils

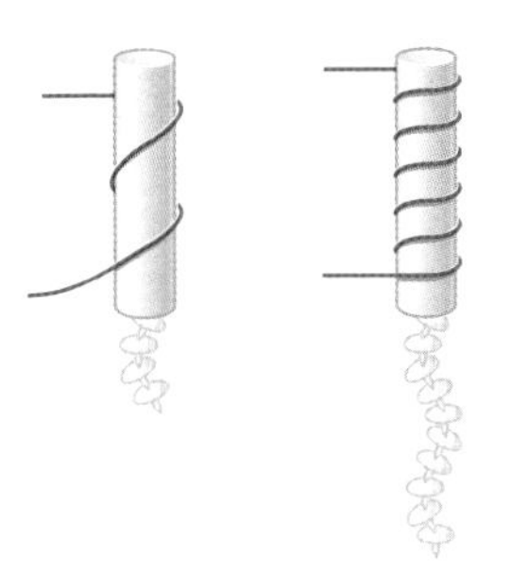

Number of coils	Number of drawing pins
2	4
4	8
6	10
8	10

Conclusion: The more coils there are, the stronger the electromagnet becomes (to a limit).

Changing the current

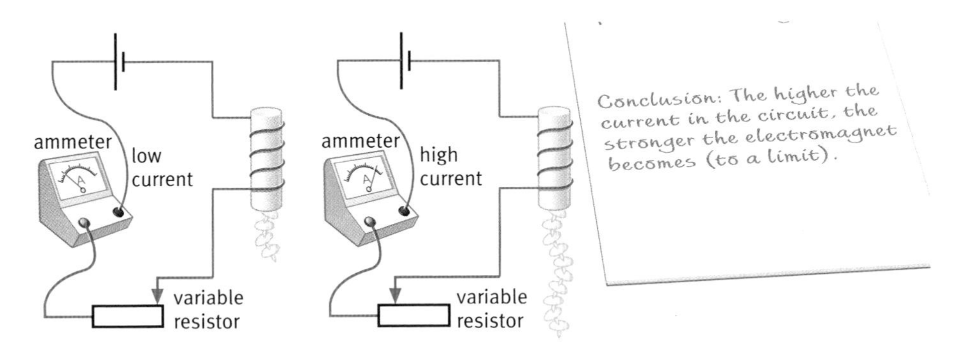

Changing the shape of the electromagnet

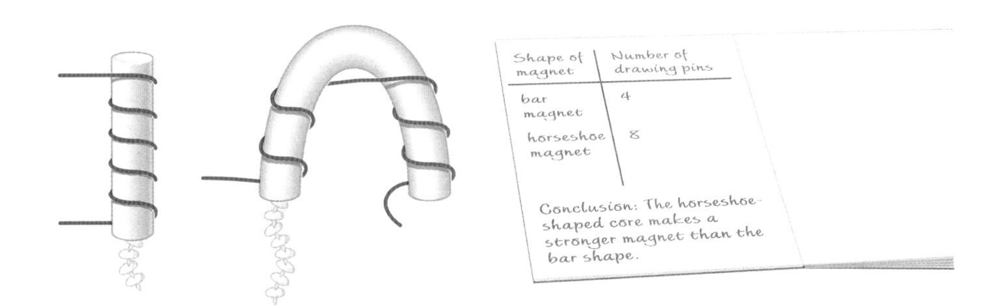

Shape of magnet	Number of drawing pins
bar magnet	4
horseshoe magnet	8

Conclusion: The horseshoe-shaped core makes a stronger magnet than the bar shape.

Guess what?

If we are investigating three things (factors) that can change, then in each part of the investigation we must keep two of the factors constant. In other words, only change one thing at a time!

1. Copy and complete using words from the Language bank:

   You can make an ______ by winding an insulated wire around a pencil to make a ______, which we call a ______. If you put a nail inside it to form a ______, and pass a current through the wire, there is a ______ around the coil. This type of magnet can be more useful than a ______ magnet.
2. What is an electromagnet, and what advantages does it have over a permanent magnet?
3. You have an electromagnet made by wrapping a wire round a pencil four times, and passing a current of 3 A through it. List three ways of making this electromagnet stronger.
4. Explain in your own words how an electric doorbell works.

Language bank 

coil
core
current
electric bell
electromagnet
magnetic field
permanent magnet
relay
solenoid

More about electromagnets

- How can we explain how electromagnets work?

The magnetic field around an electromagnet

Iron filings and plotting compasses show up the invisible magnetic field around a bar magnet. You can also use them to show the magnetic field lines around a wire carrying a current. Iron filings make a circular pattern. A compass needle shows lines of force going around the wire.

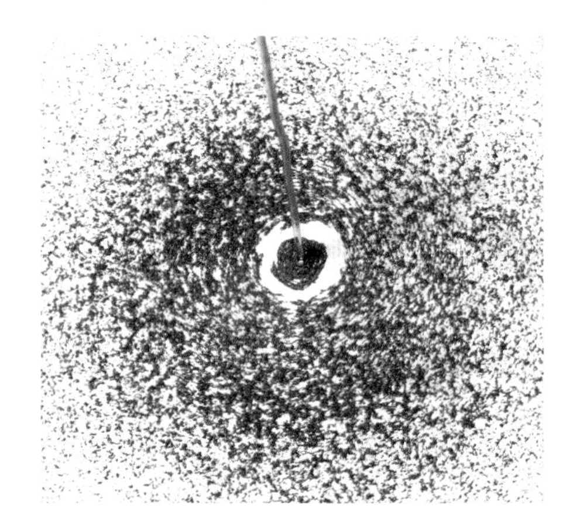

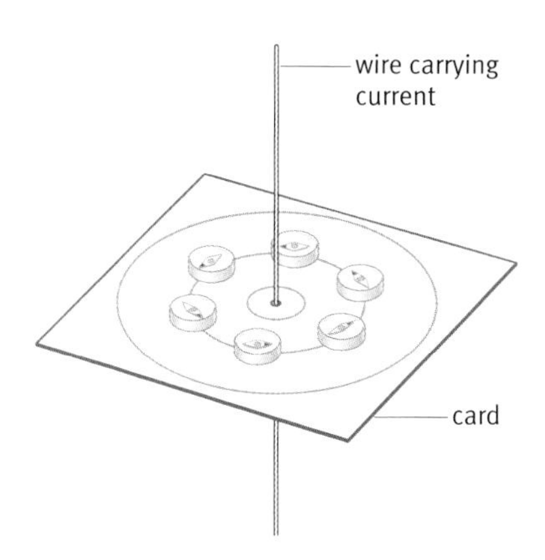

The iron filings and the plotting compasses show that there is a magnetic field acting in a circle around the wire.

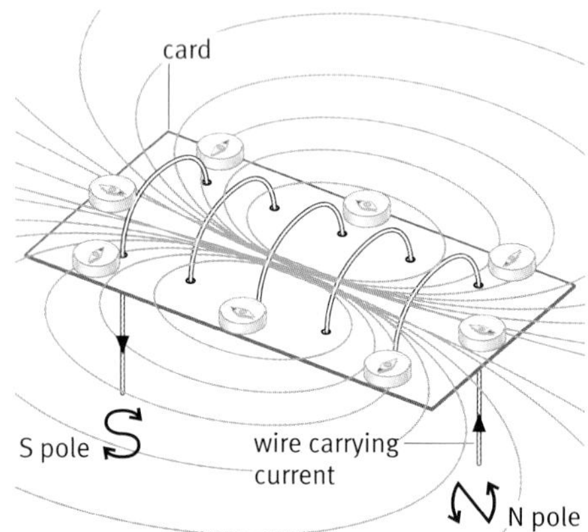

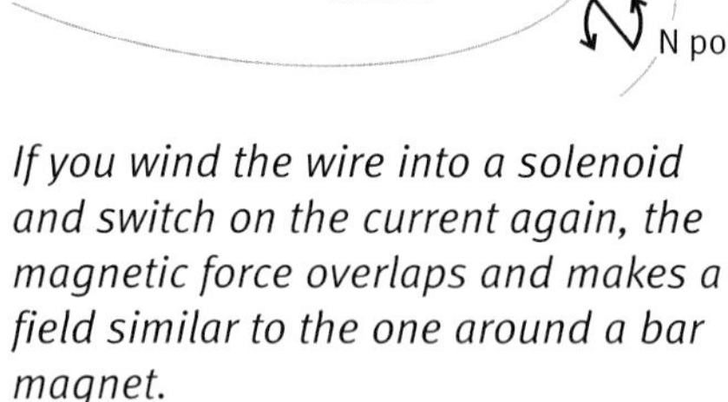

If you wind the wire into a solenoid and switch on the current again, the magnetic force overlaps and makes a field similar to the one around a bar magnet.

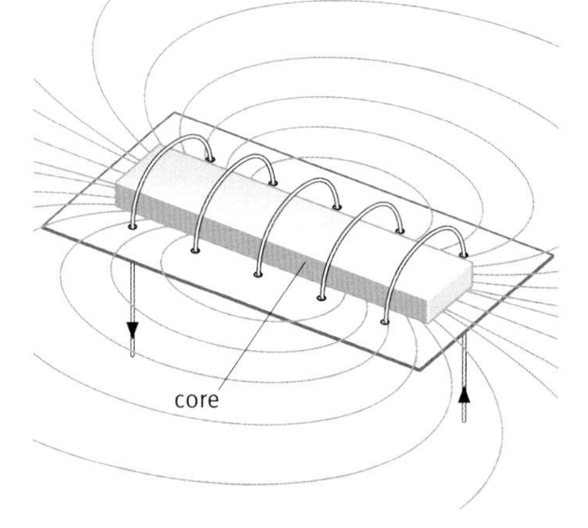

Adding a soft iron core makes the lines of force closer together, showing that the field around the electromagnet has got stronger.

What causes magnetism?

Magnetism is not fully understood, but scientists think that in magnetic materials like iron, the individual atoms can act like tiny magnets. Large groups of atoms align themselves to form an area where they all point in the same direction, called a **domain**. In demagnetised materials the domains are in random directions. In magnetised materials many of the domains line up, and this causes the magnetic effect. This description is called the domain theory, shown on the next page.

Guess what?

What is soft iron? Hint: you can't squash it in your hand! Iron is a ***magnetically soft*** material, which means it is magnetised quickly when you turn on the current, but it also loses its magnetism quickly when you switch off. Steel is ***magnetically hard***, which means it is magnetised slowly but it keeps its magnetism for longer.

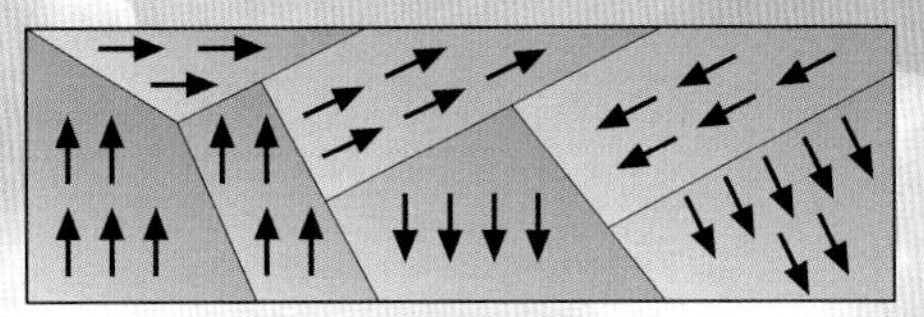
demagnetised material – domains random

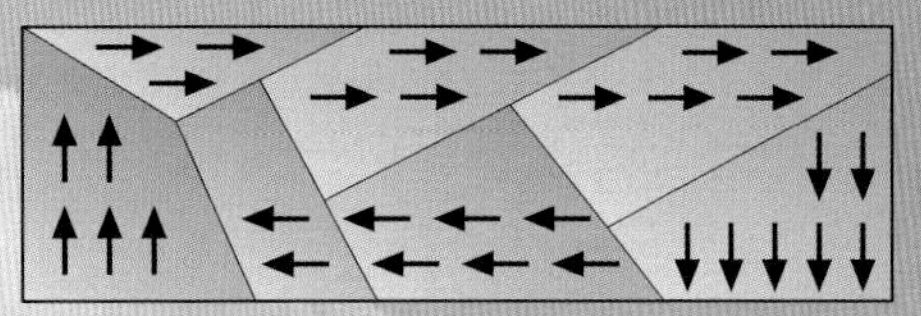
magnetised material – domains aligned in a loop

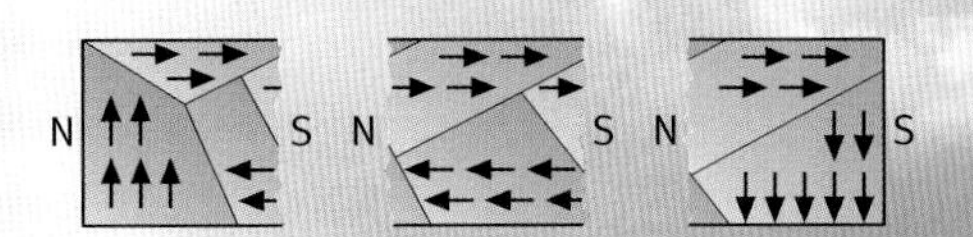

If you could break a magnet into little pieces, the domains would still be aligned. This is why several small magnets can be made from one large magnet.

However, if you drop a magnet or bang it with a hammer, the domains become randomly aligned again, which demagnetises the magnet. This is why you should never drop a magnet.

Guess what?

We can't detect a magnetic field using our senses, but some other animals can. Some birds migrate thousands of miles, navigating without a compass! Their bodies can sense the Earth's magnetic field.

The rocks in the Cuillin mountains on the Isle of Skye contain lots of iron. This can cause problems for people who go walking there.

1. Copy and complete using words from the Language bank:
   Wires carrying a ______ have a circular magnetic ______ which can be shown using iron filings or a compass. A ______ has a magnetic field similar to that of a bar magnet. The ______ theory tries to explain why magnetism happens.
2. Draw the lines of force you would expect to see around a solenoid with a soft iron core.
3. Why should you never use a compass near an electric fence?
4. Walkers often find that their compasses don't work properly in the Cuillin mountains. Try and account for this observation.

Language bank

aligned
current
demagnetised
domain
electromagnet
lines of force
magnetic field
magnetically soft/hard
magnetised
random
soft iron
solenoid
wire

Checkpoint

1 Magnetic materials

Choose the correct list of materials that are magnetic and copy it out.

iron, steel, copper, paper
steel, iron, nickel, copper
steel, iron, nickel, cobalt
iron, paint, aluminium, metals

2 How magnets behave

Copy and complete this table about how two magnets behave when put together. Use the words 'repel' and 'attract' to fill the spaces.

Pole	Pole	Result
north	north	
north	south	
south	south	
south	north	

3 About magnets

Copy and complete these sentences, unscrambling the words.

Around a magnet is a **micenagt lifed**. We can show this using **roin gifsnil**. The lines of force are close together at the **selop**. This is where the field is strongest.

The **Ethar** also has a magnetic field. We make use of this in **vannigoati**.

4 Electromagnets

Look at the three pairs of diagrams. In each pair say which would pick up more drawing pins.

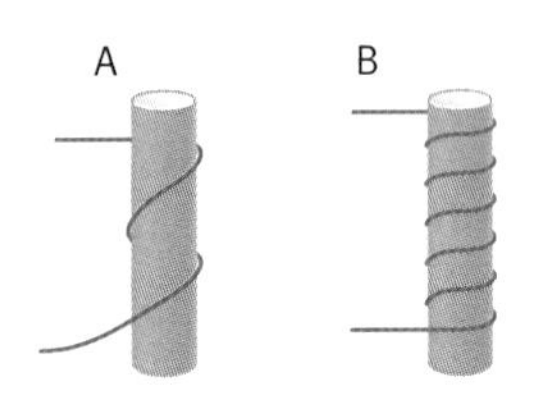

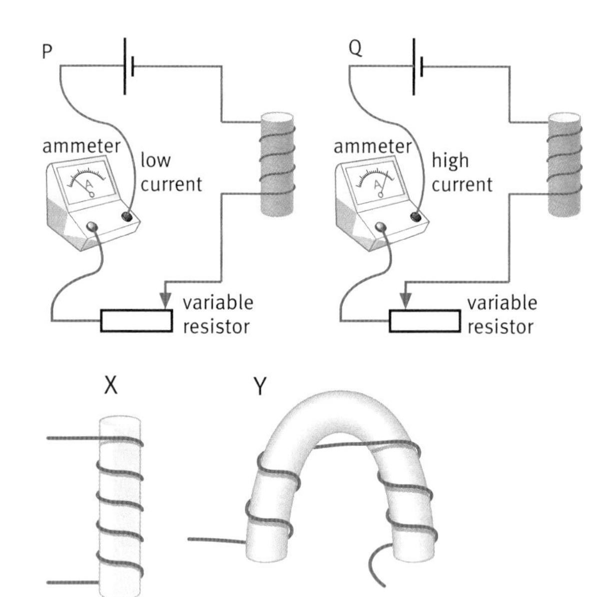

5 Switching on

How does an electric shower use an electromagnet? Choose the correct answer.

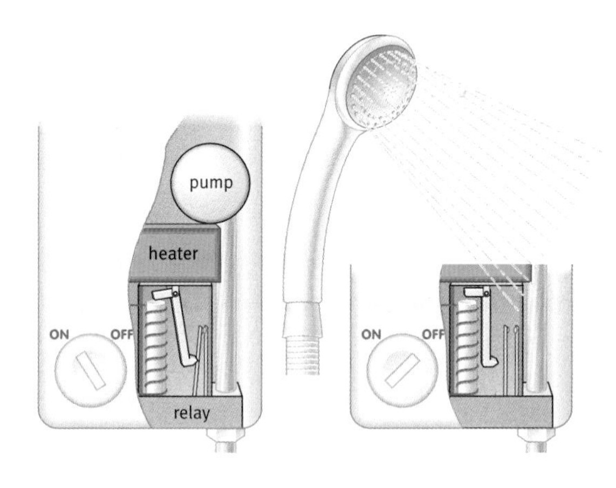

You turn on a low-current circuit which turns on the electromagnet, and this switches on another low-current circuit.

You turn on a low-current circuit which turns on the electromagnet, and this switches on a high-current circuit.

You turn on a high-current circuit which turns on the electromagnet, and this switches on another high-current circuit.

You turn on a high-current circuit which turns on the electromagnet, and this switches on a low-current circuit.

Light

Before starting this unit, you should already be familiar with these ideas from earlier work.

- Light travels out from a light source in straight lines. What do you see if an object such as a tree blocks the path of the light?
- Some materials let light through – we call them transparent materials. Which word describes materials that do not let light through?
- A shiny surface such as a mirror reflects light. Is a mirror transparent?
- We see a light source such as a torch when the light from it enters our eyes.

You will meet these key ideas as you work through this unit. Have a quick look now, and at the end of the unit read them through slowly.

- When light travels from a source, it is transferring energy. Light energy from the Sun is transferred all the way through space and comes in through your window, lighting up the room. A light bulb transfers electrical energy to light energy so you can see.
- Light travels in waves. It does not need a **medium** to transmit it. It radiates out in all directions from a light source, travelling very quickly. Light travels much quicker than sound.
- We draw **ray diagrams** to show how light beams travel, using a straight line with an arrow to show the direction of the light.
- When a light ray meets an opaque object, some light is **reflected** and some is **absorbed**. Smooth shiny surfaces reflect light in an orderly way, but rough materials **disperse** the light – they scatter it in all directions.
- Light reflecting from a smooth surface obeys the **law of reflection**.
- When light goes from one transparent material to another, such as from air to water, it changes direction. This is called **refraction**.
- We can split up white light into the colours of the rainbow, called a **spectrum**. This splitting of light is called **dispersion**. It happens when light travels through a prism.
- Coloured filters change the colour of the light passing through them. They transmit light of one colour and absorb the other colours.
- Objects look different colours in lights of different colours.

Travelling light

How does light travel?

Where is the light in this room? It is all around the room. It comes as sunlight through the window, and is scattered in all directions, filling the room with light energy. When the electric lights are switched on, the light radiates out, transferring energy through the room and letting us see things.

Light sources.

Light sources

The light in the room has been given out by the electric lights and the Sun. Hot objects give out heat energy, and they also tend to give out light energy. Some chemical reactions, and even some living things, also give out light. An object that gives out light energy is called a **light source**. We can see other objects because they **reflect** the light.

Does light travel fast?

Look at the picture opposite. The people on both yachts see the flash from the lighthouse as the light energy radiates outwards. The light gets to the red yacht just 0.000 07 seconds later than it gets to the blue yacht. But the sound of the foghorn takes about a minute longer to reach the red yacht than the blue yacht. Sound travels at 330 m/s, while light travels much faster at 300 000 000 m/s.

The same thing happens in a thunderstorm. The flash of lightning and the sound of the thunder both happen together, but unless the storm is right overhead, you see the flash before you hear the bang. The speed of light is much faster than the speed of sound.

Journey	Time taken for light to travel
100 m	0.000 000 3 seconds
Sun to Earth	8.5 minutes
Moon to Earth	1.3 minutes
Alpha Centauri (our nearest star after the Sun)	4 years

How does light travel?

Light travels in waves. Like radiated heat, it doesn't need a material or **medium** to travel through. Light energy is given out by a source, and it travels out in all directions in straight lines.

A few simple experiments will prove that light travels in straight lines.

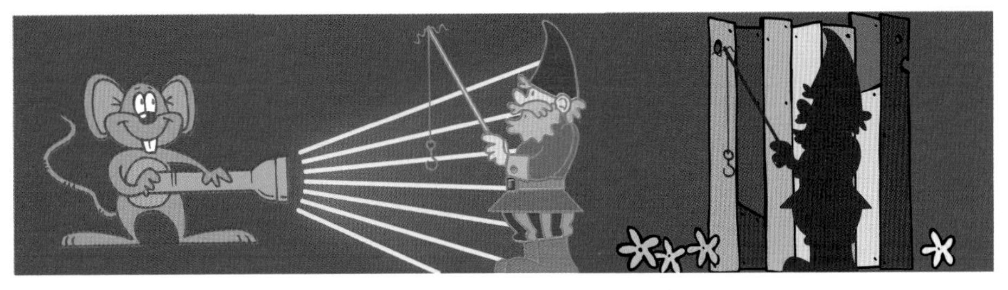

The light can't pass through the gnome so a shadow forms.

The sunbeams travel in straight lines through a gap in the clouds.

The girl can't see her ear because the light can't travel round the bend of the pipe.

Look at the cards with a hole in below. The light travels in a straight line so it passes through both holes. We draw **ray diagrams** to show how light beams travel. We draw the light rays as straight lines with arrows.

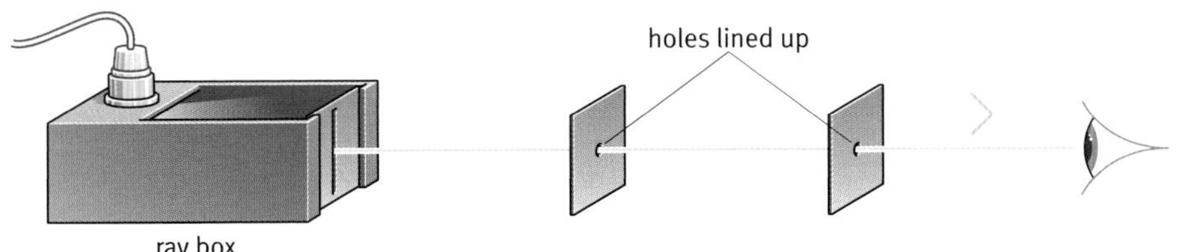

The light travels from the source in straight lines in all directions. One ray goes through the two holes, so the eye can see it. This is why you can't see all of a room through a key hole.

1 Copy and complete using words from the Language bank:

Light ______ radiates or travels out in all directions from a light ______ . The ______ of light is much faster than the ______ of sound. We show the path that light has travelled in a diagram by drawing a straight line called a ______.

2 The Sun is a light source, but the Moon is not.
  a Explain what is meant by a light source.
  b How can we see the Moon if it is not a light source?

3 Describe a piece of evidence that suggests light travels in straight lines. (Find an example not mentioned on these two pages.)

Guess what?

The distances between stars and galaxies are so vast that we don't measure them in kilometres. The numbers would be too big to make any sense. Light travels a distance of 9461 million million kilometres in a year, and we call this distance a ***light year****. The distance from Earth to Gienah (the brightest star in the constellation Cygnus, the Swan) is 680 000 million million kilometres, which is 72 light years.*

Language bank

energy transfer
light energy
light year
medium
radiates
ray
ray diagram
reflect
shadow
sound
source
speed of light
speed of sound
straight lines

Dull, shiny and see-through

- What happens when light meets an object?
- How do we see things?

What happens when light travels from a source and hits an object? The answer depends what the object is like.

If the object is transparent:
Virtually all the light passes through a **transparent** (or see-through) material. The light energy is transmitted through materials such as glass, Perspex and water.

If the object is translucent:
Some of the light passes through a **translucent** material, such as frosted glass. Some light energy is transmitted through the material, but some light energy is **absorbed** by the material and some is **reflected**.

If the object is opaque:
Most of the light is **reflected** from the surface of an **opaque** material. No light energy is transmitted through, though some might be absorbed. The smoother and shinier the surface is, the more light it reflects. (Shiny objects are not light sources – they just reflect the light from a source.) Opaque objects include you, dogs, buses, mirrors and most things.

How we see

We see things because light travels from a source to an object, and then bounces or reflects off the object and into our eyes. There are special cells at the backs of our eyes which are sensitive to light. These detect the light and send messages to the brain about what we are seeing.

The light reflects off the gold ring in an orderly way into interested eyes.

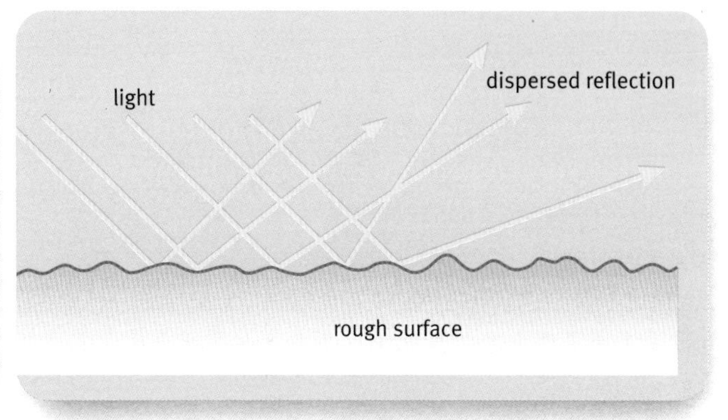

Rough materials scatter or ***disperse*** *the light. It is not reflected in an orderly way, so rough objects don't look as bright as shiny ones.*

Bar codes

In 1949, N. J. Woodland and his team were the first to file a patent for bar codes. A bar code is a pattern of parallel bars and spaces which gives information about a product. At the checkout, a laser scans the pattern and a computer turns the pattern of reflected light into a code number. This identifies the product from a database and its price comes up on the till.

1 Copy and complete using words from the Language bank:

We see objects because ______ travels out from a ______ to them. It can bounce or ______ off an object and into our eyes. Some materials are ______, which means they transmit light energy through them. ______ materials let only some of the light through, while ______ objects reflect and ______ the light energy instead of transmitting it.

2 State whether each material is transparent, translucent or opaque.

a a microscope objective lens
b a piece of wood
c a CD
d tinted glass in a stretched limo

3 Jed watches too much TV. He thinks that light travels from his eyes towards objects. Explain to him how we see, including diagrams in your explanation.

Language bank 

absorb
bar code
disperse
light
opaque
orderly
reflect
scatter
see-through
source
translucent
transmit
transparent

Mirror, mirror

- How do mirrors reflect light?
- How are images formed?

Most things reflect some light, or you wouldn't be able to see them. Translucent and even transparent materials reflect some light. Opaque materials, and especially shiny ones like mirrors, reflect light the best.

Reflecting on beauty.

Reflection

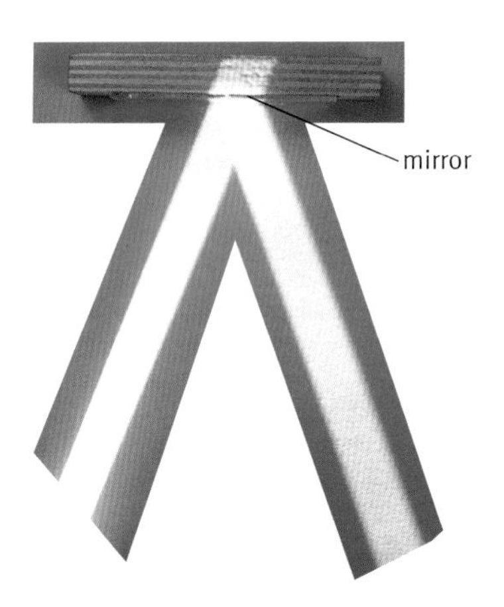

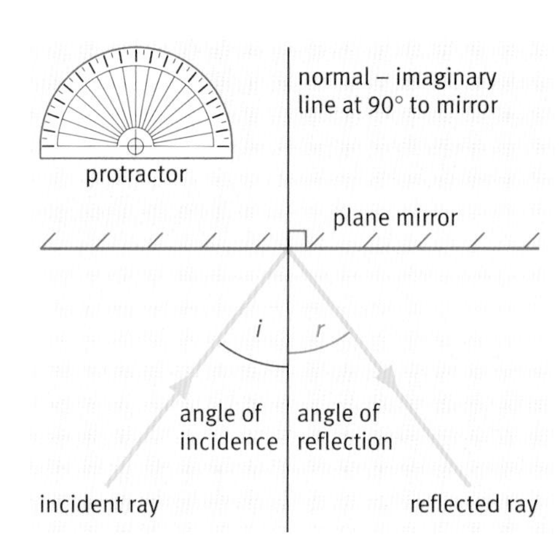

A plane mirror (flat mirror) has a very smooth surface, so it reflects light in a very orderly way. The **normal** is an imaginary line drawn at right angles to the mirror. **The reflected ray** has the same angle to the normal as the ray that arrived (the **incident ray**). We call these angles the **angle of incidence** and the **angle of reflection**, as the diagram above shows.

The reflected ray bounces off the mirror at the same angle to the normal as the incident ray. The table shows some results of measuring the two angles. There are a couple of tiny differences, but the mirror obeys the **law of reflection**:

angle of incidence = angle of reflection

Angle of incidence	Angle of reflection
10	11
20	19
30	30.5
40	40

Image is everything

When the incident ray changes direction as it is reflected from a mirror, we can see an **image**. We see the object behind the mirror, even though it is not really there. This is because our brain is fooled by the change of direction, and it follows the light back in straight lines to where it seems to come from.

The image appears the same distance behind a plane mirror as the object is in front, but it is **laterally inverted**. This sounds complicated, but you see it every time you look into a mirror. The mirror image has your left on your right and your right on your left.

The image shows the left-hand side on the right, and the right-hand side on the left.

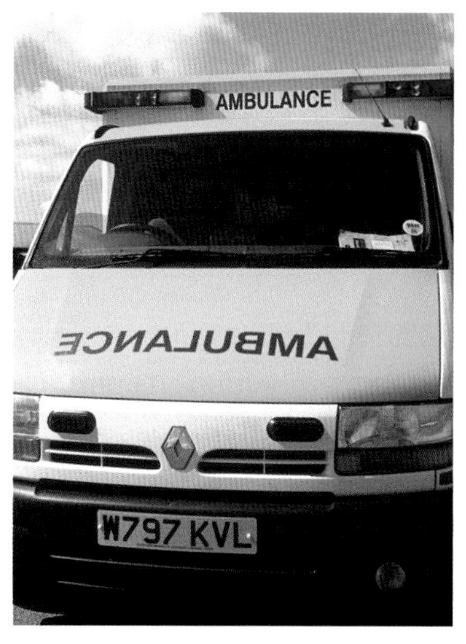

The word 'AMBULANCE' is laterally inverted, so it looks the right way round in the rear view mirror.

Using reflection

High-visibility strips use reflection to get you noticed.

The periscope has two mirrors which help the child see over large objects (like adults).

1 Copy and complete using words from the Language bank:

Light bounces or reflects from a plane ______ in a predictable way. The ______ ray arrives at the surface, and the ______ ray leaves. The angle of ______ is equal to the angle of reflection. These angles are measured from the ______, an imaginary line at 90° to the reflecting surface.

2 Which of these sentences are true and which are false?

a Only mirrors reflect light.

b The normal is a line at 45° to the mirror.

c The image from a plane mirror is laterally distressed.

3 Describe how a periscope works.

Language bank 

angle of incidence
angle of reflection
image
incident ray
laterally inverted
law of reflection
normal
periscope
plane mirror
reflected ray
reflection

8K.4 Refraction

Can light be bent?

When light goes into water, or comes out of it for that matter, the light changes direction. Its path is bent at the boundary where air meets water. We call this bending **refraction**. The ruler shows this happening.

Because of this bending, a fish in water looks nearer the surface than it really is. Aborigine hunters have trained themselves to correct for this when fishing so that they catch their tea successfully.

The ruler looks bent. The light reflected from it is bent or refracted as it comes out of the water and into the air. Water and air are both transparent media, but they are different.

A closer look at refraction

What happens to the light rays when they are refracted?

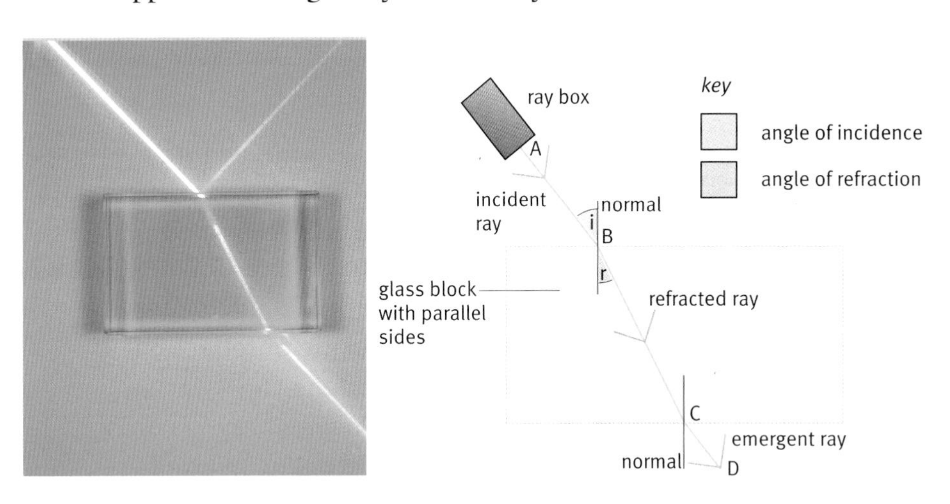

At B, the light ray bends towards the normal when it enters the glass from the air. This is because glass is more optically dense than air and it slows down the light. At C, the light ray bends away from the normal again when it travels from the more optically dense glass to the less dense air.

When light travels into a medium that is more optically dense, the **angle of refraction** is always smaller than the **angle of incidence**.

Why does the light change direction when it slows down or speeds up? This model can help you understand what happens.

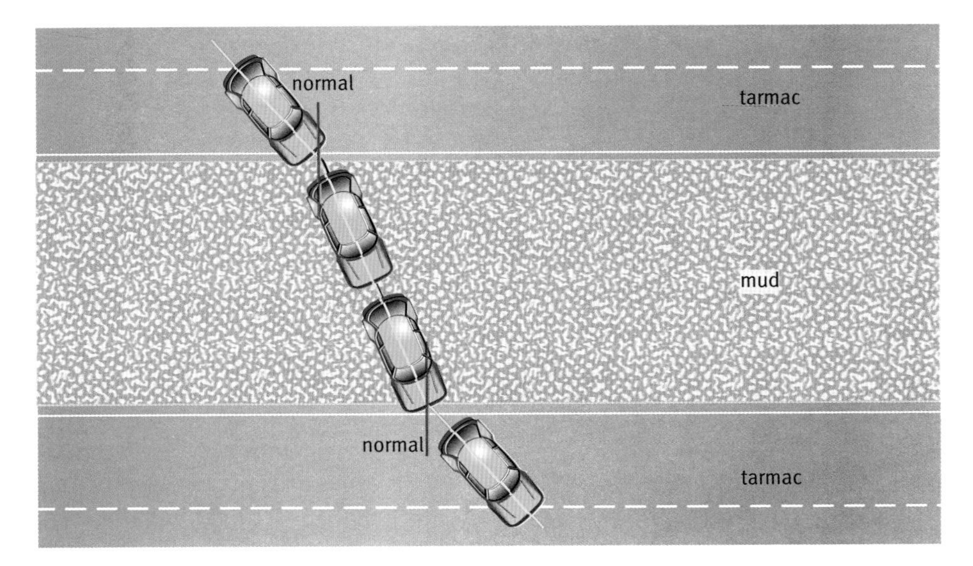

The car approaches the mud at an angle. When it hits the mud, the right front wheel slows down while the left one keeps travelling fast. The car turns towards the normal. When the left wheel enters the mud too, the car travels in a straight line again, but its direction changed at the boundary.

As the car leaves the mud the opposite happens. The right wheel speeds up first as it hits smooth tarmac, but the left wheel is still in the mud. This turns the car away from the normal.

Guess what?

You can make a coin appear and disappear! Put a coin in a cup and move your head so you just cannot see it. Keep your head still and get someone to pour water into the cup. The coin will appear! It's magic ...

Why does a ruler in water look bent?

When rays of light from the bottom of the ruler meet the air–water boundary, they bend away from the normal. Your brain thinks light rays travel in straight lines, so it assumes the rays have come from point X, not from the end of the ruler. This is why the pencil looks bent.

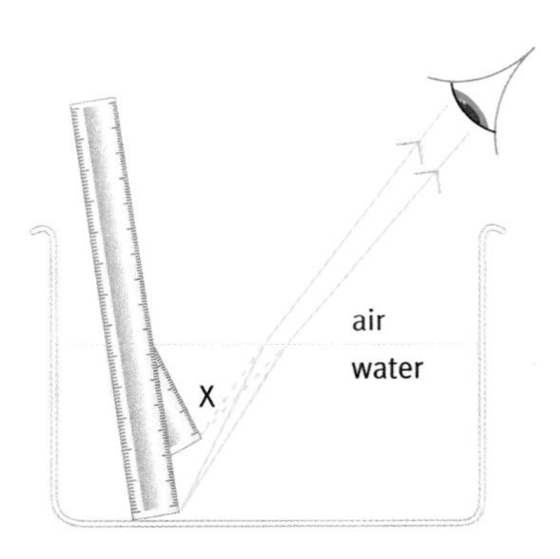

1. Copy and complete using words from the Language bank:
   Light changes direction at the ______ between two different media. Light bends towards the ______ when it travels from an optically less dense ______ to a more dense medium. A medium is any ______ material.
2. Sketch a diagram with light rays to show why a fish looks neaer the water surface than it is. Remember that light bends away from the normal when it travels from water into air.
3. Using a model of a toy car on tarmac and mud, try to explain to another student why light bends when it travels from one medium to another.

Language bank

angle of incidence
angle of refraction
bending
boundary
medium
normal
optically dense
refracted
refraction
straight lines
transparent

Rainbows and spectra

S

What is a spectrum?

All the colours of the rainbow

If you pass a ray of white light through a triangular-shaped block of glass (a **prism**), you can see the colours of the rainbow! We call these colours a **spectrum**. The white light is split up or **dispersed** into different colours. This is because violet light is refracted the most, and red light the least, with the other colours to different degrees in between.

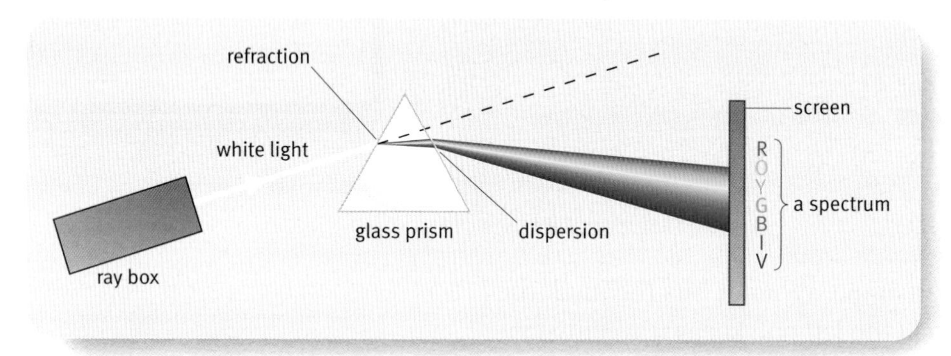

We normally say that there are seven colours in a spectrum, but indigo is hard to see. The colours blend into one another making a continuous spectrum, rather than separate individual colours.

Dispersion can be reversed! If you pass the spectrum made by the first prism into a second prism, the colours are recombined to form white light again.

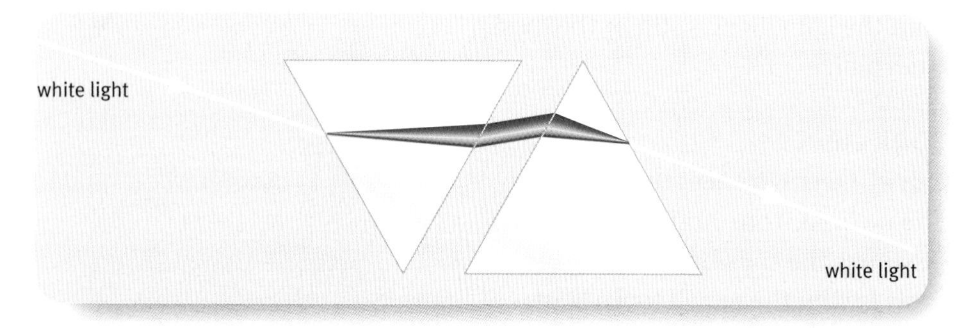

Isaac Newton

Mention Newton and most people think of gravity and apples falling on people's heads. But Newton also did many experiments finding out about white light. He observed that rays of white sunlight were split into a spectrum when passed through a prism. He realised that some colours were refracted more than others at the boundary. This meant that different colours deviated from a straight path to different degrees, and were split from each other.

Not satisfied with six colours, he included indigo (which most people have difficulty seeing) because he believed in the mythical significance of the number seven.

Guess what?

Newton's disc *is a circle that has all the colours of the spectrum. If you spin it, the seven colours seem to add together and appear white (well nearly white). Try making one for yourself.*

I can see a rainbow … or is it a spectrum?

A rainbow is formed by:

- refraction (bending)
- dispersion (splitting)
- reflection (bouncing).

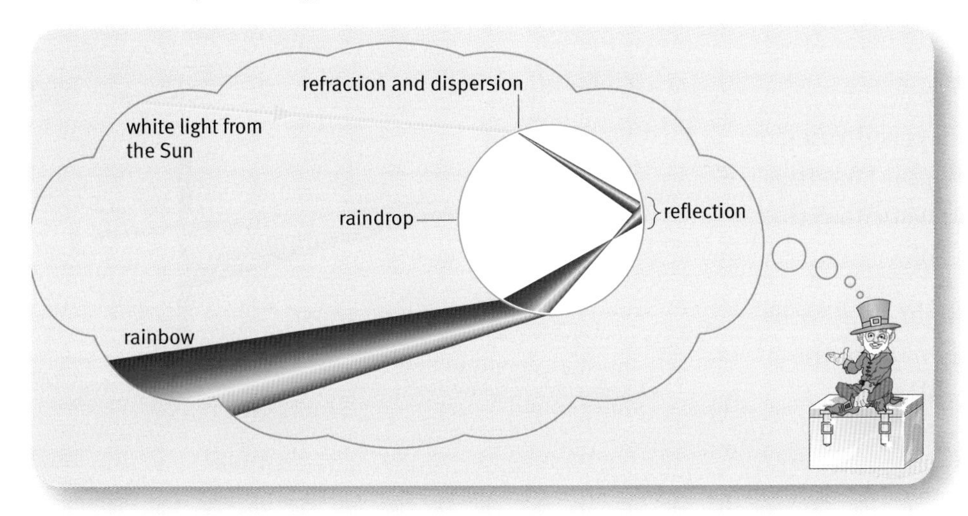

When white light from the Sun enters the raindrop, it is bent (refracted). The refraction splits (disperses) the light into the seven colours of the spectrum. The spectrum bounces (or reflects) off the back of the raindrop.

Usually an observer sees only one colour per raindrop, but there are so many raindrops that you can see all the colours of the spectrum in a rainbow.

As for the gold at the end of the rainbow … well, keep looking.

1 Copy and complete using words from the Language bank:

White light can be split up or ______ to give a range of colours. Normally we say there are seven colours in a ______, though indigo is hard to see. A rainbow forms as white light is ______, dispersed and ______ in a raindrop.

2 Which of these statements are true and which are false?

- **a** A prism adds colours to white light.
- **b** Red light is refracted less than violet light.
- **c** White light is a single colour.
- **d** The seven colours of a spectrum are not separate individual colours.

3 Make up a rhyme to help you remember the colours of the spectrum in order.

4 Explain in simple terms how a rainbow forms.

Language bank 

continuous spectrum
dispersed
dispersion
indigo
Newton's disc
prism
rainbow
reflected
refracted
spectrum
white light

What a colourful world

How can we change colour?

You can change the colour of things using filters and coloured light.

Seeing red

If you shine white light through a prism you get a spectrum of different coloured light. Pass this spectrum through a piece of red plastic (a red **filter**) and you will see only red light.

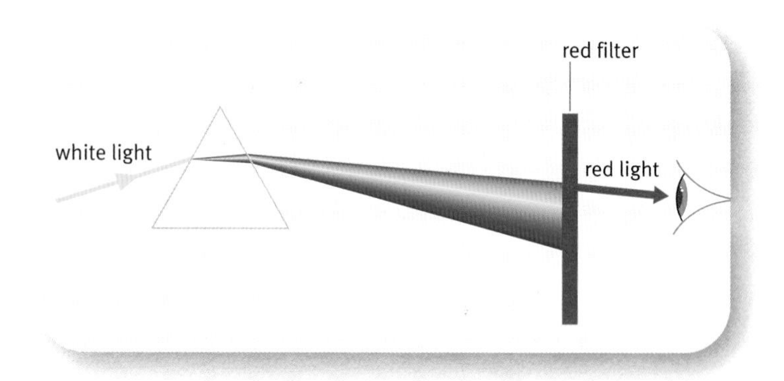

The red filter transmits only red light. It absorbs the other colours – it subtracts them from the spectrum. So this effect is called **colour subtraction**.

If you shine red light through a red filter, only the red light is transmitted. But if you shine red light through a green filter, you will see no light at all! When you can't see any light, you see black.

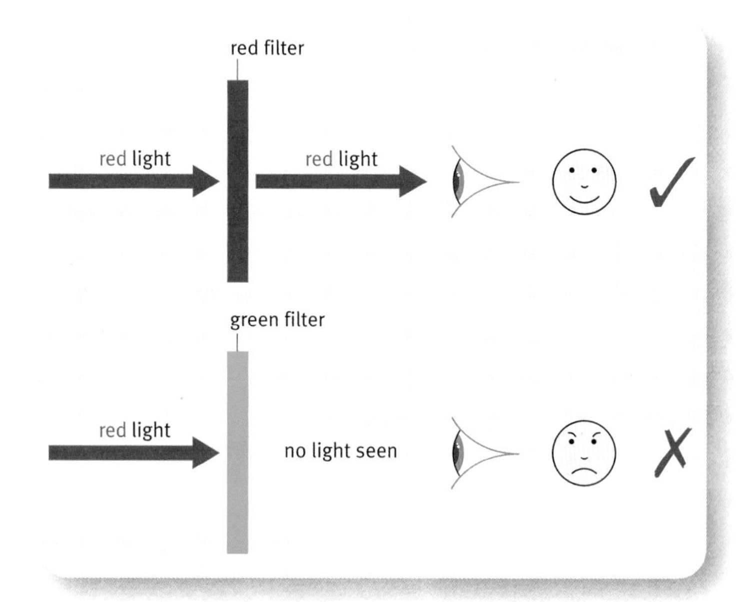

Primary and secondary colours

The **primary colours** of light are red, blue and green. We can add these together to make the **secondary colours** cyan, yellow and magenta. If you shine red, blue and green all together, you get white light.

A TV picture makes all the colours of the spectrum using dots or oblongs of just the three primary colours. Your eye merges or adds these colours so you see many combinations of colour. This is called **colour addition**.

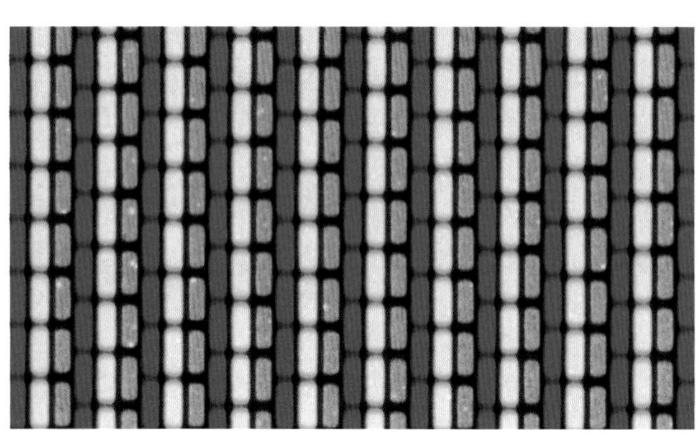

You can see the dots of the primary colours in this magnified picture of a TV screen.

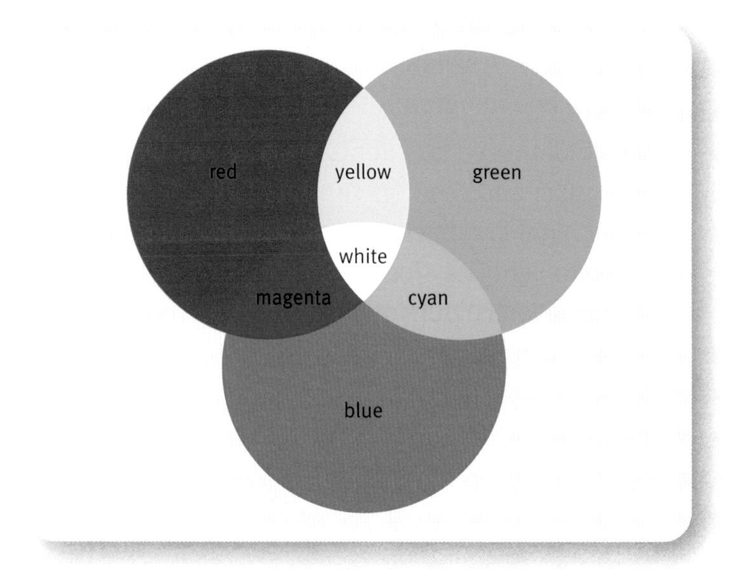

Sums with colours

When we see an object, the colour we see depends on the colour of the light going into our eyes. A banana looks yellow because it reflects, transmits and absorbs different colours of light. The light that eventually gets to our eyes from the banana makes it look yellow.

A red object in white light looks red because it reflects red light and absorbs all the other colours.

A red object in red light looks red because it reflects the red light.

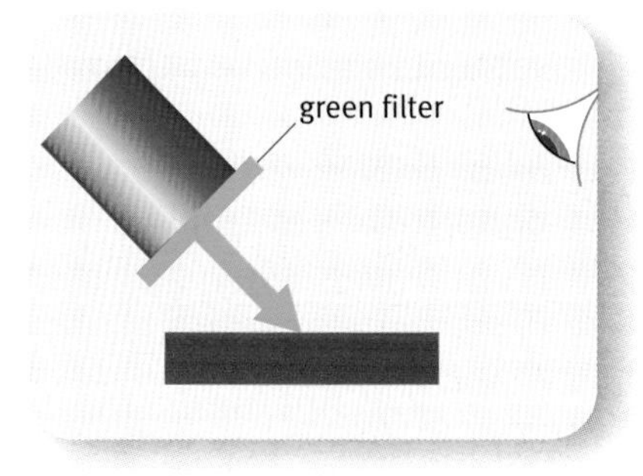

A red object in green light looks black because it absorbs the green light and does not have any red light to reflect.

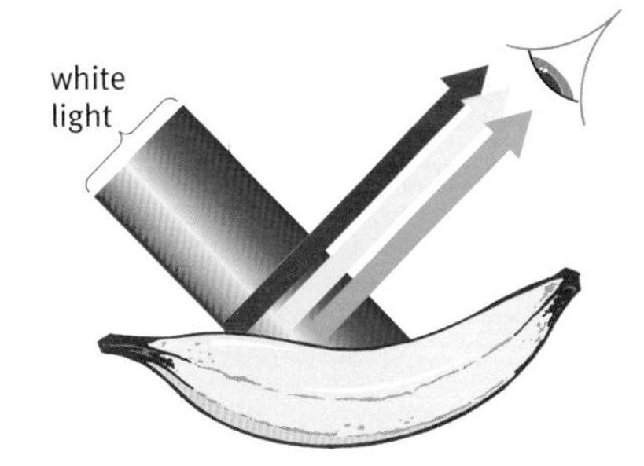

A yellow object in white light looks yellow because it absorbs some colours but reflects yellow light.

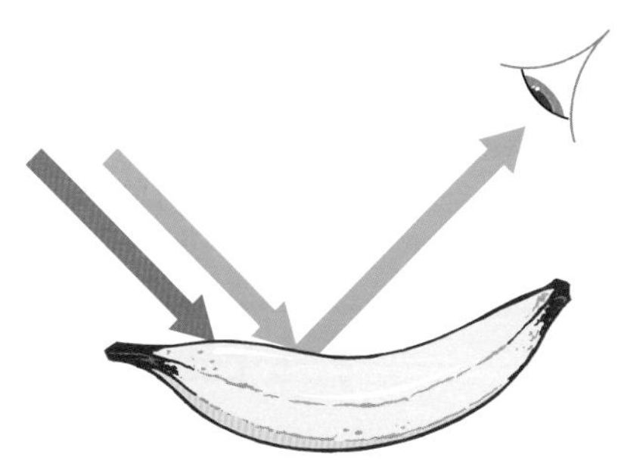

But in cyan light it will appear green because cyan light contains blue and green light.

Confused? This should help.

- A yellow banana reflects yellow light, which is green and red.
- Cyan light contains blue and green light.
- The banana absorbs the blue light and reflects the green light. There is no red light for it to reflect.
- So a yellow banana in cyan light looks green!

1 Copy and complete using words from the Language bank:
Filters absorb all colours of ______ except their own colour, which they ______. So a blue filter transmits ______ light and absorbs all the other colours.

2 What colour do these objects look in red light?
a a white ball **b** a black ball **c** a red ball

3 Why can't you have black light?

4 What colour would blue jeans look through a red filter?

Language bank

absorbs
black
blue
colour addition
colour subtraction
filter
green
light
primary colours
red
reflects
secondary colours
spectrum
transmit
white

Checkpoint

1 Travelling light

How does light travel? Choose four correct sentences and copy them down.

Light travels in waves.
Light travels in ripples.
Light travels when air particles vibrate.
Light needs a medium to transmit it.
Light does not need a medium to travel.
Light travels very fast.
Light bends when an object is in its way.
Light travels in straight lines.

2 Match the material

Match up the types of material and what happens when light meets them. Give an example of each type of material.

Types of material
opaque and shiny
opaque and rough
transparent
translucent

What happens to light
all reflected (scattered) or absorbed
some transmitted, some absorbed
almost all transmitted
reflected in an orderly way

3 Reflections

Copy this ray diagram and complete it to show how a light ray is reflected from a mirror.

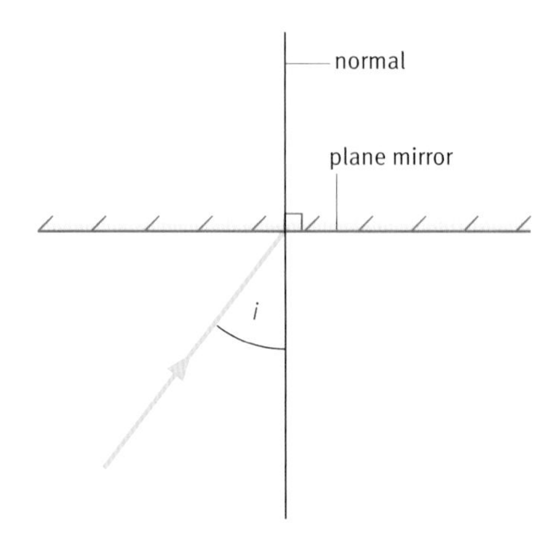

4 Magic trick

Look at the diagram. Choose three correct sentences below that explain why the ruler looks bent, and write them down.

Explanations

Light rays bend away from the normal when they leave water and enter air.
The pencil is a light source.
The pencil looks bent because of refraction.
Your brain assumes the light travelled in straight lines.
The pencil looks bent because of dispersion.
Light rays do not change speed or direction.

5 Colours of the rainbow

Copy and complete these sentences, unscrambling the words.

When white light passes through a glass **mirps**, it is split up into different colours. We call this splitting **noiseprids**.
The light splits up because different colours are **fredcrate** different amounts by the glass.
Voteli light is refracted the most and red light the least.
The seven colours make up the **crepsumt** of light.

6 What colour?

Copy and complete the table below to show what happens when light passes through coloured filters.

Colour of light	Colour of filter	Colour you see
white	blue	
white	red	
white	green	
red	red	
red	blue	

Sound and hearing

Before starting this unit, you should already be familiar with these ideas from earlier work.

- Sound travels by vibrations. What makes the vibrations when you bang a drum?
- Sounds can be high or low. How can you make the sound from a guitar or violin string higher?
- Sounds can be loud and quiet. How can you make the sound from a guitar or violin string louder?
- Sound can travel through solids, liquids and gases.
- We hear sounds when vibrations from a source travel through the air to our ears. Name your favourite sound source.

You will meet these key ideas as you work through this unit. Have a quick look now, and at the end of the unit read them through slowly.

- When sound travels from a source, it is transferring energy. A radio transfers electrical energy to sound energy.
- Sound travels as vibrations. It needs a medium to travel through. The particles of the **medium** pass the vibrations on.
- Sound travels much slower than light. It travels at different speeds in solids, liquids and gases.
- We can use an **oscilloscope** to 'see' sound waves. Loud sounds have a large **amplitude** (height); soft sounds have a low amplitude. High-pitched sounds have a high **frequency** (number per second); low-pitched sounds have a low frequency.
- Musical instruments vibrate to produce sound waves of different amplitudes and frequencies to give a range of notes and sounds.
- We hear because our ears transfer sound energy to electrical energy. Vibrations in the air enter the ear and make the **eardrum** vibrate. The vibrations are passed through the bones of the middle ear to the **cochlea**, which converts the vibrations to electrical signals. These pass along nerves to the brain.
- Frequency is measured in **hertz**. Humans hear sounds in the range of 20–20 000 Hz. As we get older our hearing range gets smaller. Other animals can hear different ranges of frequency.
- Hearing can be damaged or impaired in many ways. One way of looking after your hearing is to reduce the level of **noise pollution** you are exposed to and protect your ears in noisy situations.

Making a sound

How are different sounds made?

What makes sound? Sound is produced when something shakes or vibrates. The vibrations send out waves of sound energy which our ears detect. The sound energy is transferred to our ears.

Something that sends out sound waves is a **sound source.** Different sources vibrate in different ways, making different sounds.

The vibrating of the speaker makes the rice grains jump around.

The guitar, double bass and piano all have vibrating strings that make sound. Inside the saxophone is a vibrating column of air that sets up sound waves.

The cymbal vibrates so much that it looks blurred.

Seeing sounds

We can't see sound waves, but we can model them on a slinky spring.

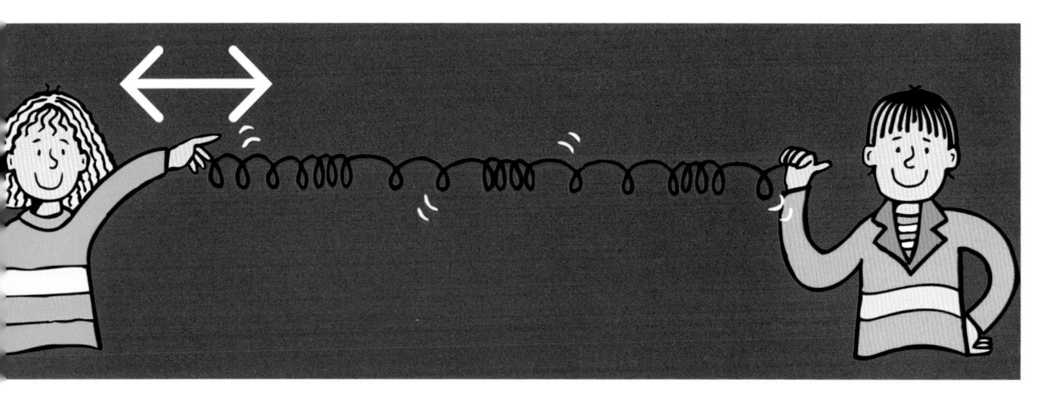

Sound energy is transferred like this. If you push and pull the slinky at one end, compressions travel along it to the other end.

A sound may be:
- quiet like a whisper, or loud like a shout – this is the loudness or **intensity** of the sound
- high like a little dog's yap, or low like a big dog's growl – this is the **pitch** of the sound.

An **oscilloscope** lets us see sound! We play the sound into a microphone. The oscilloscope shows wave patterns. They have different shapes for different kinds of sound.

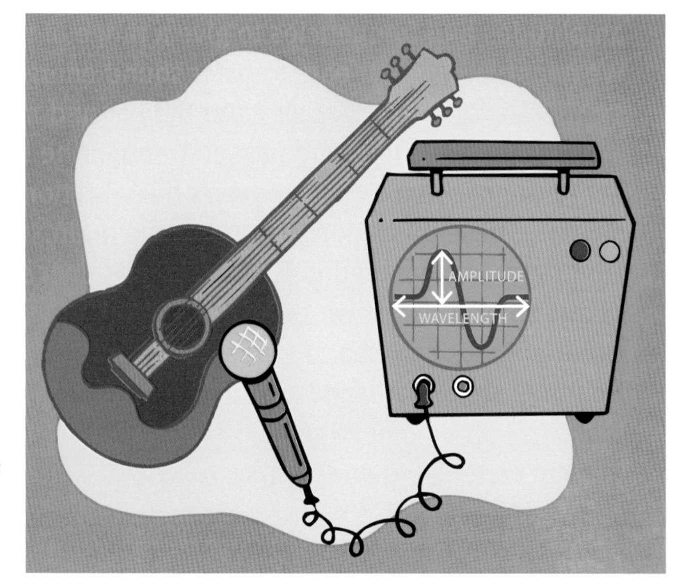

The microphone detects the sound energy. The oscilloscope transforms the sound into a shape that we can see. But sound waves in the air don't actually look like this.

Amplitude and frequency

How loud a sound is depends on the **amplitude** of the sound wave. This is the *height* of the wave on the oscilloscope. The harder you pluck the guitar string, the bigger the sound waves and the louder the sound.

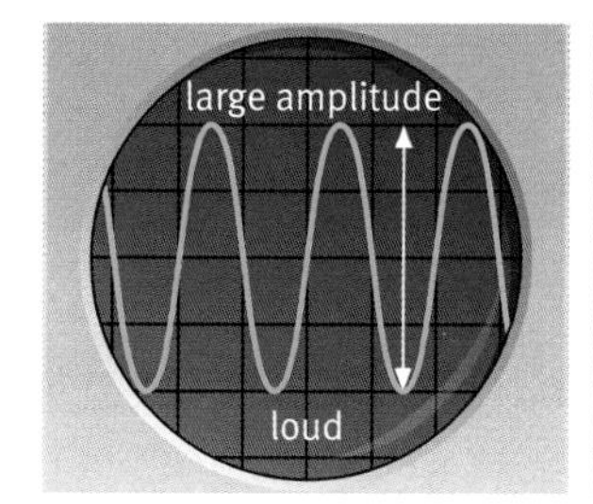

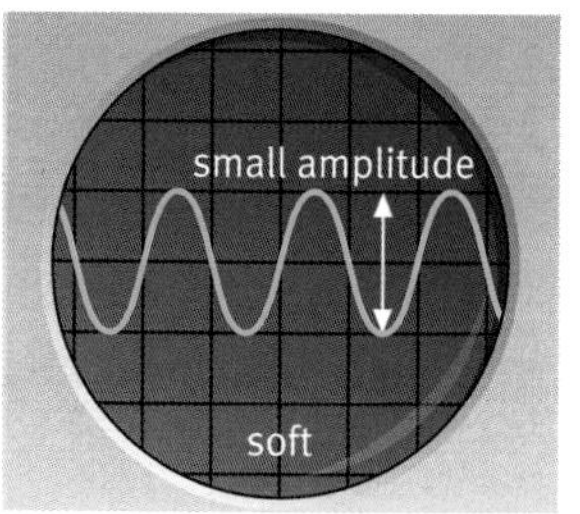

Loud or soft – it's a question of height (amplitude).

The pitch of a sound depends on the **frequency** of the sound wave. This is *how many* waves there are across the oscilloscope. A higher note makes more waves in a certain time. You can make a note higher by using a thinner guitar string, or by tightening the string or making it shorter.

The sounds shown opposite have a different pitch. But they are both equally loud. How can we tell?

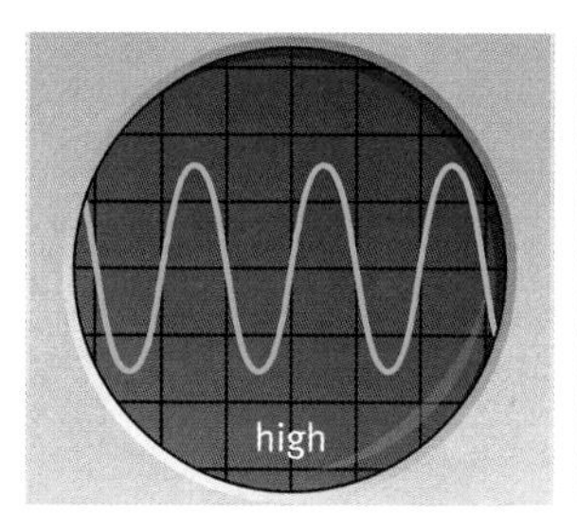

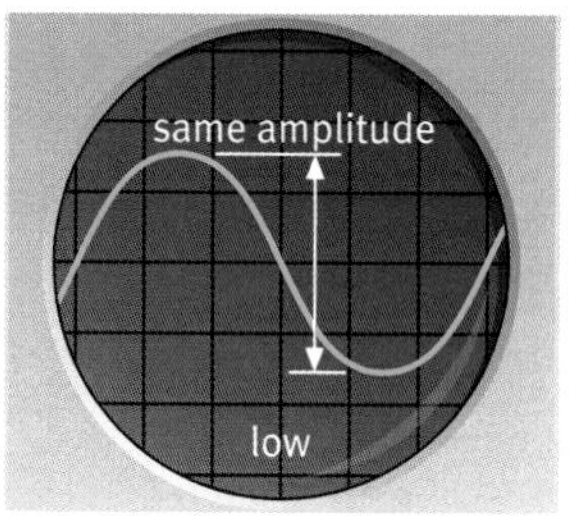

High or low – it depends on how many (frequency).

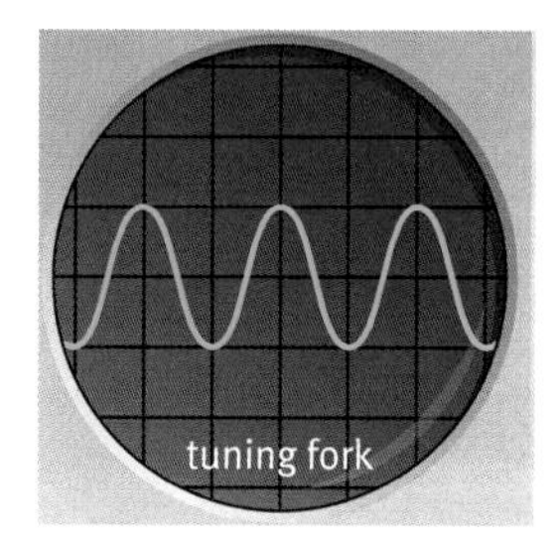

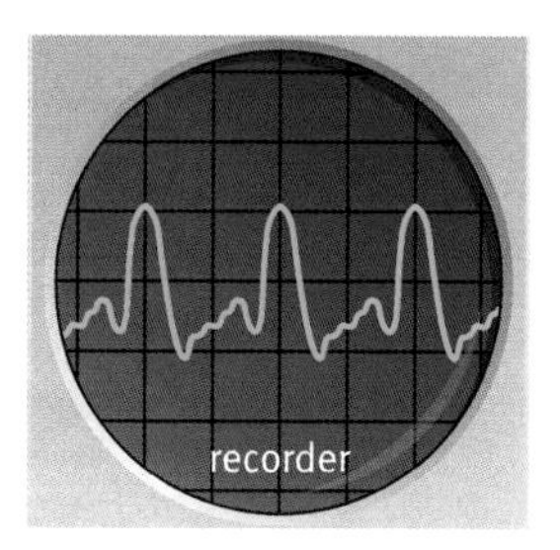

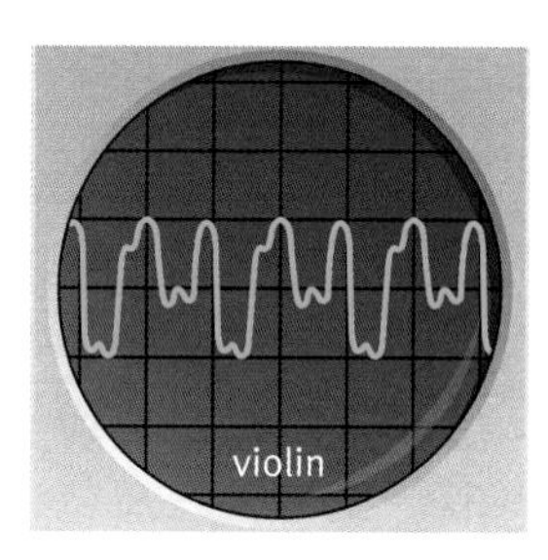

The pure tuning fork sound has a simple wave shape. The recorder and violin produce a more complex pattern, which gives them their individual timbre.

Timbre and quality

Timbre is not something a lumberjack shouts when cutting trees! It describes the quality of a note. Three sound sources might produce a note of the same loudness and pitch, but you can hear which is which. You can see above that they look different on the oscilloscope because the notes have been made by different objects vibrating.

1. Copy and complete using words from the Language bank:

   A sound is made when something shakes or _______. The vibrations send out waves of sound _______ which are detected by our _______. The higher the _______ of a sound wave, the higher will be its pitch. The greater the _______ of a sound wave, the louder it will be.
2. Describe two ways of increasing the frequency of the note from a violin string.
3. Sketch the oscilloscope traces you might see for the note of a tuning fork when tapped gently and then harder.
4. Find out what the volume control on a stereo system does to the sound it produces.

Language bank

amplitude
compression
ears
energy
frequency
intensity
loudness
oscilloscope
pitch
sound source
sound wave
timbre
vibrates
vibrations

Shifting sounds

Remember
Light travels much faster than sound. Light travels at 300 000 000 m/s in air, with sound lagging behind at only 330 m/s.

○ How does sound travel through solids, liquids and gases?

Unlike light, sound needs a **medium** to travel through. It cannot travel through a vacuum. Sound is carried by vibrations so it needs a material to vibrate, either a solid, a liquid or a gas.

Moving through a medium

Through solid ...

You can hear the sound of a train on the track long before the train arrives. The sound travels down the track faster than through the air. Unfortunately, sound energy is also transferred through solid doors and walls.

... liquid ...

Whales communicate over many miles using high-pitched sounds which travel through water. We can hear sounds in water through a ***hydrophone****.*

... and gas

Most of the sounds we hear travel through the air. But the further away you are from the source, the quieter it seems.

Guess what?

In 1827 Daniel Colladon and Charles Sturm measured the speed of sound in water on Lake Geneva. One of them struck a bell and a simultaneous flash of light signalled the other to start timing. They timed the sound through water. Their surprisingly accurate experiment showed that sound travels around 5 times faster in water than in air.

Demonstrating that sound needs a medium

In (A), we hear the bell ring. Its vibrations are transferred through the air and the glass to our ears.
hammer hits bell → bell vibrates → air in jar vibrates → glass vibrates → air outside jar vibrates → sound detected by our ears

In (B), the vacuum pump has removed the air from inside the jar. We cannot hear the bell as there is nothing to transmit the vibrations away from the bell.
hammer hits bell → bell vibrates → no air in jar to vibrate → glass does not vibrate → air outside jar does not vibrate → no sound detected by our ears

Sound transfer and particles

The particle model can help us picture what happens when sound energy passes through a material. The vibrating bell causes compressions in the air near to it. These compressions are transmitted through the air as air particles move together and apart.

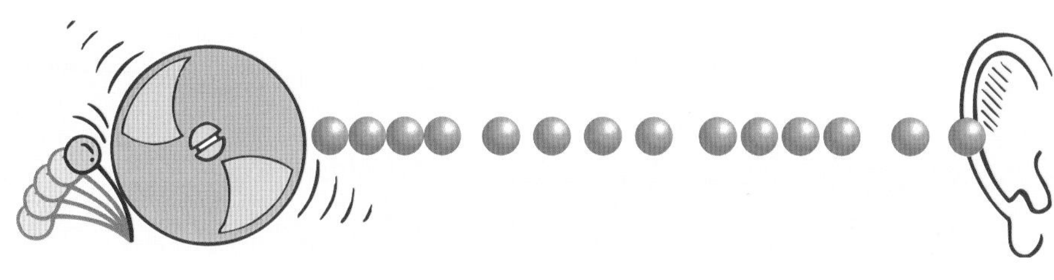

The particles transmit the vibrations through the air.

In a solid the particles are close together, so vibrations are passed quickly from one particle to the next. Sound travels fastest through a solid.

But sound does not have the same speed in all solids. In a dense solid such as steel, the particles are close together and pass the vibrations on faster from one particle to another.

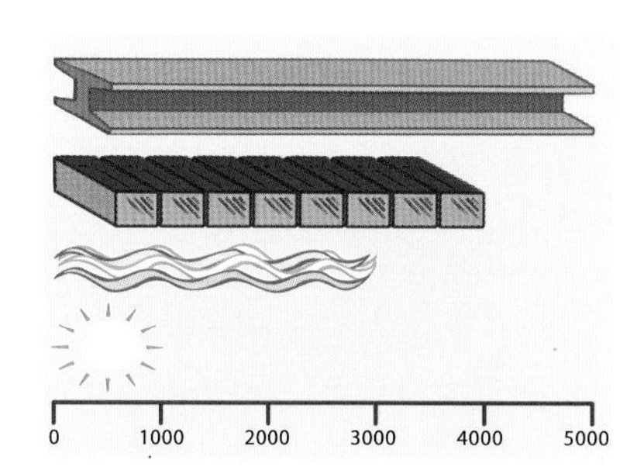

Steel transfers sound more quickly than brick, which is less dense. In air sound seems quite sluggish!

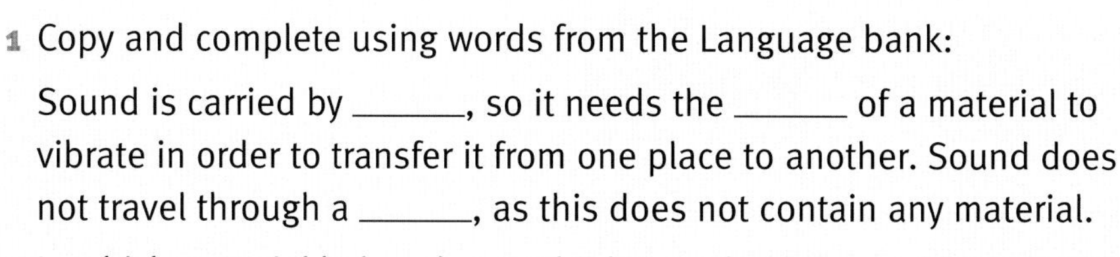

1 Copy and complete using words from the Language bank:
Sound is carried by ______, so it needs the ______ of a material to vibrate in order to transfer it from one place to another. Sound does not travel through a ______, as this does not contain any material.

2 In which material below do you think sound waves would travel the fastest? Explain your answer.
a chipboard **b** concrete **c** lead

3 An advertisement for a science fiction film said: 'They can't hear you scream in space'. Why is this statement true?

Language bank

dense
hydrophone
medium
particles
speed of sound
transferred
vacuum
vibrations

Hearing

M

How do we hear sounds?

The girl in the photo is having her hearing tested by an **audiologist** (someone who studies hearing). The earphones are linked to a computer which makes sounds of different frequencies and amplitudes. This tests the girl's **threshold** (the quietest sound she can hear) over a range of frequencies, from the lowest pitch to the highest. The sounds she can hear are known as her **audible range**.

*Frequency is measured in units called **hertz (Hz)**. A higher threshold than normal at particular frequencies might indicate a hearing problem.*

How we hear

If a heavy lorry passes close by, you can often feel its vibrations through your whole body. Hearing is similar to this – hearing means 'feeling' a sound with your inner ear. Here is how it works.

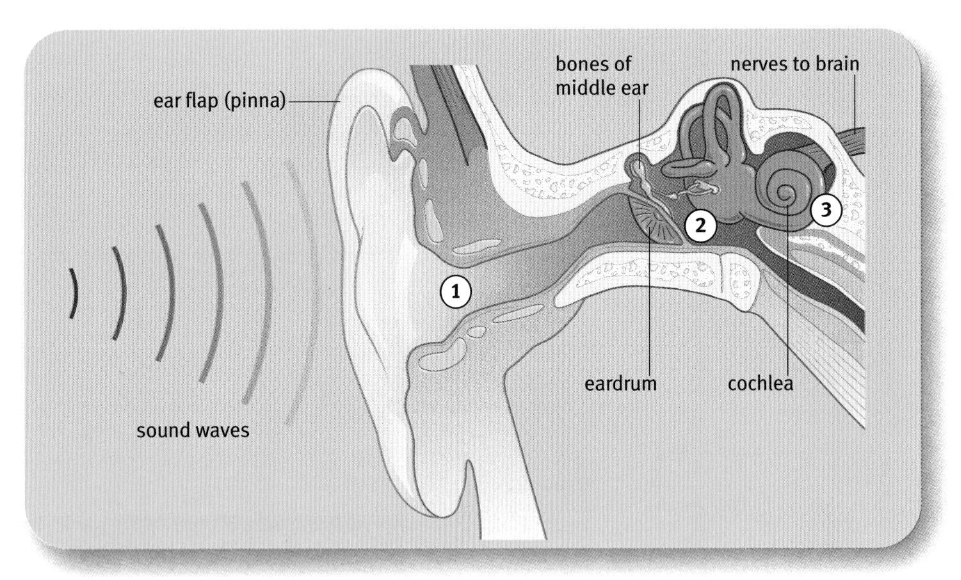

In the ear, sound energy is transformed to electrical energy. Vibrations are transferred through the eardrum to the bones of the middle ear and then to the cochlea. Electrical signals are then transferred to the brain where we 'hear' the sound.

1 Vibrating air particles are funnelled into the ear by the ear flap (**pinna**).
2 The vibrating particles cause the **eardrum** to vibrate. This in turn passes on the vibrations to the bones in the middle ear. This magnifies the vibration.
3 In the coiled structure called the **cochlea** are 17 000 or so sensitive hairs, which vibrate next. These hairs are connected to nerve cells and these send electrical signals to the brain, which registers the sound.

Do we all hear the same?

Humans hear sounds of frequencies between about 20 Hz and 20 000 Hz. As people get older, the range of sounds that they can detect tends to narrow. Dogs can hear up to around 40 000 Hz and bats up to 120 000 Hz.

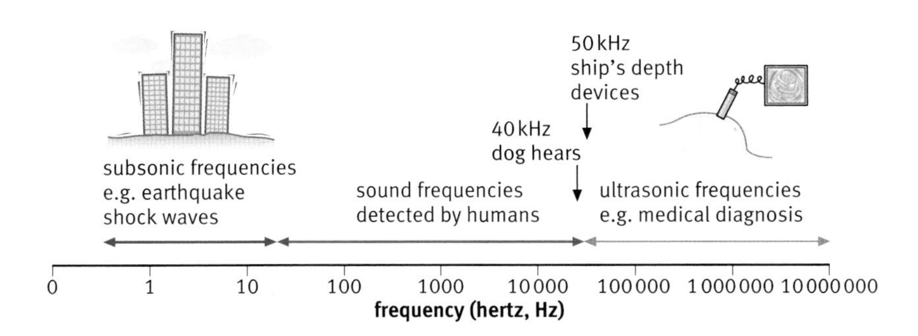

The range of frequencies we can hear is quite small. Subsonic vibrations are too low for us to hear, and ultrasonic vibrations are very high.

Guess what?

Earwigs hear through their pincers and crickets have hearing organs on their legs, shown here.

Designed to hear

A dog can detect higher frequencies than humans can. We can't hear the handler's whistles, but the dog can.

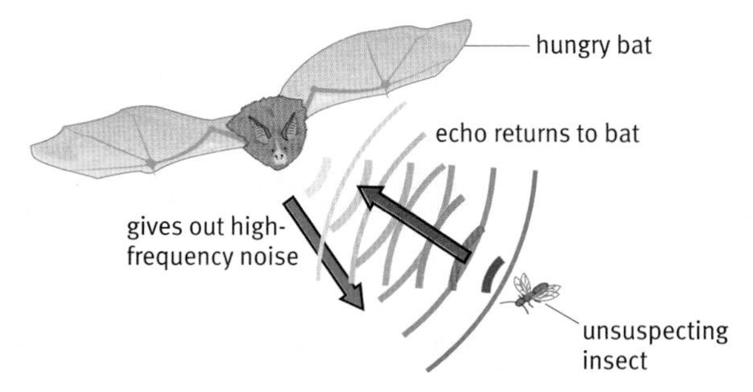

Bats use their own radar system known as ***echolocation*** *to find insects and avoid obstacles. Bats give out a high-pitched sound which reflects back from objects as thin as a spider's web. Their large ears help them detect the echoes so they can sense where things are.*

1 Copy and complete using words from the Language bank:

The _____ range is the range of sounds that a person can hear. This tends to reduce as a person grows older. In our ears, the _____ vibrates and causes the bones in the middle ear to vibrate. These vibrations are passed onto hairs in the _____ which send electrical signals to the brain.

2 The desert fox has very large ear flaps. How does this help the fox's acute hearing?

3 Find out why a person's hearing may get worse as they grow older.

4 Find out what SONAR stands for and describe its uses.

Language bank 

audible range
brain
cochlea
ear flap
eardrum
echolocation
hertz (Hz)
middle ear
pinna
subsonic
threshold
ultrasonic

Harmful sound

Can sound be dangerous?

If you are exposed to loud noises for a long time it can damage your hearing. But how loud is loud? The loudness of a sound can be checked using a sound meter which measures in units called **decibels (dB)**. The number of decibels tells you how powerful the sound is.

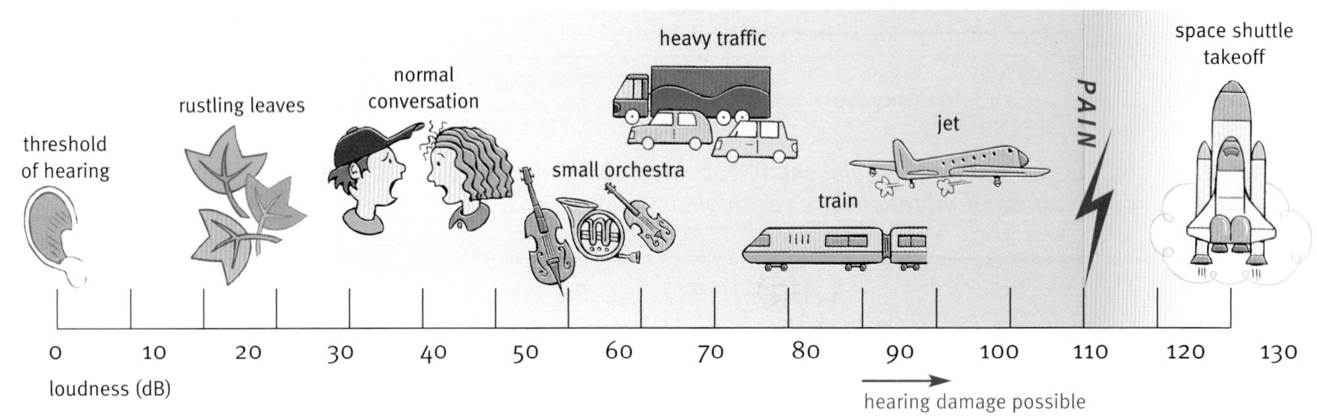

Noise pollution from airports, traffic or even noisy neighbours can make life unbearable for some. Double glazing can help with sound insulation as the air gap reduces noise pollution. But personal stereos and mobile phones also cause noise pollution.

Poor hearing

There are about 8.7 million people in the UK today who are deaf or hard of hearing, and 2 in every 1000 children aged 9–16 are deaf.

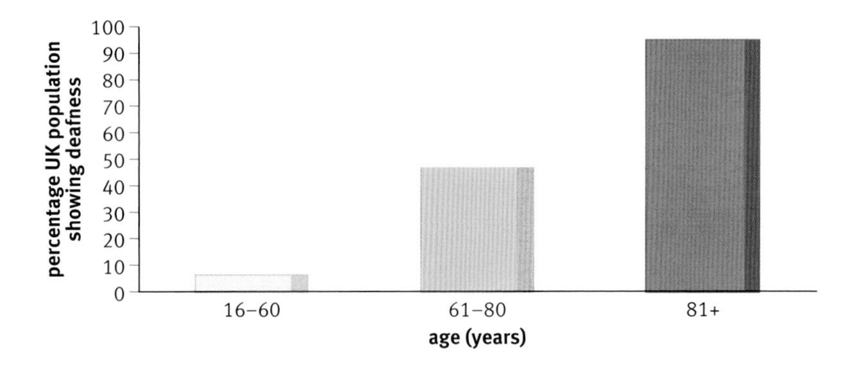

Deafness becomes more common as people get older.

Here are a few reasons why someone's hearing might not be perfect.

- A build-up of wax prevents sound entering the ear.
- Exposure to loud noises for long periods of time can damage the hairs and nerve cells in the ear.
- An accident or injury might damage the bones of the inner ear or the hairs in the cochlea.
- A burst eardrum, caused perhaps by illness, prevents the vibration being passed on to the hairs in the cochlea.
- Deafness may be caused by an inherited problem with the ear or nerves.

Guess what?

Some sound meters use a scale called the dBA scale. This takes account of the ear's sensitivity to sound.

Protecting your ears

There are laws about the maximum levels of sound that people should be exposed to. Many industries take sensible steps such as asking workers to wear ear defenders to protect their hearing.

Noise is part of many jobs, but wearing ear defenders prevents long-term damage to the ears.

Guess what?

Silence might not be golden! Many people suffer from ***tinnitus*** *– they hear a buzzing or ringing sound instead of silence. This can be very annoying and distressing. Their ears can hear sounds that are not really there but are generated by their own auditory (hearing) system. Tinnitus may be caused by exposure to loud sound.*

How does this sound?

Evelyn Glennie is a world-class percussionist who has performed all over the world to large audiences in spite of being profoundly deaf. Like many deaf people she uses her body's sense of touch to 'hear' or 'feel' her music. She has trained herself to hear sounds of different pitch in parts of her body other than her ears. For example, she feels low-pitched sounds in her legs.

1 Copy and complete using words from the Language bank:
Unwanted sound is called noise ______. Loud noises of over 140 ______ can damage hearing. It is important to wear ear ______ to protect your hearing when exposed to loud sounds.

2 How might loud noises damage your hearing?

3 What is tinnitus?

4 Using a search engine, type in 'Evelyn + Glennie' to find out more about this talented artist.

Language bank

auditory system
deafness
decibels (dB)
ear defenders
loudness
noise pollution
tinnitus

Checkpoint

1 True or false?

Decide whether the following statements are true or false. Write down the true ones. Correct the false ones before you write them down.

Sound travels out from a source, transferring energy.
Sound does not need a medium to travel through.
Sound travels as vibrations in solids, liquids or gases.
Sound travels much faster than light.

2 Sound waves

Look at the pairs of diagrams of sound waves on an oscilloscope. Match each diagram to the correct descriptions to compare the waves. What do they sound like?

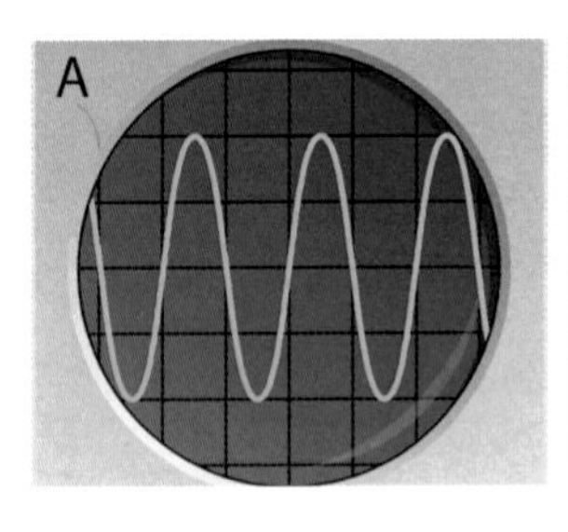

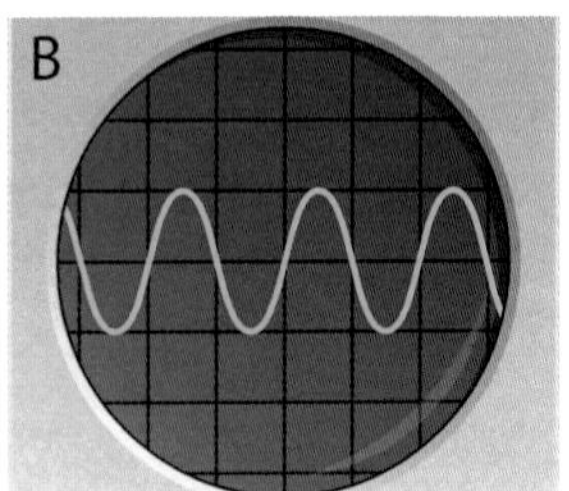

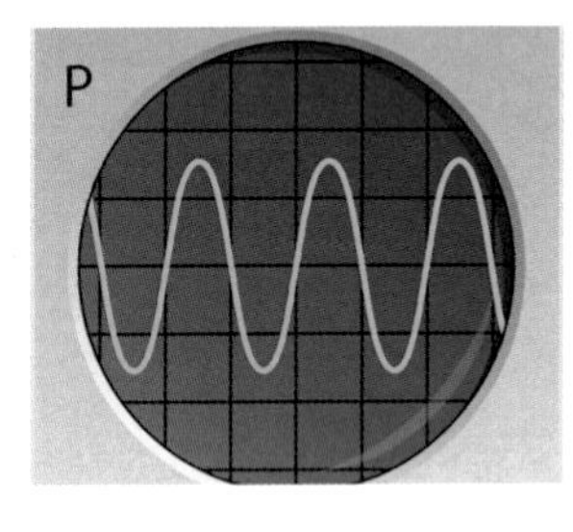

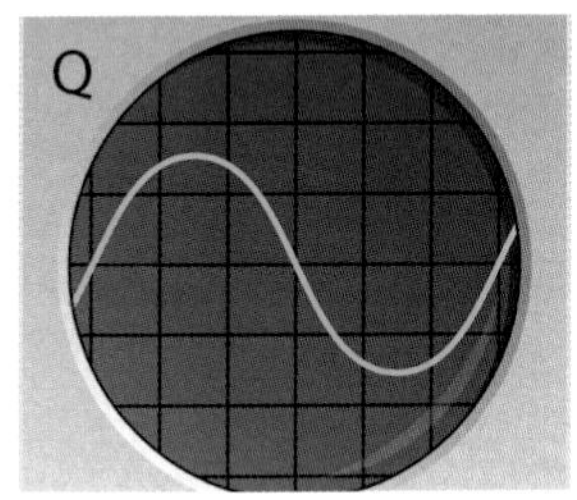

Wave descriptions
low frequency
small amplitude
large amplitude
high frequency

Sound descriptions
soft
high-pitched
loud
low-pitched

3 Fix the flow chart

The following flow chart is mixed up. Redraw it in the correct order to show how we hear.

The eardrum passes the vibrations to the bones in the middle ear.

A sound source gives out sound vibrations that pass through the air.

These convert the vibrations to electrical messages in nerves.

The bones magnify the vibrations, and they pass to the cochlea where little hairs vibrate.

The vibrations are funnelled to the eardrum and make it vibrate.

The messages pass to the brain and we hear a sound.

4 It's your choice

Copy and complete the following sentences, choosing the correct words.

The loudness of sound is measured in **decibels** / **hertz** / **metres per second**.
The frequency of sound is measured in **decibels** / **hertz** / **amplitudes**.
Humans can hear **speeds** / **volumes** / **frequencies** of sound in the range of 20 to 20 000 Hz.
Bats can hear **higher** / **lower** / **the same** frequencies as us. They find their way using **compasses** / **echolocation** / **tinnitus**.
To protect our hearing in noisy environments we use **ear defenders** / **earpieces** / **oscilloscopes**.

Glossary

Words in italic have their own glossary entry.

A

absorption, absorbed Taking into the *blood* to be used by the body.

aerobic respiration *Respiration* using oxygen.

alveolus (plural alveoli) Air sac in the *lungs* where *gas exchange* occurs.

amplitude Height of a wave.

antibiotics Chemicals used as medicines which kill *micro-organisms* inside the body.

antibodies Chemicals in the *blood* which fight disease.

arteries *Blood vessels* that carry *blood* away from the heart.

atom Particle that is the basic building block of all matter.

audible range The range of sound that a person can hear.

audiologist A doctor who is a hearing specialist.

B

bacteria Type of *micro-organism*, a single celled organism much smaller than an animal cell.

balanced diet A *diet* that provides the correct amounts of all seven *nutrients* needed for a healthy body.

basalt *Extrusive igneous rock*, often with small crystals.

belt transect Survey of the organisms present in a band through a certain area.

biodegradable Will rot away naturally in the environment.

blood Tissue that transports many substances around the body, including digested food molecules, oxygen and waste materials.

blood vessels Tubes that carry *blood* around the body.

boiling point *Temperature* at which a *pure* substance changes from a liquid to a gas.

breathing system Organ system that carries out *gas exchange*.

bronchus (plural bronchi) Tube that joins the *trachea* to the left or right *lung*.

burning Reaction of a material with oxygen, giving out *thermal energy*.

C

capillaries Very small *blood vessels* that join *arteries* to *veins*, and carry substances to cells in body tissues.

carbohydrates *Nutrient* that provides energy.

carnivore Meat eater.

cellular respiration Another name for *respiration*.

Celsius Scale used to measure *temperature*, in units of degrees Celsius (°C).

chemical change See *chemical reaction*.

chemical reaction Change in which new substances are made, which is not easily changed back.

chickenpox *Infectious disease* caused by a *virus* (especially common in children), which causes rashes and blisters.

chloride *Compound* that contains one or more *elements* chemically joined to chlorine, e.g. sodium chloride.

cilia Tiny hairs attached to cells lining the airways, that move *mucus* and trapped dust up away from the *lungs*.

circulation Transport of *blood* and *nutrients* around the body in the *blood*.

circulatory system Organ system that transports *blood* around the body, carrying many substances to where they are needed.

clot *Blood* hardens and seals off a cut or wound to stop the bleeding and prevent *micro-organisms* entering the body.

cochlea Organ in the ear that converts vibrations to electrical signals.

community Collection of plants and animals that share a *habitat*.

compound Substance containing *atoms* of more than one *element* chemically joined up.

conductor Substance that allows heat or electricity to pass through it.

consumer Organism that eats (consumes) other organisms in a *food chain*.

convection Transfer of *thermal energy* in which the energy is transferred by the movement of particles in convection currents in a *fluid*, as warmer parts of the fluid expand and rise through cooler parts.

core (of Earth) Central part of the Earth.

crust Outer solid layer of the Earth, which floats on the *mantle*.

D

decibel (dB) Unit of loudness.

deposition *Sediment* is laid down when the transport agent e.g. river no longer has enough energy to carry it.

diet The combination of all the foods a person eats.

digestion Breaking down of large food molecules into smaller ones which the body can *absorb* and use.

digestive enzymes *Molecules* made by the body which speed up the breakdown of food.

digestive system Organ system that carries out *digestion*.

dispersed Light scattered in all directions.

dispersion White light is split up into its constituent colours, e.g. by passing it through a *prism*.

dyke Vertical *intrusion* of *magma* where *igneous rock* forms.

eardrum Membrane in the ear that transmits sound vibrations from the air to the bones of the middle ear.

echolocation Using sound to find the way, e.g. by bats.

egestion Removal from the body of undigested waste that remains after *digestion*.

electromagnet *Magnet* formed by a *solenoid*, often with a core inside.

element Substance that cannot be split into anything simpler, that has *atoms* all of the same kind.

enzymes *Molecules* made by the body which speed up *chemical reactions* in the body.

epidemic Widespread occurrence of a disease in a community.

erosion *Weathering* of rocks and *transportation* of the fragments.

evaporation Change of state from liquid to gas without boiling, in which the more energetic particles of the liquid escape from the surface.

exfoliation Onion skin weathering, in which the surface of a rock flakes and falls off due to the repeated heating and cooling of the rock through the day and night.

exhale Remove air from the *lungs*.

extrusive igneous rocks *Igneous rock* formed on the Earth's surface.

fats *Nutrient* that provides a store of energy and is needed for cell membranes.

fibre Another name for *roughage*.

filter (light) A *translucent* material of a certain colour.

fissure Crack.

fluid Liquid or gas.

foliation Wavy pattern of bands often seen in *metamorphic rocks*.

food chain Diagram that shows the feeding relationships between certain organisms in a *habitat*. It shows what eats what and the transfer of energy.

food web Network of interlocking *food chains*.

formula Combination of *symbols* used to represent a *molecule* or a *compound*.

fossil Remains of a once-living plant or animal preserved in rock.

fractional distillation Method of separating mixtures of liquids such as liquefied air.

freeze–thaw weathering *Weathering* of rocks due to the repeated freezing and thawing of water, which expands when it freezes and makes cracks larger.

frequency Number of waves per second.

fungi Type of *micro-organism* that may be single-celled or larger, and feeds off other living things.

G

gabbro Dark coloured *igneous rock*.

gas exchange Exchange of the gases carbon dioxide and oxygen in the *lungs*.

geologist Scientist who studies rocks.

glucose Simple sugar (*carbohydrate*) which is a source of energy for the body, used in *respiration*.

granite *Intrusive igneous rock* with large crystals and speckled appearance.

H

habitat Place where an organism lives.

heating Transfer of *thermal energy*.

herbivore Plant eater.

hertz (Hz) Unit of *frequency* (1 kHz = 1000 Hz).

I

igneous rock Rock that forms when hot liquid rock solidifies.

image Produced when light is *reflected* in a mirror – we can see the object somewhere else.

immune If you are immune to a disease, your body can make *antibodies* to fight the disease quickly so you do not catch it.

impure Contains two or more or more substances in a *mixture*.

incident ray Ray of light which approaches something and may be *reflected* or *refracted*.

infection Entry of a *pathogen* into the body, causing an *infectious disease*.

infectious disease Disease that spreads from one organism to another, caused by *micro-organisms*.

infrared radiation Type of light energy, emitted by warm objects.

ingestion Taking in food.

inhale Take air into the *lungs*.

inoculation Treating with a *vaccine* to increase immunity to a disease.

intrusion Movement of *magma* into spaces in solid rock above, where the magma cools and forms *igneous rock*.

intrusive igneous rocks *Igneous rock* formed inside the Earth.

joule (J) Unit for measuring energy.

large intestine Part of the *digestive system* where undigested food remains after *digestion*, and water is absorbed.

laterally inverted Left becomes right and right becomes left, as when something is reflected in a plane mirror.

lava Hot liquid rock (*magma*) that has reached the Earth's surface, usually from a volcano.

law of reflection Angle of incidence = angle of reflection.

light source Something that emits (gives off) light energy.

light year Distance travelled by light in one year; unit used to measure large distances in space.

line transect Survey of the organisms present on a line in a certain area.

liver Organ that secretes bile into the *digestive system*, which breaks up fat globules and neutralises acid from the *stomach*. The liver also has many other functions.

lodestone A type of rock that is *magnetic*.

lungs Organs where *gas exchange* takes place.

lysozymes *Enzymes* in sweat and tears which kill *micro-organisms*.

M

magma Hot liquid rock in the Earth.

magnet Object that repels another *magnet*.

magnetic field The space around a *magnet* where its magnetic force acts.

magnetic material Material that experiences a force in a *magnetic field*.

magnetic shielding Blocking of a *magnetic field* by a *magnetic material*.

magnetically hard Material that is hard to *magnetise* and demagnetise.

magnetically soft Material that is easily *magnetised* and demagnetised.

magnetised Made into a *magnet*.
mantle Semi-liquid part of the Earth between the *core* and the *crust*.
measles *Infectious disease* caused by a *virus*, in which there are red spots on the skin.
melting point Temperature at which a *pure* substance changes from a solid to a liquid.
metal Type of *element* that is usually solid at room temperature, shiny, hard and a good *conductor* of heat and electricity.
metamorphic rock Rock that has undergone some kind of change, usually caused by increased heat and/or pressure.
microbes Another name for *micro-organisms*.
micro-organisms Small (microscopic) organisms.
minerals In biology: essential *compounds* that provide *elements* needed in small amounts in the *diet*. In geology: grains of a single *compound* found in rocks.
mixture Two or more substances mixed together but not chemically joined.
molecule Group of *atoms* chemically joined up.
mucus Sticky substance that lines many internal surfaces of the body. In the airways mucus traps dust and other particles to clean air entering the *breathing system*.

N

non-metal Type of *element* that not usually shiny and is often a poor conductor of heat and electricity. Many non-metals are gases at room temperature.
normal Imaginary line at 90° to a mirror or lens.
north-seeking pole The *pole* of a *magnet* that is attracted to the Earth's north pole, marked N and often painted red.
nutrients Substances in foods that supply the chemicals needed for a healthy body.

O

obsidian Dark glassy volcanic (*igneous*) rock.
oesophagus Tube that carries food from the mouth to the *stomach*.
omnivore Plant and meat eater.
opaque Material that light cannot pass through.
oxidation Reaction of oxygen with another substance to make an *oxide*, e.g. magnesium with oxygen to make magnesium oxide.
oxide *Compound* that contains one or more elements chemically joined to oxygen, e.g. magnesium oxide.

P

palaeontologist Scientist who studies *fossils*.
pancreas Organ in the *digestive system* that produces *digestive enzymes* which act in the *small intestine*.
pathogen *Micro-organism* that causes *infectious diseases*.
periodic table Table that lists all the *elements* and groups similar elements together.
photosynthesis Process by which green plants use carbon dioxide and water in the presence of sunlight to make sugar (*glucose*) and oxygen.
pinna Outer ear, that funnels the sound down the ear canal to the *eardrum*.
pitch How high or low a sound is.
plasma Straw-coloured watery liquid in *blood* that transports digested food molecules, hormones and *antibodies* around the body.
platelets Fragments of cells found in the *blood* which help blood to *clot* in order to seal off cuts and wounds.
pole Part of a *magnet* where the *magnetic field* is concentrated.
population The number of organisms of a certain species living in a *habitat*.
porous Has little holes in its structure, so allows fluids to pass into it.
precipitate Solid formed in a *chemical reaction*, which falls out of the solution.
predator Animal that eats other animals.
prey Animal that is eaten by other animals.
primary colours Red, blue and green are the primary colours of light.
prism Glass block, often triangular in shape, used to split white light into a *spectrum*.
producer Green plant, which produces its own food, found at the start of a *food chain* or *food web*.

product Substance that is made in a *chemical reaction*.

properties Describe what something is like, e.g. for a material the properties include its colour and how it reacts.

protease *Enzyme* that digests *proteins* (e.g. trypsin is a protease).

protein *Nutrient* that is needed for growth and repair of cells.

pure Contains only one substance (*element* or *compound*).

pyramid of biomass Diagram showing the mass of each organism at each stage of a *food chain*.

pyramid of numbers Diagram showing the number of each organism at each stage of a *food chain*.

Q

quadrat Frame often one metre square used in fieldwork to sample and survey a *habitat*.

quartzite Type of *metamorphic rock*.

R

radiation Transfer of energy in waves, that does not need a medium to travel through.

ray diagram Diagram that shows what happens to rays of light.

reactant Substance that reacts in a *chemical reaction*, and is changed into new substances.

rectum Last part of the *digestive system*, where waste is stored before being *egested*.

red blood cells Cells in the *blood* that transport oxygen and carbon dioxide around the body.

reflect Allows light to bounce off it.

reflected ray Light ray which has been reflected.

refraction Bending of light as it passes into a different medium.

respiration The chemical reaction that releases energy from food such as *glucose* in the body.

rock cycle A summary of all the processes that act on rocks and change them from one type to another.

roughage Material in the *diet* which the body cannot *digest*.

S

secondary colours Colours made by combining two *primary colours*. Cyan, magenta and yellow are the secondary colours of light.

sediment Rock particles that are being transported, e.g. in a river, or have been *deposited*.

sedimentary rock Rock that forms from deposits of fragments of other rocks.

seismologist Scientist who studies earthquakes.

sill Horizontal *intrusion* of *magma* where *igneous rock* forms.

small intestine Part of the *digestive system* where *digestion* is completed and digested food molecules are *absorbed*.

solenoid Current-carrying coil of wire that can act like a bar *magnet*.

sound source Something that makes a sound (gives out sound energy).

specific (of enzymes) Acts only on one reaction or group of reactions.

spectrum All the colours of the rainbow, that combine to make up white light.

starch Carbohydrate found in foods such as potatoes, bread and pasta.

stomach Organ in the *digestive system* that produces acid and *digestive enzymes*.

strata Layers.

sulphide *Compound* that contains one or more *elements* chemically joined to sulphur, e.g. iron sulphide.

symbol One or two letters used to represent an *element*.

T

temperature How hot or cold something is.

thermal conduction Transfer of *thermal energy* in which the energy is transferred from one moving particle to the next in a solid.

thermal energy Heat energy.

thermometer Device used to measure *temperature*.

tinnitus Constant ringing in the ear, often caused by exposure to loud noises.

trachea Main tube that carries air from the mouth or nose down into the *lungs*.

translucent Material that allows some light to travel through it, but some is reflected or absorbed.

transparent Material that allows light to travel through it.

transportation Movement of rock *sediment* e.g. by wind, water or ice.

vaccine Weakened or dead *micro-organisms* put into the body to stimulate *antibody* production to make you *immune* to the disease.

veins *Blood vessels* that carry *blood* towards the heart.

villus (plural villi) Small finger-like structures in the *small intestine* that increase the surface area for the *absorption* of digested *nutrients*.

virus Type of *micro-organism* that does not have cells.

vitamins Essential substances needed in small amounts in the *diet*.

weathering Breaking up of rocks into smaller fragments by physical, chemical or biological processes.

white blood cells Cells in the *blood* that help fight disease.

word equation Equation using words to represent a *chemical reaction*.

Index

Acknowledgements

t= top, l = left, r = right, c = centre, b = bottom.

Cover photo: Corbis UK Ltd and Pictor

We are grateful to the following for permission to reproduce copyright material in this book:

pi Corbis UK Ltd; p7 Corel; p8l Corbis UK Ltd., p8r David Turnley/Corbis UK Ltd. ; p9 Zooid Pictures; p10 Corbis UK Ltd.; p11 Corbis UK Ltd.; p12bl&br Corbis UK Ltd., p12t Pictor International/ImageState/Alamy; p14 Richard T. Nowitz/Corbis UK Ltd.; p17 PhotoDisc; p18t Action Images, p18b Zooid Pictures; p19t Martyn F. Chillmaid, p19c&b Corbis UK Ltd.; p20 Corbis UK Ltd.; p21 Corbis UK Ltd.; p22bl&br Corbis UK Ltd., p22t Science Photo Library; p23l Science Photo Library, p23r Matt Meadows/Peter Arnold Inc./Oscience/Photo Library/Science Photo Library; p24 Neal Simpson/Empics; p26bl&br&t Corbis UK Ltd.; p27 Jim Zuckerman/Corbis UK Ltd.; p29 PhotoDisc; p30l Dr Klaus Boller/Science Photo Library, p30c Lester V. Bergman/Corbis UK Ltd., p30tr&br Corbis UK Ltd.; p31bl John Durham/Science Photo Library, p31br Mick Rock/Cephas Picture Library, p31t Eye Of Science/Science Photo Library; p32tl Lester V. Bergman/Corbis UK Ltd., p32bl Peter Turnley/Corbis UK Ltd., p32tr David Scharf/Science Photo Library, p32br Dan Sinclair/Zooid Pictures; p33l Jeffrey L. Rotman/Corbis UK Ltd., p33tr Custom Medical Stock Photo/Science Photo Library, p33br Richard T. Nowitz/Corbis UK Ltd.; p34l CNRI/Science Photo Library, p34r Biology Media/Science Photo Library; p35 John Durham/Science Photo Library; p36t&b Corbis UK Ltd.; p39 Corel; p40 Corbis UK Ltd.; p41tl Bruce Adams/Eye Ubiquitous/Corbis UK Ltd., p41bl Simon Fraser/Science Photo Library, p41tc Tania Midgley/Corbis UK Ltd., p41bc Dr Morley Read/Science Photo Library, p41tr Eric Crichton/Corbis UK Ltd., p41br Chris Mattison/Frank Lane Picture Agency/Corbis UK Ltd.; p42l&r Corbis UK Ltd.; p43 James King-holmes/Science Photo Library; p44l Corbis UK Ltd., p44c Michael & Patricia Fogden/Corbis UK Ltd., p44r Gary W. Carter/Corbis UK Ltd.; p45 Steve Austin/Papilio/Corbis UK Ltd.; p47l Tony Wilson-Bligh; Papilio/Corbis UK Ltd., p47r Corbis UK Ltd.; p49 PhotoDisc; p52t&b Corbis UK Ltd.; p55tl Andrew Lambert Photography, p55cl Bettmann/Corbis UK Ltd., p55bl Lawrence Migdale/Science Photo Library, p55tr Martyn F. Chillmaid/Science Photo Library, p55cr Andrew Lambert Photography, p55br Lester V. Bergman/Corbis UK Ltd.; p56t&b Adam Hart-Davis/Science Photo Library, p56 Digital Vision Ltd.; p57t&b Alfred Pasieka/Science Photo Library; p58l&r Martyn F. Chillmaid; p59l&r Martyn F. Chillmaid; p60cl&cc Martyn F. Chillmaid, p60bl Martyn F. Chillmaid/Science Photo Library; p60bc&tr Corbis UK Ltd., p60cr Charles D. Winters/Science Photo Library, p60br Corbis UK Ltd.; p62 Charles D. Winters/Science Photo Library; p63 PhotoDisc; p64tl Martyn F. Chillmaid, p64cl Andrew Lambert Photography, p64tr Andrew Lambert Photography/Science Photo Library p64cr Martyn F. Chillmaid, p64br Charles D. Winters/Science Photo Library, p64br Adam Hart-Davis/Science Photo Library; p65t&b Corbis UK Ltd.; p66l&cl Martyn F. Chillmaid, p66cr Lawrence Migdale/Science Photo Library, p66r Martyn F. Chillmaid; p67(all) Martyn F. Chillmaid; p68(all) Martyn F. Chillmaid; p69bl&t Martyn F. Chillmaid, p69br Corbis UK Ltd.; p70t&b Zooid Pictures; p71l Courtesy of BOC, p71r Corbis UK Ltd.; p72 Andrew Lambert Photography/Science Photo Library; p73t&b Corbis UK Ltd.; p75 Corel; p76bl Corbis UK Ltd., p76tc Geophotos, p76bc Sinclair Stammers/Science Photo Library, p76br Corbis UK Ltd., p76t Geoscience Features Picture Library, p76c De Beers; p77(all) Geoscience Features Picture Library; p78l&c Geophotos, p78r Martyn F. Chillmaid; p79l&r Martyn F. Chillmaid; p80tl&bl Corbis UK Ltd., p80tr Richard T. Nowitz/Corbis UK Ltd., p80br&c Martyn F. Chillmaid; p81bl&bc&br Martyn F. Chillmaid, p81t Geoscience Features Picture Library; p82bl&br Corbis UK Ltd., p82t David Muench/Corbis UK Ltd.; p83l Robert Holmes/Corbis UK Ltd., p83c Richard A. Cooke/Corbis UK Ltd., p83r Geophotos; p84tl Geoscience Features Picture Library, p84bl Bernd Mellmann/Alamy, p84tr Geophotos, p84cr Tom Bean/Corbis UK Ltd., p84br Geoscience Features Picture Library; p85l Kevin Schafer/Corbis UK Ltd., p85r Sinclair Stammers/Science Photo Library; p87 Corel; p88tl&cl Geoscience Features Picture Library, p88bl Geophotos, p88bc&tr&br Corbis UK Ltd.; p89 Geoscience Features Picture Library; p90t Gregory Dimijian/Science Photo Library, p90b Geoscience Features Picture Library; p91tl Ric Ergenbright/Corbis UK Ltd., p91bl&br Martyn F. Chillmaid, p91tc Geophotos, p91tr Geoscience Features Picture Library; p92l Charles Mauzy/Corbis UK Ltd., p92c&r Geoscience Features Picture Library; p93tl H.D. Thoreau/Corbis UK Ltd., p93bl&tr&br Geoscience Features Picture Library; p97 Corel; p99tl Samuel Ashfield/Science Photo Library, p99bl Andrew Lambert Photography, p99c Adam Hart-Davis/Science Photo Library, p99r Chris Priest & Mark Clarke/Science Photo Library; p100t&b Corbis UK Ltd.; p101 Zooid Pictures; p102tl&cl&tr&cr&ca&cb Martyn F. Chillmaid, p102b Corbis UK Ltd.; p106cl&cr Dr. Arthur Tucker/Science Photo Library, p106bl&br Corbis UK Ltd., p106t Bettmann/Corbis UK Ltd.; p107t Glen Dimplex UK Limited, p107b Greg Mathieson/Rex Features; p108 Photo courtesy of Knauf Insulation Limited; p109 Paddy Gannon; p113 Photodisc/Getty Images; p116 Zooid Pictures; p118 Richard Megna_Fundamental Photos/Science Photo Library; p119 Martyn F. Chillmaid; p122 Martyn F. Chillmaid; p123 Roger Antrobus/Corbis UK Ltd.; p125 PhotoDisc; p126bl&br Corbis UK Ltd., p126t Michael Freeman/Corbis UK Ltd.; p128t&c&b Martyn F. Chillmaid; p129 Paul Shambroom/Science Photo Library; p130t Stuart Westmorland/Corbis UK Ltd., p130c Jerome Martin/Rex Features, p130b Oxford University Press; p131l&r Shout; p132bl&br Corbis UK Ltd., p132t Adam Hart-Davis/Science Photo Library, p132c Oxford University Press; p136 Vaughan Fleming/Science Photo Library; p139 PhotoDisc; p140t Dan Sinclair/Zooid Pictures, p140b John Slater/Corbis UK Ltd.; p141l&r Corbis UK Ltd.; p144 Richard T. Nowitz/Corbis UK Ltd.; p145l Marc Henrie, p145r Andrew Syred/Science Photo Library; p147tl Mark Fuller/Leslie Garland Picture Library/Alamy, p147tr Dan Sinclair/Zooid Pictures, p147b Nils Jorgensen/Rex Features.

Photo research by Zooid Pictures Limited.
Technical illustrations are by Oxford Designers & Illustrators.
Cartoons are by John Hallet.